汤姆·索亚历险记

【美】马克·吐温（Twain,M.） 著

高静怡 译

吉林美术出版社 | 全国百佳图书出版单位

图书在版编目（CIP）数据

汤姆·索亚历险记 / （美）马克·吐温（Twain,M.）著；高静怡译. -- 长春：吉林美术出版社，2014.6（2019.8重印）
书名原文：The Adventures of Tom Sawyer
ISBN 978-7-5386-8272-4

Ⅰ.①汤… Ⅱ.①马…②高… Ⅲ.①儿童文学—长篇小说—美国—近代 Ⅳ.①I712.84

中国版本图书馆CIP数据核字（2014）第065445号

汤姆·索亚历险记

作　　　者	（美）马克·吐温（Twain,M.）
译　　　者	高静怡
出　版　人	赵国强
责　任　编辑	林　鸣　马　杰
封　面　设计	李劲松
开　　　本	880mm × 1230mm　　1 / 32
字　　　数	180千字
印　　　张	7.5
版　　　次	2014年6月第1版
印　　　次	2019年8月第2次印刷
出　　　版	吉林美术出版社
发　　　行	吉林美术出版社图书经理部
地　　　址	长春市人民大街4646号
	邮编：130021
电　　　话	0431—86037809
网　　　址	www.jlmspress.com
印　　　刷	三河市骏杰印刷有限公司

ISBN 978-7-5386-8272-4　　　　　　定价：58.00元

序

本书所描述的大多数冒险都真实发生过，其中的一两件是我自己经历过的，其他的则是我的同学经历过的。哈克贝利·费恩这一人物形象来源于生活，汤姆·索亚也是如此，但是他不是来源于某一个人，而是我认识的三个男孩性格特点的结合体，所以他属于混合型建筑。

本书所涉及的那些怪异的迷信在书中故事发生的时代——三四十年前——在西方的孩子和奴隶中间颇为流行。

尽管我写本书的目的是给孩子们提供点娱乐，我还是希望大人们不要因此就不去看它，因为我也计划着可以用一种委婉的方式让大人们看到曾经的自己，看到他们当时的所思所想所谈，看到他们曾经热衷的事情是多么的稀奇古怪啊。

作者

一八六七年于哈德福特

[目录]

第一章

"汤姆!"

无人回应。

"汤姆!"

无人回应。

"这孩子到底是怎么回事?真是纳闷儿,你这个汤姆!"

这个老妇人把眼镜向下一拉从镜框上方看了看房间,接着她又把眼镜向上一推从镜框的下方看了看。她很少或者说从来都没有透过镜片来找一个像小男孩这样的小东西。这副眼镜可是她资质的体现,是她心中的骄傲,它天生就是来显示她的"风度",并不是拿来用的。她可是带着一副炉盖儿都能看清楚东西。她茫然地看了一会儿,然后用并不凶恶但却十分响亮的声音——这声音连桌椅板凳都能听见——说道:"好吧,我发誓如果让我逮着你,我就——"

她这句话没能说完,因为这时她正弯着腰,用一把扫帚在床底下猛捅,捅一下就得停下喘口气,结果除了一只猫什么都没捅出来。

"我这辈子从来没有见过这种男孩!"

说着,她走到了敞开的门口定住了脚,然后朝满院子的西红柿藤和曼陀罗草丛中张望,但是没有发现汤姆。所以她提高了嗓门向远处吼道:

"汤——姆——"

她身后传来一阵窸窣的声音,于是她转过了身,刚好抓到了一个紧身短上衣的衣摆，逮住了他。"好啊，我早该想到你会躲在那个小储存室里，你在那里干吗呢？"

"什么都没干。"

"什么都没干！看看你的爪子，再瞧瞧你的嘴，那糊的都是什么？"

"姨妈，我不知道。"

"好吧，我知道，是果酱，那是果酱，对吧？我警告过你不下四十遍了如果你敢碰我的果酱，我就会扒了你的皮，快点去拿柳条鞭！"

鞭子已经抡到了空中——大难就要临头了——

"天啊，姨妈，快看你身后那是什么！"

老妇人转过了身，在惶恐之中捏起了裙子，就在这时，这个小鬼转身就跑了，他爬上了高高的木栅栏，逃之夭夭。他的姨妈——波丽站在那里待了一会儿，然后突然轻声地笑了。

"该死的小鬼，我怎么就不长记性呢？他要诡计把我耍到这个份上，我怎么还不吸取教训呢？但是老了终归是糊涂了啊，俗话说，老狗学不了新招。可是我的上帝啊，他从来不耍同样的把戏，我怎么知道下一次他又会想出什么鬼主意？"

他似乎知道能捉弄我多久才会引得我发怒，他还知道只要他设法哄我一会儿或者引我发笑，那么这事儿就算完了，他就不会挨揍了。我没有对这孩子尽到责任，这一点上帝可以作证。正如《圣经》上说，孩子不打不成器。我知道我这样溺爱他是有罪的，这让我们俩都受折磨，他是个有一肚子鬼主意的孩子，可我呢，他是我死去的姐姐的孩子，可怜的小家伙，我就是下不了狠心去责罚他。每一次我原谅他时我都会良心不安，每一次我鞭打他我却又难受得心都要碎了。算啦，算啦，就像《圣经》上说的，人为母生，光阴荏苒，多有患难。我还真是同意这一说法，他下午准是要逃学的，那我一定要履行我的义务，让他明天干点活儿，来惩罚他。让他周六干活是有些困难，因为所有的孩子都在享受假期，而且他最恨的就是干活，但是我必须要对他尽到责任，否则我就是把这个孩子给毁了。"

汤姆确实逃了学，而且玩得很开心，他回到家正巧赶上帮助吉姆这个小黑鬼劈做晚饭用的柴火，锯第二天用的木头——至少他能及时地回来把自己经历的事情讲给吉姆听，而实际上吉姆干了所有活计的四分之三。汤姆的小弟弟（确切地说是他同父异母的弟弟）西德尼早已干完了自己的活（捡拾碎木条），因为他是一个很安静的小孩，从来不会去冒险，也不会给大人添麻烦。在汤姆吃晚饭并抓住这个大好的机会偷糖吃的时候，波丽姨妈向他问了些问题，这些问题比较狡诈，而且非常巧妙，因为她想要设套，让他自己露馅儿。像其他一些头脑简单的人一样，她很自负地认为自己天生就有暗中整人的手腕，而且她很喜欢使用一些实际上轻易就能被人识破，毫无诡计可言的伎俩。她说道：

"汤姆，学校里有些热，对吧？"

"是的。"

"非常的热，对吗？"

"是的。"

"你想去游泳吗，汤姆？"

汤姆的心头掠过一丝恐慌——有一种被怀疑的感觉。他偷偷察看了波丽姨妈的脸色，见她不动声色，于是他便说：

"不——呃，我不是很想去。"

老太太伸出了手，摸了摸汤姆的衬衫，说道：

"嗯，你现在也不是很热。"

她心中窃喜，因为她发现了衬衫是干的，可没人知道她此举的真正用意。但是汤姆猜透了她的意思，所以他决定先发制人。

"一些小孩往我们头上浇水，你瞧，我的头发还是湿的呢。"

波丽姨妈没有想到自己竟忽略了这个简单的证据，从而错失了良机，她心里暗自苦恼了一番，不过马上她就想出了一个新主意：

"汤姆啊，你头发淋湿是用不着把我给你缝的衣领解开的，是吧？把外套解开给我看看！"

汤姆脸上所隐藏的不安消失了，他解开了外套，波丽姨妈发现他的衣领好端端的缝在那里。

"好吧，真见鬼，跟你坦白了说，我觉得你肯定是逃学去游泳了，但是我这次就原谅你了，汤姆，我相信你就像俗语说的那样，是个烧焦了毛的猫，但内在是比外在好的。"

一方面她有些难过，因为自己的智谋计划落空了，另一方面却有些高兴，因为汤姆偶尔也会乖乖地听话。

不料此时西德尼开口说了话：

"咦？我明明见你用白色的线给他缝的衣领，怎么现在却成了黑的啊？"

"真是的啊，我确确实实是用白色的线缝的，你这个汤姆！"

不过汤姆根本没等到她说完就开溜了，并在他跑出门的时候放话道：

"西德尼，我一定会揍你一顿。"

汤姆跑到一个安全的地方，把那两根戳在他外套翻领上的大针检查了一番，两根针上都绕着线，一根针上是白线，一根是黑线，汤姆自言道：

"要不是西德尼这么一说，她一准察觉不到。真讨厌，有时候她拿白线缝，有时候又用黑线，真希望她永远只用一种线缝——她这样，我根本都分不清什么时候用的什么线——但是我打赌，我一定要揍西德尼一顿，一定要给他点颜色瞧瞧。"

汤姆不是村子里的模范小孩，他深知模范小孩是什么样子的，所以他对他们深恶痛绝。

不到一两分钟他就把他所有的烦恼忘得一干二净了，并不是因为他的烦恼相比于成人的烦恼而言算不了什么，而是因为一件十分有趣的事情将它们从他脑海中暂时赶走了——正如成人沉浸在新事物中将所有的不幸忘了一样。这一新鲜有趣的事情就是口哨的一种奇妙吹法，这是他刚从一个黑人那里学来的，他现在正练个不停呢。这种口哨听起来就像鸟在啁啾一样，婉转动听，吹的时候要将舌头不停地贴向上颚。读者们，如果你们曾经是个小男孩的话，你们可能还记得怎么吹。他勤奋而专注地练着，很快就掌握了其中的诀窍。于是他走上了街头，一边走着一边吹着动听的调子，他的心中充满了喜悦，就跟一个天文学家发现了新行星一样，开心极了。但若论起谁的这种喜悦更加强烈，更加深刻，更加纯粹的话，天文学家无疑会输给这个小子。

夏天的夜晚很长，天还没有黑，汤姆正忙着检查自己的口哨有没有吹好，一个陌生人来到了他的面前——一个比他块头稍大点的男孩。在贫穷破落的圣彼得堡村子里，任何新面孔，不管年龄多大，不管是男还是女，都是很新奇的。这个小男孩穿得很体面——在周末都能穿得很体面着实让人吃惊。男孩头上戴着一顶十分精致的帽子，身穿一件又新又干净的蓝色紧身上衣，裤子也是崭新崭新的，他竟然穿了鞋子——要知道今天可只是星期五。他甚至还打了个领带，那是一条颜色鲜亮的领带，他这身时髦的打扮让汤姆气不打一处来，汤姆一直瞪着这个男孩，他越盯着他，就把自己的头抬得越高，同时男孩一身华丽的装扮就越来越让他感觉到自己衣衫褴褛。他们谁都没有说话，如果一个孩子动了一下，另一个也会跟着动，但只是向一侧移动，走成了个圆圈。两个人始终脸对脸，互相盯着对方，最终，汤姆说了话：

"我能揍你一顿！"

"那我倒想看看你怎么揍。"

"哼，我真的可以揍你。"

"不，你根本揍不了我。"

"我当然能揍你。"

"不，你不能。"

"我能。"

"你不能。"

"能。"

"不能。"

经过了短暂的尴尬沉默，汤姆又开口了：

"你叫什么名字？"

"这也许跟你没有任何关系。"

"哼，我保证这会变成我的事。"

"好吧，那你干吗不试试呢？"

"你要是说更多的话我就会这样做。"

"更多——更多——更多！我说了，你做啊。"

"哼，你以为你很聪明，是吗？如果我想的话，我把一只手背在身后，只用另一只手就能揍扁你。"

"哈，你干吗不揍我呢，你光说你能揍我。"

"我当然会揍你，要是你惹我的话，我一准儿揍你。"

"是啊是啊，像你这样的人我见多啦。"

"你这个喜欢卖弄的人，你以为你很了不起，对吧？瞧你那帽子！"

"要是你不喜欢我的帽子，你也得忍着，你绝对不敢把我的帽子打下来，谁要敢这样做，我就让他死得很难看。"

"你这个骗子！"

"你才是个骗子。"

"你只会吹牛，根本都不敢打架。"

"哼——哪凉快哪待着去吧！"

"你再说——要是你再敢无礼的话，我就要拿石头把你的头砸下来。"

"哈，你是会这么干哦。"

"当然，我会这么干。"

"那你怎么不做呢？你一直都在嚷着要干什么来着？你干吗不这样做啊，因为你害怕。"

"我才不害怕。"

"你就怕。"

"我不怕。"

"就怕。"

又是一阵子的沉默，两个人互相鄙视着转着圈，不久他们就肩架着肩，汤姆说：

"快从这滚开！"

"你才滚开！"

"我才不会。"

"我也不会。"

于是他们就这样站着，每个孩子都把一只脚向后退一步抵在地上，使出了吃奶的劲，并死死地仇视着对方。但是没有人能够占上风，在他们争斗得汗流浃背，满脸通红之后，每个人都泄了点气儿，但仍然警惕着对方。这时汤姆说道：

"你这个傻帽胆小鬼，我要把这告诉我的大哥哥，他用小拇指都可以撂倒你，我一定会让他这么做的。"

"我会怕你的大哥哥？我有个比他还强的哥哥，更可怕的是，他能把他从那个栅栏上扔过去。"（其实两个哥哥都是想出来的）

"你撒谎。"

"你说的才像是在撒谎。"

汤姆用他的大脚趾在土灰中画了一条线，他说：

"你胆敢踩过这个界，我就会把你揍得站都站不起来。看谁敢来试试！"

这个新来的小孩马上就踩了过去，并且说道：

"现在好了，你刚说你要这么干，那我看看你敢不敢这么干。"

"你可别逼我，你最好当心点。"

"好啊，你说你会这么干，那你为什么不干呢？"

"老天作证，给我两分钱我就会这么做。"

这个新来的小孩马上从自己的口袋中掏出两个铜板，嘲弄地把它们拿了出来。

然后汤姆一巴掌把它们扇到了地上。

两个孩子立刻就滚在了土灰中，像两只猫一样抱在了一起，在接下来的一分钟里，他们撕扯着对方的头发和衣服，对着对方的鼻子又是揍又是抓，弄得他们俩浑身都是灰，却还是得意扬扬的。不一会儿局势就明朗了，汤姆的身影在尘土中清晰了起来，他坐在这个新来的小孩的身上，用拳头不断揍他。

"求饶吧！"汤姆说着。

男孩却只是挣扎着。他哭了起来——主要是被气的。

"快求饶吧！"汤姆不停地抢着拳头。

最终，男孩憋住了，说了声"我求饶"，汤姆放他起来，然后说："这下你该学着点了，下次最好看清楚你想捉弄的对象。"

男孩弹弄着衣服上的灰走开了，他一边哭一边骂，时不时地还回头看看，一边摇着头一边威胁着汤姆下次要是逮着他，一定会让他好看。汤姆嘲讽着他，并得意扬扬地走开了，等到汤姆一转身，男孩就拿起一块石头向他砸去，正好打到了汤姆背上，然后这个男孩像个羚羊一样，拔腿就跑了。于是汤姆就一路追着这个叛徒，找到了他住在哪里。汤姆在他家门外站了一会儿，害怕他的敌人会突然冲出来，但是敌人只从窗户里望了望他，就消失了。最终，敌人的妈妈出来了，她骂汤姆是个坏小子，是个没教养的野孩子，并命令他赶快离开，然后汤姆就离开了，但是他说自己只是暂时放过他，哪天一定会再教训他。

那天晚上，他很晚才回家，当他小心翼翼地从窗户爬进屋子的时候，刚好碰见等着捉他的姨妈，当姨妈看清了他这一身的灰之后，原先想让他在周六干苦活的打算变成了坚定的决心。

第二章

终于到了周六，在这一天，一切事物都是美好的，阳光明媚，到处生机盎然。每个人心里都哼着歌儿，年轻人更会忍不住唱出来。每个人都兴高采烈的，走起路来两脚生风。洋槐树上花朵盛开，沁人的香气在空气中弥漫开来。

村外高高耸立的卡迪夫山披着绿色的植被，山峰不远不近，看起来就像一块"乐土"，它是那么的梦幻，静谧，让人无限向往。

汤姆走在一条人行道上，他拎着一大桶石灰水，扛着一把长刷子。在勘测了一番栅栏后，汤姆霎时就没了高兴的心情，他惆怅了起来。这些高大的栅栏可是有三十码长，九尺高啊！此刻，生活对他而言乏味极了，简直就是一个很大的负担，他垂头丧气地拿起刷子沾了点灰浆对着最顶上的木板刷了一下，然后又将此动作重复了一遍，又刷了一下。看看那刚刷过的白色木板，就那么一丁点儿，再看看那没刷过的木板，根本望不到边，汤姆懊恼地坐在了一个木桶上。这时，吉姆提着一只锡桶从门口蹦蹦跳跳地跑了出来，他一边跑一边还唱着《布法罗的女孩们》。在汤姆看来，从镇上的泵站拎水回来实在讨厌不过了。但是现在，他觉得这好像没那么糟糕。他记得泵站那儿有好多小伙伴。白人孩子、混血儿、黑人孩子，都在那儿迫不及待地等着提水，大家在那儿玩耍、交换玩具、吵吵闹闹，活像一群小云雀。他还记得虽然那个泵站离家不过一百五十码，吉姆每次都要耗上一个小时才能把一桶水打回来，有的时候甚至得有人去叫他，他才能回来。汤姆对吉姆说：

"听着，吉姆，如果你能替我刷点儿，我就去帮你打水。"

吉姆摇了摇头，说：

"我不能这样做，汤姆少爷，老太太嘱咐我在去拎水的路上一定不能停下来和别人玩。她说她就知道你会叫我刷栅栏，她交代我只能干自己的事，她会亲自来看看你干得怎么样了。"

"天啊，你可不能在意她说了什么，她总是这样说话的。把桶给我吧，我一分钟之内就能回来，她不会知道的。"

"不行啊，汤姆少爷，老太太会把我的头拧下来的，她肯定会这么做的。"

"她？她连打人这种事都没干过，只不过会用顶针在你头上敲敲罢了，谁会受不了这个呢，我跟你说啊，她就是讲话很凶，但是骂骂你又伤不了你——只要你别把她惹哭就没事儿。吉姆啊，你帮我刷会儿，我就给你个石子儿，这可是块儿白色的石子儿，怎么样？"

"嘿，老实跟你说，这真是不错，但是汤姆少爷，我可真是害怕老太太。"

"要是你帮我的话，我还会给你看看我发炎的脚趾。"

吉姆毕竟只是个凡人，他哪儿受得了这么多诱惑啊。他把水桶搁在了地上，从汤姆那儿拿过了白石子儿。可不到一会儿，吉姆就捂着他火辣辣的屁股，拎着水桶飞快地跑上了街道，而汤姆也使劲儿地刷起了木板。原来是波丽姨妈从田里干完活回来了，此时她手里拿着拖鞋，眼里流露出胜利的眼神。

但是汤姆没干多久就又泄气了，他开始想起他原本在星期六应该有的欢乐，越想心里越伤心。一会儿那些自由的小子就会蹦蹦跳跳地跑过来，做着各种各样好玩儿的事情。他们肯定会嘲笑他竟然还要干活儿——他一想到这个，脸就羞得发烫。他把自己所有的财产都掏了出来并仔细地看了一阵——几个残缺不全的小玩具，几个大理石子儿，还有些破烂儿。这些东西足够用来换别的小孩给他干活，但却连半个小时的自由时光都换不来。于是他把这些玩意儿都又揣回了兜里，放弃了想要收买别人的想法。在这个紧要关头，他突然想到了一个好主意，一个妙不可言的好主意！

他拎起了刷子，静静地刷了起来。不一会儿，本·罗杰的身影最先出现了，在所有的男孩中汤姆最害怕他的奚落。本走起路来就像是在做三级跳——显示他是多么的开心，并且还打算干些更有乐子的事，他正啃着一个苹果，不时地还发出长长的动听的声音，紧接着又会用低沉的声音叫着"叮——咚——咚，叮——咚——咚"，他这是在学一艘蒸汽船呢，当他越走越近时，他又放慢了脚步，跑到道路中间，夸张地做出让船倾向右侧的样子，并费力地调转了船头，让船停下来了，仿佛船已吃水九英尺深，他这又学起了"大密苏里号"。他既是一艘船，又是船长，还要当汽笛。所以他得想象自己正站在蒸汽船的顶层甲板上发号施令，并且还要去执行这些命令。

"快停船，伙计！丁——零——零！"船几乎都停下来了，他缓慢地踱向人行道。

"调转船头！丁——零——零！"他夹紧了双臂，使劲儿地向下杵着。

"右舷向后！丁——零——零！嚓呜！嚓——嚓呜——呜——嚓呜！"他一边喊着，一边用右手画着一个大圆圈，这代表着一个四十英尺的大转轮。

"左舷向后！丁——零——零！嚓呜——嚓——嚓呜——嚓呜！"他又抡圆了左手比画着个大轮子。

"右舷停！丁——零——零！左舷停！丁——零——零！右舷前进！停下！外舷轮慢慢转过来！丁——零——零！嚓呜——呜——呜！抛前缆绳！快点儿！快点吧，再把后缆绳放下！你愣在那里干吗？把绳套绕船桩弄好！对，就这样！伙计，熄火！丁——零——零！"

"唏！唏！唏！"（他在模仿阀门放气的声音）

汤姆一直专心致志地粉刷着——丝毫不理会这艘蒸汽船。本先是盯着他看了一会儿，接着他说：

"嗨，日子过得挺滋润的嘛。"

汤姆没有回答他，只是用艺术家似的眼光端详着他最后刷的那块儿板，然后拿起刷子轻轻地刷了一下，接着又像刚才那样，对着他的作品审视了一番。本往汤姆身边凑了过来。汤姆看着那只苹果，馋得直咽口水，但是他正镇定地刷着。本说：

"嗨，小子，你在工作啊，对吧？"

"呀，是你呀本，我压根儿就没注意到你呢。"

"我可是要去游泳的，你想去吗？但是你是想待在这里干活儿的，是的，你当然是这样想的。"

汤姆卖了个关子，说道：

"你把这个叫作干活儿？"

"不是吗？这不是在干活儿是什么？"

汤姆继续刷着栏杆，故意装作不在乎地说：

"好吧，这可以算是在干活儿，也可以不算。我只晓得，这种活计很适合汤姆·索亚。"

"天啊，不是吧，你说你喜欢干这个？"

汤姆的刷子继续飞舞着。

"喜欢？我可不知道为什么不该喜欢。哪个男孩能有机会天天刷栅栏啊？"

这句话让本大吃一惊，心里觉得是那么回事。于是他停止了啃苹果。汤姆轻盈地挥舞着他的刷子——不时地后退几步看看刷的效果——在这补一刷，在那涂一下——然后再审查下效果，本注视着他的一举一动，越看越感兴趣，越看越着迷。然后他说：

"哦，汤姆，让我刷一会儿吧。"

汤姆想了一想，他差点儿就答应了下来，但又改变了注意：

"不，这可不行，这可是个很难的活计。你知道波丽姨妈对这个栅栏十分地挑剔——这可是当街的一面啊。如果这是后面的栅栏我当然不介意让你刷会儿，她当然也不会介意。但事实上，她很在意这个栅栏刷得好不好，所以要万分小心才行。我敢打赌，一千个男孩甚至两千个男孩中都没有一个有本领把它刷好。"

"是吗？哎呀，你就让我试试嘛，就刷一点儿。汤姆，要是我是你，我就会让你刷。"

"本，老实说，我是同意让你刷刷的，但是波丽姨妈——唉，吉姆本来就想刷的，但是她根本不让他干。西德尼也想刷，她也不干。你看到我是怎么刷的了吗？如果你来刷的话，要是出点什么事儿——"

"行了啊，我一定会很小心的，快让我试试吧。我把我的苹果核给你怎么样？"

"唉，这样啊，不，本，这可不行。我怕——"

"我把苹果都给你！"

汤姆把刷子给了他，表现出极不情愿的样子，但是他心里可是美滋滋的。于是，当刚才的那个"大密苏里号"蒸汽船在太阳下大汗淋漓地干活儿时，这个退休的艺术家就坐在阴凉地儿的一只木桶上，跷着二郎腿，大嚼着苹果，并计划着怎样猎杀更多天真的小羊羔。这样的小笨蛋还真不少，没过一会儿就有很多男孩走过来，他们起先都会嘲弄一番，但结果都留下来刷栅栏了。当本玩够了的时候，汤姆又跟比利·费雪做起了买卖，这次他得到了一只修好了的风筝。当比利又玩够的时候，詹尼·米勒用一只死老鼠和一个用来挂它的弹簧买到了刷栅栏的机会。就这样，不断有男孩来刷栅栏，他们刷了一个小时又一个小时。于是下午过了一半的时候，汤姆就从早上那个从贫民窟里出来的穷小子变成了一个真正的富有的人。除了我提到过的家当，他还多了十二个大理石子儿，一个犹太人的破竖琴，一块透明的蓝玻璃片，一个线轴做的大炮，一个什么锁都开不了的钥匙，一截粉笔，一片儿酒瓶的玻璃瓶塞，一个锡皮做的士兵，一对蝌蚪，六个爆竹，一只独眼的小猫，一个门上的铜片，一直拴狗的颈圈——但是没有狗，一把小刀，四个橘子皮，还有一个破旧的框格窗。

汤姆这半天过得太舒适了，有一大群伙伴陪着他，栅栏也刷了三遍！如果不是他的白灰浆没有了，他能让村子里的每个男孩都破产。

汤姆自言自语道，这个世界其实也没那么乏味啊。他发现了一个人类行为的伟大定律，尽管他自己都不知道。这一定律就是：如果想让一个大人或一个小孩渴求地做一件事，那么只需让这件事变得难以得手就行了。如果汤姆是一个伟大聪明的哲学家，就像本书的作者这样的话，他就会弄明白，原来工作就是指一个人被迫要去做事，玩耍就是指一个人自愿去做事。这样想他就能理解为什么做假花和蹬轮车就是工作而玩九柱戏或者登勃朗峰就只能算是娱乐。在英国有很多绅士，他们在大夏天会驾着四轮大马车走上二三十英里，他们愿意这样做是因为他们可是花了大笔的钱才得到驾马车的这种特权。但是如果你要给他们钱让他们这样做，就会把这桩事的性质转变成为工作，他们就会撒手不干了。

第三章

　　汤姆去找波丽姨妈的时候，她正坐在屋里一个敞开的窗户旁，这个舒服的房间位于屋子的后部，它既可以当卧室使用，也可以当餐厅和图书室用。夏日的空气暖暖的，屋子里的静谧让人感觉到十分惬意，屋里弥漫着花朵的芬芳气味，窗外蜜蜂懒洋洋地嗡嗡叫着。这一切都舒服得恰到好处，让正在织毛衣的波丽姨妈不由得打起了盹儿，她的猫也趴在她的腿上打起了瞌睡。她将眼镜向上推到了花白的头发上以防它掉下来。她本以为汤姆早就撂下活儿跑没影儿了，没想到他竟然这样理直气壮地走到了她的面前。汤姆说道：

　　"姨妈，我现在可以去玩了吗？"

　　"什么？你想去玩儿？你刷了多少啦？"

　　"我全干完啦，姨妈。"

　　"汤姆，不要跟我撒谎——我可受不了这个。"

　　"我可没撒谎啊，姨妈，我真的做完了。"

　　波丽姨妈对汤姆的这种话可是一点都不相信。于是她起身亲自去看了看，如果汤姆说的能有百分之二十是真的她都满足了。当她看见整个栅栏全都刷成了白色，而且是认认真真刷了好几遍的，她甚至还能在地上看见一条石灰滴下的印，她的惊讶简直无以名状。她说道：

　　"嘿，真是没看出来啊，太出乎我的意料了，汤姆，你要是想干一件事的时候还真是能干得非常漂亮。"然后她觉得表扬得有点过头了，就又补充几句："但是，我不得不说，你想认真干事的情况少之又少，嗯，去玩吧，但是你可要记住了，再怎么玩，你一个星期也要在家里待一会儿，否则我可是要抽你了。"

波丽姨妈对汤姆漂亮地完成了工作感到非常满意，她把他领到小储存室里，然后给他挑了个又大又甜的苹果，在她把苹果拿给汤姆的同时，她又讲了一大通道理，说是只有付出了极大的努力获得的奖励才最有意义。当波丽姨妈从《圣经》里挑出一句恰当的话来作为训诫时，汤姆就趁机捞走了一个面包圈。

然后汤姆蹦蹦跳跳地出去了，正好看见西德尼爬上通往二楼后房间的室外楼梯。霎时，空中就飞满了大量的土块儿，它们打着旋儿奔向了西德尼，其猛烈程度就像下了一场冰雹。在波丽姨妈反应过来并冲出来营救西德尼之时，他已经被六七块土块儿砸中了。而此时汤姆已经越过栅栏跑得无影无踪了，虽然在他的身子旁边就有大门可以走，但是在紧急时刻，这个大门显然不如栅栏更能阻碍姨妈的追打。他现在心里开心极了，因为他终于为自己报仇了，谁叫西德尼要提醒姨妈衣服的线是白的，给他带来麻烦。

汤姆绕过了街区，转到了姨妈家牛棚后面的那条泥泞小道。他目前可算是完全逃过了姨妈的追捕和惩罚，于是汤姆就偷偷跑到了村子里的"小广场"上，在那儿男孩儿们会按约过来打群架。汤姆是其中一支部队的将军，他的心腹之交——乔·哈泼则是另一支部队的将军。这两个伟大的指挥官才不会屈尊来参与战斗——那种战斗可是只适合他们手下的虾兵蟹将——他们会坐在一块高地上下达命令，然后由他们的副官传令。在一番苦战之后，汤姆的军队打赢了，接下来就是双方清点亡将，互换战俘以及协商下次交战条件。在他们定出下次的交战时间之后，两个部队都分别整理队形，踏着大步走开了，汤姆也就一个人回家了。

当他路过杰夫·撒切尔家时，他看见花园里有个陌生的小女孩，那是一个有着一双水灵灵的蓝眼睛的姑娘，金黄色的头发梳成了两个长长的辫子，上身穿着一条白色长裙，下面配一条绣花裤，美丽极了。这位刚刚戴上桂冠的英雄瞬间就不战而降了，一个叫艾米·劳什的姑娘从他的心中彻底消失，没了踪影。他本以为自己爱她爱得发狂，甚至觉得自己对她的热情都可以称得上是爱慕了，他费了好几个月来讨她欢心，而她答应了他才不到一个星期，他当这个世界上最幸福最骄傲的男孩也不过短短七天。然而，面对眼前的这位姑娘，艾米瞬间就从他的心头溜去了，像一个普通的访客结束了旅程一般。汤姆偷偷地瞅着这个新的天使直到他发现她看到了自己。然后汤姆装作不知道她在这儿一般，开始用各种男孩子惯用的方式炫耀自己，以此来引她发笑，赢得她的芳心。汤姆傻乎乎地耍弄了好一阵子，他一边做着各种惊险的体操动作，一边瞟向小女孩，却发现她正朝屋里走去，汤姆跑到了栅栏边，倚在栅栏上独自伤心，他多希望她可以在外面多待一会儿啊。小女孩走在台阶上时停顿了一会儿，却又走向了房门。当她抬脚上门槛时，汤姆重重地叹了口气，但是他马上又欣喜了起来，因为她在进门消失之前向栅栏外丢过一朵三色紫罗兰。

于是汤姆又跑了回去，在栅栏外左右徘徊，像之前那样不停地炫耀，一直折腾到傍晚。但是这个小女孩再也没有露面，汤姆还是安慰自己道，她可能一直在窗旁站着，注视着他的举动。最后，他还是不情愿地回家去了，那小脑袋瓜里充满了各种幻想。

整个晚饭期间，汤姆都极其兴奋，连波丽姨妈都不住地怀疑这个小孩儿是不是脑袋里进什么了。为向西德尼扔土块这事他挨了好一顿训，但是汤姆似乎毫不在意。他还企图在姨妈眼皮子底下偷糖吃，却被抓到，狠狠地打了手。汤姆说：

"姨妈，当西德尼偷糖吃的时候你都不惩罚他。"

"那肯定了啊，西德尼从来都不会这么折磨我，而你呢？只要我一不留神儿，你就在偷糖吃。"

"等到姨妈进了厨房之后，西德尼开心地将手伸向了糖罐——他得意扬扬地看着汤姆，这让汤姆简直难以忍受。但是西德尼抓糖罐的时候手滑了一下，罐子一下子掉到了地上打碎了。这下，汤姆可是欣喜若狂，但是他极力地抑制住这种狂喜并保持沉默。他告诉自己一定不能说一句话，就算姨妈出来了，他也得牢牢地坐稳，直到姨妈发问，他才能说出来。天下再也没有比看着那个宠儿受罚更痛快的事儿了。汤姆真是喜不自胜，这个老妇人很快就回来了，当她看到这满地碎片之后，愤怒的火光从她那副眼镜中射出，这一秒，汤姆对自己说："哈哈，好戏终于来啦！"可下一分钟，汤姆就被一只大手打趴到了地上，当这只大手高高扬起准备再次拍下时，汤姆吼道：

"停！你这是在干什么啊？你打我干吗啊？是西德尼打碎的！"

波丽姨妈停在了那里，一脸茫然，汤姆眼巴巴地看着她，指望她道个歉，但是当姨妈发话的时候，她只说：

"哼，你这挨得也不吃亏，我不在的时候你肯定也干了其他一些捣蛋事儿，这就够打你一顿了。"

说了这些之后，波丽姨妈心里有些愧疚，她就想说些话安慰他，但是她觉得说了只会显得她做错了似的，所以她不得不禁止自己这样做。于是她就保持着沉默干别的事儿去了，心里却是乱糟糟的。汤姆跑到一个角落里生闷气儿，他沉浸在了自己的悲伤里。他知道姨妈心里肯定在向自己说着对不起，所以他虽然面上悲恸欲绝心里却很满足。他可不能发出任何和解的信号，也不能对对方有所理睬，他明知道有一个充满渴望的目光时不时地透过眼泪落在自己身上，但他硬是不予理会。他想象着自己躺在床上病得要死了，而他的姨妈跪在他的身旁祈求他说一句原谅自己的话，但他将脸转向了墙壁，直到死也没有说一个字。啊，她那时会是什么感觉呢？他又想象自己淹死在了河里，卷曲的头发湿淋淋的，可怜的小手僵硬着，被人从河边抬了回来，他悲伤的心终于得以安息。她那时会多么悲痛地扑到他的身上，泪如雨下，不停地祈求上帝把他还给自己，再也不会这样折磨他了！但是他却躺在那儿一动不动，身子冰冷，与世长绝了——这么一个受苦受难的小人儿终于不用再悲伤了。汤姆全身心地投入到自己的想象中，喉咙哽咽，不时地抽泣着，最后眼泪哗哗地流了出来，顺着他的鼻子淌了下来。汤姆现在正享受着这种悲伤的心情，它是如此的神圣，他绝不能容忍任何世间鄙俗的喜悦或者是任何恼人的欢乐打扰此刻的情绪。后来他的表姐玛丽手舞足蹈地跑了进来，她在乡下不过待了一个星期，却搞得跟待了一个世纪似的，进了家门那一刻，她开心极了，又是唱又是跳的，这时汤姆顶着漫天的乌云从另一个门溜了出去。

他独自一人游荡着，远远地离开了男孩儿们玩耍的地方，找了个僻静的地儿专心地沉溺到自己的精神家园里。河里的一只长木筏吸引了他的注意，他走了上去坐在了木筏的边上，凝视着这无边无际的河水，期待着自己能突然不知不觉地被淹死，这样他就不用去面对人生中注定要经历的磨炼。接着他想到了那朵花，于是他把它拿了出来。这枝花朵已经皱巴巴的并且枯萎了，这就更加增强了他对于自己悲惨命运的幸福感。汤姆遥想着如果她知道的话，会不会同情自己，会为他哭泣吗？她会想要搂着他的脖子安慰他吗？或者说她会像这个冷漠的世界一样无情地转身走开？这一想象带给了他一种虽然痛苦但却很享受的快乐，他在脑子里一遍又一遍地回味着，然后又从不同的角度都想了一遍，直到他实在什么都想不出来了。最后，他叹着气站起身，在黑暗中离开了。

大概是晚上九点半或是十点钟的光景，他走上了孤独的街头，这里住着他心中那位不知姓名的"伊人"。他在这停了一会儿，竖着耳朵却什么声儿也没听到，只有一支蜡烛昏黄的烛光，映在了二楼窗户的窗帘上。那位纯洁的姑娘是不是就在那儿呢？他爬上了栅栏，蹑手蹑脚地穿过了一排花丛，直到他站到了窗户下面。汤姆深情地久久注视着窗口，然后又仰卧在窗下，捏着他那朵可怜的小花，双手合在胸前。他就这样死了——在这个冰冷的世界里，孤身一人，没有任何东西可以遮身避寒，没有一双慈祥的大手拂去他额头上的虚汗，在巨大的痛苦到来之时没有一个温暖的脸庞惋惜地靠向他。而她，在早上的时候将会看到他身影——老天啊，她会为他可怜的没有生命的躯体掉一滴眼泪吗？当她看到一个如此年轻鲜活的生命就这样早早地凋谢了，她会轻声叹息吗？

　　窗子被打开了，一个女仆突兀的声音瞬间就打破了这神圣的静谧，随后一大盆子水浇了下来，把这个有心殉难的可怜人淋得透湿！

　　这个快要被水呛死的英雄一下子跃了起来，他喷着鼻息，用来缓解这会儿的难受。这时空中嗖嗖地飞过了什么东西，伴随着一阵咒骂，紧接着又有玻璃破碎的声音。只见一个小孩的身影飞快地跃过了栅栏，消失在了黑暗中。

　　不久，汤姆就脱了衣服上床了，他坐在床上映着烛光查看自己湿透了的衣服，西德尼醒了过来，他刚想说冷嘲热讽的话，就对上了汤姆凶狠的眼神，于是他觉得自己还是乖乖睡觉不说的好。汤姆没有做恼人的祷告就睡觉了，而西德尼则在脑袋里默默记下了汤姆的这次懒惰行为。

第四章

太阳从静谧的地平线上冉冉升起，暖暖的阳光犹如上帝的赐福洒向了这个安详的村庄。吃完早饭后，波丽姨妈带着全家开始祷告，祷告的内容是《圣经》里的一些生硬的节选，穿插着一些她自己的发挥，勉强可以凑到一起。当到达高潮部分的时候，她表现得就像自己是摩西站在西奈山巅上一样，吟诵出了摩西十诫。

然后汤姆扭了扭腰，煞有介事地准备开始背诵他要背的那节诗，而西德尼几天前就把要背的背好了，汤姆此时使出了吃奶的劲儿来背他那五节诗，他选了"登山宝训"这一部分，因为他找不到比这还短的部分了。

时间快过了半个小时的时候，汤姆才对他要背的东西搞清了个大概，而且也就只能记住这么多了，因为他的心此时正在人类思想的长河里穿行，他的手正不停地捣弄着什么，玛丽一把拿过书本要考他，汤姆背得磕磕巴巴，就像在雾里使劲儿地找路似的。

"可以得到保佑的是——是——"

"穷人——"

"对，就是穷人，穷人可以得到保佑——在——在——"

"天堂——"

"在天堂，对，穷人可以在天堂得到保佑，因为他们——他们——"

"他们——"

"因为他们，啊，穷人可以在天堂得到保佑，因为天堂是他们的，悲悯的人可以得到庇护，因为他们——他们——"

"必——"

"因为他们必——"

"必——"

"因为他们必——天啊，我真是记不得这是个什么字！"

"必须！"

"哦！是必须！因为他们必须——必须——啊——这个——必须悲悯——呃——呃——可以得到保佑的是——是——呃——是悲悯的人，因为他们必须——呃——必须什么来着？玛丽，你干吗不告诉我呢？你为什么对我这么刻薄？"

"天啊，汤姆，你这个可怜的糨糊脑袋，我不会捉弄你，我才不会这样做呢，你必须要重新去背，不要灰心，汤姆，如果你下功夫背的话——如果你真这么认真背的话，我就会给你个好玩意儿，好啦，现在快去背吧，做个好孩子。"

"真的啊，玛丽，你要给我什么？快告诉我吧。"

"不要问啦，汤姆，你是知道的，我说是个好东西就会是个好东西，我可不骗人。"

"那你发誓你说的是真的，我就去再背一遍。"

汤姆真的就背了一遍，在好奇心和对奖励的期待双重压力下，他非常顺溜地背了出来。

玛丽给了他一把价值一角二分钱的崭新的巴洛牌小刀，他捧过这把小刀，突如其来的幸福让他激动得站都站不稳了，虽然这把小刀切不了什么东西，但是它可是正宗的巴洛牌的啊，这代表着极大的荣耀——至于后来西部的男孩们如何会想到这样的武器有可能会被假冒，从而名誉受损，真真是一个谜，而且可能永远都是个谜。汤姆拿着刀在橱柜上划了几下，他还准备在书桌上划，但却被叫去换衣服，上主日学校。

玛丽给他拿了一盆水和一块肥皂，他走到了门外面，把盆子放在一只小板凳上，然后把肥皂在水里蘸了一蘸，搁在了一旁，接着便撸起了袖管，将水轻轻地洒在地上，然后走到厨房里，拿起挂在门后的毛巾使劲儿地擦脸，但是玛丽拽走了毛巾说：

"你真是不害臊啊，汤姆，你可不能这么坏，你用水洗个脸又伤不了你。"

汤姆被说得有点窘迫，接着玛丽又给他倒了一盆水，这回，他盯着水盆站了一小会儿，然后下了很大的决心，深吸了一口气开始洗了起来。随后他走进了厨房，此时他两只眼睛紧闭着，双手摸索着去找毛巾，肥皂水顺着他的脸流了下来算是他洗过脸的证明。但是当他的脸从毛巾里钻出来的时候，效果并不是很令人满意，因为洗干净的部分到下巴和额头那儿就突然没有了，像一个面具一般罩在他的脸上。这面具以外的地方可是黑乎乎的一片，就像一块没有浇灌过的土地一般从脸往下向脖子上周围蔓延开来。玛丽可是看不下去他这样，麻利地给他拾掇好，这之后，他看起来才像个男人，才是她的同胞兄弟，他们的肤色才没有什么差别。汤姆的头发被梳得油亮整齐，他那头短短的鬈发被从中间分开，匀称地贴在头上。（汤姆可是暗自花了很大的工夫想把他的鬈发弄平，他使劲儿地把头发压在头上，因为他觉得长着鬈发看起来像个女人一样，这可给他的生活添了不少苦头。）然后玛丽又给他拿出了那套这两年周日才能穿的衣服——这些衣服干脆被称为"那套衣服"——所以我们现在就可以看到他到底有几身行头。在他自己穿好了之后，玛丽不得不再重新给他整理好，她把他整洁的紧身上衣纽扣一直扣到脖子那里，将他宽大的衣领一直翻到肩膀上，再给他上下拍拍，然后给他戴上了那顶斑点草帽。他现在看上去漂亮多了，但是也不舒服极了，而实际上，汤姆还真有他看上去的那样不舒服，因为他不得不保持整个衣服必须是干干净净的，这让他感到非常束缚。汤姆真希望玛丽可以忘了还要穿鞋子，但是他的希望落空了，玛丽像通常那样给他的鞋子擦了鞋油然后拿了出来。汤姆现在急得发了脾气，他说自己一直在被强迫做各种他不愿意做的事。但是玛丽劝他说：

"你就忍会儿吧，汤姆，这可是好孩子应该的着装。"

于是汤姆一边嘟囔着一边穿上了鞋子，玛丽也马上就打扮好了，然后这三个孩子就出发去上主日学校了——那是一个让汤姆深恶痛绝的地方，但是西德尼和玛丽却很喜欢那里。

主日学校上课时间是九点到十点半，接着就是做礼拜，三个孩子中的两个往往自愿留下来听牧师布道，另一个当然也会留下来——是因为某种强烈的原因。如果教室的高背无坐垫长凳都能坐满的话，可以容纳三百人，教堂大楼比较简陋，房顶上装着一个松木料做成的匣子算是教堂的尖塔了。汤姆后退到教堂门口，跟一个同样穿着"周日正装"的伙伴搭讪道：

"嘿，比尔，你有黄票吗？"

"有啊。"

"你想要我用什么来换呢？"

"那你会给我什么呢？"

"一块甘草糖还有一个鱼钩。"

汤姆把东西拿出来给他们展示了一下，这些小孩感到很满意，他们马上就偷偷地交换了物品。在这之后，汤姆又用一对大白石换了三张红票，又拿一些小玩意儿换了两张蓝票。当别的男孩进来的时候，他都一一拦下，要跟他们换各种颜色的票子，他们换了能有十分钟甚至是十五分钟之久。现在，他跟着一群穿着干净、吵吵闹闹的小孩进了教堂，走到了座位上，不一会儿就跟最开始进行买卖的那个小孩吵了起来。老师是个严肃的老头儿，他马上阻止了他们的争吵，但是老师刚转过身去，汤姆就扯了一下前排男孩的头发，当这个男孩回过头时，他却装作正在认真看书。不一会儿，他又拿针扎了另一个男孩，他这样做只是为了听听这个男孩悲惨地叫一声："天啊，疼死了！"为此，他又被老师训斥了一顿。汤姆班上整个就是这种气氛——吵闹无序，总是出各种状况。当他们背诗时，没有一个能背得滚瓜烂熟，每个人都要不时地给点提示。但是在他们提心吊胆地背完之后，每个人总能得到张小蓝票作为奖励。每一张票上面都印有一段《圣经》的内容，每一张票可都是要背出两节诗才能换来的，十张蓝票的价值等于一张红票的价值，而且可以用十张蓝票去换一张红票，而十张红票等于一张黄票，红、黄票之间也可以这样进行兑换。如果你能拿到十张黄票的话，校长就会奖你一本平装版的《圣经》（这在当年日子好的时候四毛钱一本呢）。我的读者们啊，你们有多少人会有情趣并且认真背上两千节《圣经》啊？但是玛丽就用这种方式得到了两本《圣经》，那可是她两年努力学习的成果。还有一个德裔的男孩甚至得过四本或五本《圣经》，他曾一口气儿背出了三千节诗，但也由于这事儿，他用脑过度了，所以从他背完的那天起就有些痴呆了——这对于学校而言是个极大的悲哀，因为过去每逢重大场合，校长就会叫这个孩子出来"秀两下"。其实只有一些高年级的学生才会想着要多得点儿票子，才会愿意重复枯燥的背诵来得到一本《圣经》，所以，能得到一次奖赏是一件非常宝贵而且引人注目的事，受奖的学生当天尾巴都能翘上天了，显示出自己非常伟大，非常优秀的样子。而看见这种情景，每一个学生的胸中都会燃起熊熊大火，心里暗暗树起雄心壮志，这种高昂的气势可以持续一两个星期。对汤姆而言，他的精神世界里可能不会渴望得到这种奖励，但是毫无疑问，他整个身心都长时间地向往着奖品所带来的荣耀和声誉。

等到了讲话的时间，校长走到了全体学生的面前，他手里拿着一本合上的赞美诗集，食指夹在书页中间，示意学生们安静下来。当一个主日学校的校长按照惯例做他那简短的演讲时，一本赞美诗集在手是必不可少的，就像一个在音乐会上独唱的歌手手里必须要拿上一张乐谱一样——不过这究竟是为什么还是一个谜，因为不管是校长手里的赞美诗集还是歌手的乐谱都不会被打开。这个校长身材瘦长，大概有三十五岁，留着沙色的胡子和头发，上衣的竖领十分硬挺，领边都几乎要盖到耳朵了，领角向前杵着直逼他的嘴角——这衣领就像一堵墙一样，让他不得不只能往前看，要是他想往两边看看，就只能连同身体也转过来。他的下巴下扎着一个领结，这个领结又大又宽，跟一张钞票似的，周围还带有流苏花边。脚下蹬着的靴子尖直直地往上翘着，这样做在当时是很时髦的，穿上靴子看上去就好像是踩在滑雪板上一样——这可是几个年轻人将鞋尖抵在墙上又认真又努力地压了好几个钟头才弄出来的效果。沃尔特先生神态诚挚，事实上他的内心也一样的诚实与纯粹。他在宗教方面处事总怀着敬畏的心，把它们与生活的日常琐事分开来对待，因此他自己都没有意识到他周日讲话的声音已经形成了一种特殊的语调，这种语调在平时可是绝对听不到的。他开始用这种方式讲话了：

"现在，孩子们，我要求你们全都坐得又直又正，注意力集中，至少给我集中个一两分钟。对，很好，就是这样，这才是好孩子的表现。我看到某个小女孩还在往窗外看——恐怕她以为我在窗户外头的某个地方呢——可能正在某个枝头上给一群小鸟讲话呢。（全场一阵认可的窃笑）我想要告诉你们我非常高兴能看到这么多张阳光、干净的小脸聚集在这里，学习着如何做正确的事，做高尚的人。"

校长说了诸多此类的话语，我想我没必要把剩下的都写下来给你们看。这种言辞千篇一律，我们大家都很熟悉。当校长讲到后三分之一时，大家变得骚动起来，一些坏男孩开始打架、鼓捣一些新花样儿。争吵声、私语声在教室里传开了，甚至连西德尼、玛丽这样通常不会被撼动的坚石都受到了影响。但是当沃尔特的声音变得低沉时，大家就突然坐好不出声了。校长宣布讲话完毕，全班就都显现出一种默默的感激之情。

大部分同学的窃窃私语都是由一件不平常的事引起的——有贵宾驾到：撒切尔律师，以及陪伴在他身边的一位苍老的男人，一位头发灰白、身体健壮且肥胖的中年绅士，还有一位端庄的女士，很显然她是这位绅士的夫人，这位女士还牵着一个孩子。一看到那个小孩，汤姆就变得躁动起来，他坐立不安，心烦气躁，心中还受到了良心的谴责——他现在可不敢看艾米·劳伦斯的眼睛，他再也不能忍受她充满爱意的眼神。他看见这个新来的小女孩走进教堂时，心中瞬间就燃起了爱之烈火，他马上就开始以他所能想到的方式进行各种炫耀，一会儿拍一下这个，一会儿扯一下那个的头发，一会儿又做起了各种鬼脸，总而言之，他用尽了能吸引一个女孩的所有手段来赢得她的赞赏。他的欢呼雀跃中闪过一丝尴尬——他想起了在这个女孩的公园中遭遇的丢人事，但这缕不快很快就被欢喜的海浪冲刷得不见踪影了。这群贵宾被引到了代表最高荣誉的座位上，沃尔特在结束演讲之后，立刻就把他们介绍给了大家。这个中年男子竟然是一个很了不起的人物：县里的大法官，这可是孩子们见过的最具威严的人物了，所以大家都很好奇他到底是什么做成的，才会这么牛。孩子们很想看看这种大人物大声吼叫会是什么样子，但又很害怕他会这么做。他来自二十英里外的康士坦丁堡——他一定到过很多地方，见过大世面——他甚至见过县法庭——据说法庭的屋顶是锡做的。教堂里弥漫着庄严的气氛，空气里悄无声息，一排排水灵灵的眼睛瞪得大大的。他们都看向大法官撒切尔，当地撒切尔律师的哥哥。杰夫·撒切尔马上迎上去，和这个伟大的人套近乎，好让整个学校的人都羡慕羡慕。他要是听到了同学们的私语，心里准会欢喜地唱歌：

"看啊，吉姆！他正朝台上走呢。看，快看！他还要跟他握手——噢！他正在跟他握手啊！说真的，你不希望你现在就是杰夫吗？"

沃尔特觉得自己在这位大人物面前应该"秀两手"，他四处忙活着，参与各种事情，发号施令，到处指指点点，几乎每个地方他都要说些什么。图书管理员也不停地"秀两手"：他抱着一堆书一会儿跑到这，一会儿跑到那，嘴里嘟嘟囔囔地不停地说着，但只有昆虫学家才乐意听他说话。年轻的女老师也在积极地"秀两手"：俯身安慰那些才挨过板子的同学，用温暖可爱的手指抚摸着那些坏小孩，充满爱意地拍着那些好孩子。年轻的男老师也来"秀两手"：浅浅地斥责着学生，展示着自己的权威以及对学校纪律的重视。几乎所有的老师，不管男女，都能在讲坛旁的图书馆里找到事情忙活，而且他们忙活的事情通常要两三个小时才能做完（他们表面上还装作非常着急的样子）。小女孩们也以各种方式表现着自己，小男孩们则兴奋地扔着纸团，扭打成一片，来展现自己。讲坛上的那位大人物正襟危坐，面带微笑却不失威严地看着整个屋子，他正沐浴在自己的光辉里——因为他也在"秀两手"。

沃尔特校长现在特想干一件事，这事儿能让他心中的欢乐膨大成狂喜。那就是，能给某个同学颁发《圣经》做奖品，从而展现出一个空前盛大的场面。有一些同学有几张黄票，但是没一个能攒够——他已经询问了好几个优秀的学生，要是那个德裔小孩可以完好地站在这里的话，他宁愿用自己的一切去换。

可是此刻，这个希望完全就是个泡影，然而出乎意料的情况发生了，汤姆·索亚拿着九张黄票、九张红票、十张蓝票走上了前台，他要求换一本《圣经》。这一举动简直就是个晴天霹雳，哪怕再过十年，沃尔特都不会觉得这个小鬼有可能得奖——但是现在这些凭证完好无损地摆在了他的面前。于是汤姆被请到了台上，和大法官以及其他的贵客站在一起，这可成了这十年间的头号新闻。这个结果在过去的十年间成了最出乎意料的事，这位新的英雄竟然可以站到法官大人的身旁，和他同台并肩，这下学校的孩子们就有两个伟大的人物可以凝视了。男孩子们都嫉妒得眼睛发红——那些曾把票子拿给汤姆换刷栅栏的特权的孩子们痛苦不已，但为时已晚，他们给的票子大大地增加了汤姆的财富，才成就了他今天的辉煌。男孩们鄙视着自己，竟然被这个如青草中的毒蛇一般狡诈的骗子给骗了。

　　奖品发给汤姆时，校长为了维持场面不得不强打起精神，但是很显然这个可怜的老头儿并不是发自内心地想要给他奖励，因为他的直觉告诉他这个小孩是耍了诡计才拿够票子的，他真是怀疑这个小孩有能力背出两千节《圣经》——他肯定连背二十节都成问题。

　　艾米·劳伦斯这会儿感到既骄傲又开心，她努力地让汤姆看到自己的脸——但是他根本就不看她。她觉得很纳闷儿，接着她感到一丝不安，一缕怀疑浮上心头，又被她撵走了——马上却又萌生了。她看到了，她看到他鬼鬼祟祟地朝某个方向瞟了一眼，她一下子就明白了，瞬间，她的心都碎了，她嫉妒极了，又感到很生气，于是她哭了起来，她现在恨每一个人，尤其是汤姆（她这样想着）。

　　汤姆被介绍给法官，但是他的舌头此时打了结，紧张得呼气也不均匀了，他的心颤栗着———一部分是由于大法官的威严，但是主要还是因为他面对的是她的爸爸。此刻若是夜晚，那么汤姆就会拜倒在他的脚下，将他奉若神明。大法官将手放在汤姆的头上，称他为一个小男子汉，他问了问汤姆的名字。这个男孩结结巴巴地喘着气说：

"汤姆。"

"不，我想问的不是汤姆——是——"

"托马斯。"

"对，这就对了，我就知道你的名字不只是汤姆，非常好，我打赌你还没说你的姓呢，告诉我吧，好不好？"

"托马斯，快告诉这位绅士你的姓，"沃尔特说道，"说的时候不要忘了说声先生，你可不能忘了礼节。"

"先生，我叫托马斯·索亚。"

"很好，真是个好孩子，好孩子！真是好，好小伙儿啊。两千节诗可真是够多的——真的非常非常多。你虽然为了背这个吃了很多苦头，但是你一定不会后悔的，因为知识比世界上任何东西都贵重。知识造就伟人和好人，将来有一天，你会成为一个伟人和一个好人，托马斯，到那时，你再回头看看，你会觉得你孩提时每周日来上主日学校是多么的值得。那时你会想说：'多亏了我的老师们教我学习——多亏了那个优秀的校长鼓励我，看着我成长，给我《圣经》作为奖励——一本精致的《圣经》——我永远都将它保存在我身边——多亏了各位圣贤将我教育成人！'托马斯——你不会收任何钱来出卖这两千节《圣经》——你绝对不会的。现在，你不会介意跟我和这位女士说点你学过的东西吧？你肯定知道所有十二门徒的名字。你不会介意告诉我耶稣最初任命的那两个门徒的名字吧？"

汤姆抠着一颗纽扣洞，他看上去局促不安，红着脸，眼睛盯着地面。沃尔特先生的心也跟着他一起沉了下去，他暗自想着，这个小孩肯定连这个最简单的问题都答不出来——为什么法官要问他这个呢？他觉得自己现在有必要说两句：

"告诉这个绅士吧，托马斯——不要害怕。"

托马斯仍然不吭声。

"好吧，我知道你会告诉我的，"这个女士说道，"这两个门徒的名字是——"

"大卫和哥利亚！"

让我们发发慈悲，拉上幕帘，别再往下看了吧。

第五章

　　大约是十点半的样子，小教堂的那口破钟开始打铃了。人们随即聚集起来去听牧师上午的讲道。主日学校的孩子们在教室里分散开，跟他们的父母一起坐在长椅上，以便监督。波丽姨妈也来了，汤姆、西德尼和玛丽都跟她坐在一起——汤姆被姨妈安排在过道边坐着，这是为了让他尽量远离敞开的窗子以及窗外那极具诱惑的夏日风景。过道里走来了一大群人：以前生活滋润，但是现在却很落魄而且已经上了年纪的邮政局长；市长以及他的老婆——除了这个市长，人们倒还有一些不必要的东西；治安官，道格拉斯寡妇——她已经四十岁了，但却仍然漂亮精明，慷慨大方，她有着一副好心肠，家境阔绰，她那位于山上的宅子可是村里唯一气派如宫殿的房子，每逢过节，圣彼得堡人最能自夸的就数她的热情好客以及出手大方；还有那德高望重，身材伛偻的沃尔德少校及其夫人；远道而来的新贵族里弗森律师；接下来就是村子里的头号美女，后面跟着一群身穿上等细麻布衣服，扎着彩色绸带，惹人爱怜的女孩们；再下来就涌进了镇里所有的年轻职员——他们刚还站在一起啃着甘蔗，围成一个圈，吮着手指头，痴痴地看着这群姑娘，直到最后一个女孩从他们的包围中冲出来他们才进来；最后进来的是模范男孩威利·马福森，他对自己的母亲体贴入微，好像她是雕花玻璃做的一样。每次他都领着母亲来教堂，这已成了所有妈妈们的骄傲。但是男孩子们都恨他，因为他太听话了，而且，大人们动不动就拿他来教训自己。他那白手绢从屁股口袋里露出来了一截——每个星期天都是这样的，好像每次都是不小心露出来了一样。汤姆根本就没有手绢，所以他可瞧不起那些拿手绢擦鼻涕的人。

现在会众已经完全集合完毕，那口破钟又响了一次，用来警告那些落在后面的人。之后，教堂里笼罩着一种庄严的肃穆，只有边座上的唱诗班还在窃笑、交头接耳。一直以来，在做仪式的过程中唱诗班里总会有人不住地窃笑、说悄悄话。曾经倒是有一个有教养点的唱诗班，可是我已经忘记了他们现在在哪里唱诗了。那是很多年前的事，我现在几乎都记不起来什么了，不过我想应该是在国外。

牧师分发了赞美诗本，然后他用一种在当地十分受崇敬的特殊音调，津津有味地把诗读了一遍。接着用适中的音量开始了朗读，然后他的声音稳步升高，直到渐渐攀爬到某个高度，再将最高音落到的那个字重读了出来，接着音调骤然下降，就像从跳板上一跃而下一样：

他人奋战争荣，血洒疆场；

我岂能安坐绣榻，由人抬入天堂？

人们认为他是个非常优秀的诵读者，在教堂举行"恳亲会"时，他总是被叫来读诗，每当他读完时，女士们就会把手扬起然后让它们无力地落到腿上，她们还会转着眼睛，摇头晃脑，仿佛在说："这简直太美好了，难以用语言诉说啊，人间能有如此美妙的声音真是太好了啊。"

唱完赞美诗后，牧师大人斯普格拉先生宛如一个公告牌一样，念着诸如会议、团体等的通知，他就这样喋喋不休地念着，好像要念到世界末日那天才会停下——这个古怪的习俗在美国一直保留至今，就算在当下这个报纸满天飞的年代，这种习俗仍出现在各个城市。通常情况下，一个传统习俗越是不合理，就越是难以革除。

现在，牧师开始做祷告了，这是篇题材广泛，面面俱到的佳作：

它为教堂祈祷，为教堂里的小孩儿们祈祷，为村里的其他的教堂祈祷，为村子祈祷，为全县祈祷，为整个州祈祷，为州里的官员祈祷，为美国祈祷，为美国的教堂祈祷，为议会祈祷，为总统祈祷，为政府的官员祈祷，为那些在波涛汹涌的大海上颠簸的可怜水手祈祷，为在欧洲君主制以及东方专制的铁蹄下呻吟的千万劳苦大众而祈祷，为那些领受了圣光和福音却还闭目塞听的人祈祷，为遥远的海岛上的异教徒们祈祷。最后牧师祈求他将要说的话能够得到上帝的恩典和宠爱，能够像一粒埋在沃土中的种子一样，季节一到，就会有个大丰收。阿门。

随后在一阵衣服的沙沙声中站着的人们都坐下去了，本书所讲述的那个男孩并不喜欢这篇祷词，他只是忍受着这一切——也许他根本就忍不了。在整个过程中，他都焦躁得不得了，有意无意地听着牧师所讲的细节——因为他没有听进去，但是他熟悉牧师每次都要讲的这些陈词滥调——只要祷词中加入一丁点儿新的内容，他的耳朵就能辨别出来，然后就会对这些新内容恨之入骨。他觉得加进这些新内容一点也不公平，可恶极了。在牧师布道的中途，一只苍蝇飞了过来落到了他前面的椅子背上，它一会儿用爪子搓来搓去，一会儿用前腿儿挠着头，挠得十分起劲儿，好像非要把头挠下来不可一样，这样它那细线一样的脖子就看得一清二楚。它又用后腿不停地扒拉着翅膀，好像在熨燕尾服一样想把翅膀捋平。它安详自若地打扮着，好像知道此时停在这儿非常安全一样。汤姆看着这只苍蝇的一举一动，心里痒痒得难受极了。而且事实上这只苍蝇现在确实是安全的，因为汤姆想伸手去抓它——但又不敢——他相信只要他在祷告的过程中做这样的事，他的灵魂就马上会受到惩罚。但是当牧师说完最后一句话后，他就攥起手并悄悄地把手伸了出来，牧师刚一说完"阿门"，这个苍蝇就变成了战俘。他的姨妈瞅见了他的行为，呵斥他放了这只苍蝇。

牧师念完了祷文，就用单调的声音絮叨起来，他说的东西太枯燥了，很多人都瞌睡得直点头——他讲的是地狱之火的问题，地狱之火是那么的可怕，但是注定可以被拯救的人少之又少，所有的人简直都不值得被救。汤姆数着布道词的页数，在每次去教堂之后，他都能知道布道词都有多少页，但是除此之外，他几乎啥也不知道。然而，这一次，他对布道词感兴趣了那么一小会儿，这位牧师描绘了一幅千禧年之际全世界人民团聚在一起的宏伟又形象的画面：狮子和羊羔歇息在一起，小孩子牵引着它们。但是汤姆却完全没有感受到牧师所描述的悲怆以及盛大，这对他一点教育意义也没有起到。他只一心想着那个主人公在众人面前是多么的威风，一想到这，他的脸上不自觉地就挂起了神采，他暗暗想道，要是那个狮子比较温顺的话，他真想当那个小孩。

随着牧师继续讲着无聊的东西，汤姆又重新陷入了痛苦之中，他很快想起自己还有一个宝贝，于是把它拿了出来。这是一个大个儿的黑色甲壳虫，它的下巴特别的大——汤姆叫它为"大钳甲虫"。它被放在一个装雷管用的盒子里，这个甲壳虫被拿出来后做的第一件事就是夹他的手指，汤姆本能地弹了一下指头，甲壳虫就被甩到了过道里，摔了个四脚朝天。汤姆把手上的手指头放到嘴里吸了吸，甲壳虫仰在那里，无助地扑棱着爪子，但是却翻不过来身。汤姆看见了它的样子，很想把它抓回来，但是他够不着。其他的人因为实在是对布道词不感兴趣，也注意到了这只甲壳虫，他们也盯着它瞅。后来，一只四处游荡的鬈毛狮子狗慢慢地走了过来，夏日静谧、暖暖的空气把它搞得懒洋洋的，有些郁闷，于是厌烦了被圈着，它走出来想要透透气。它看见了这只甲壳虫，此时甲壳虫正高高地翘着尾巴，摇摆着想要起来。它小心翼翼地勘测着地上的这个东西，随后又绕着它转了几圈，然后又保持着一个比较安全的距离嗅了嗅，接着又绕着它走了几圈，这下它胆子变得大些了，然后就靠近嗅了嗅。紧接着，它张开嘴，谨慎地咬向它，可惜没有咬到，于是它又咬了一下，接着是第二下，显然它已经开始享受这种消遣了。然后将肚皮贴地放在两个前爪之间，继续玩着它的游戏，最后它玩腻了，变得有些漫不经心，心不在焉了。于是打起了盹，下巴一点一点地往下耷拉，最后碰到了它的敌人。结果被这个甲壳虫夹了一下，只听见一声惨叫，狮子狗的头摇晃了起来，而甲壳虫被甩出了两米之远，这次它又被摔了个四脚朝天。过道上的人们看到这儿，心里乐开了花，有些人甚至拿扇子或手帕遮住了脸，汤姆也着实的开心。这条狗看起来很傻，可能它自己也是这么觉得的。它心里充满了愤怒，想着怎么样去报仇。所以它走近了甲壳虫，准备再一次小心翼翼地进攻，它从甲壳虫的周围都攻击了一遍，前爪拍在距甲壳虫一米的地方，甚至用牙凑近了咬，它摇头晃脑地折腾了好一阵儿直到耳朵又耷拉了下来。这下它又一次厌烦了，试图去打一只苍蝇来自娱自乐，但是它并没有从中获得乐趣，接着它围了一会儿蚂蚁玩，鼻子紧贴着地面，结果又很快就玩累了，于是它打起了哈欠，呜呜地叫着，完全忘记了甲壳虫的存在，结果就一屁股坐在了甲壳虫上面！然后，就听到一阵痛苦的狂叫，这只狗沿着过道一边跑一边继续狂叫。它继而穿过了圣坛前面的讲台，跑到了另一边的过道上，然后跑过了好几个门口，一直跑到了回家的路上。它越跑叫越疼，最后就像一个毛茸茸的彗星一样闪着光亮，以光速跑到了自己的轨道上。终于，这只疼得要疯了的狗突然脱离了轨道，冲到了主人的大腿上，主人把它从窗户那儿赶了出去，它的疼痛才慢慢地减退，那痛苦的声音才渐渐消失在了远方。

而此时，教堂里的人们都憋着笑，涨红了脸，牧师也停下了布道，不过他很快又讲了起来，但他却讲得磕磕巴巴，给人留下深刻印象的可能性已经消失殆尽了。因为即使他讲到最严肃的地方，也会有后排的人躲在椅子背后面抑制不住地笑，好像这个可怜的牧师讲了一个大笑话一样。当这场磨人的讲话终于结束，牧师也为大家做了祷告之后，人们如释重负般地得到了解脱。

汤姆·索亚十分高兴地回了家，他暗自想着，神圣的礼拜出点岔子还真是蛮有趣的。只有一点他觉得有些罪恶感，那就是虽然他乐意让狮子狗跟他的甲壳虫一起玩耍，但是他觉得自己不该把它从口袋里拿出来。

第六章

很快星期一的早上到了，汤姆觉得很不爽，每个星期一他都这么觉得，因为星期一标志着一个星期悲惨的学校生活又开始了。他极不情愿地开启了这一天，他宁愿压根儿就没有放过假，因为这会让禁锢在学校这几天显得更加枯燥。

汤姆躺在床上鼓捣这事儿，他真希望现在生病了，这样就能待在家不去上学了，而这也还是有可能的。所以他仔细检查了一下自己的身体，但是什么病都没有发现，于是他又检查了一遍。这次他觉得自己能勘测出肚子疼的症状，于是他开始抱着极大的希望，自己鼓着劲儿，但是很快他的肚子疼就减轻了，最终一点也不疼了。他还是不死心，又打起了别的主意。突然，他有了一个新发现——上颚的一个牙齿松动了。这真是太走运了！他刚要开始呻吟，就像他说的，这叫作"启动第一步"，他又想起了如果他跟姨妈抱怨他的牙疼死了，姨妈就会把它拔出来，那样的话才真会疼死了。所以他想不如把牙先留着，另外再想办法。可是过了好一会儿，他什么也没想出来，突然他想到一个医生曾对他提到过一个病人，该病人得了一种病，躺了两三个星期，差点把手指头都烂掉了。所以这个男孩赶忙把他疼痛的脚趾从被子里伸出来，翘得老高来检查检查，但是现在他并没有发现异常症状，然而，能有目前这个状态就已经很值得来碰一碰运气了。所以他精神高度集中，不停地呻吟起来。

但是西德尼仍然迷迷糊糊地睡着。

汤姆更加起劲儿地呻吟着，想象着自己已经感受到了脚趾的剧痛。

可是西德尼还是没醒。

于是汤姆大张旗鼓起来，他边喊着"西德尼！西德尼"边摇他。

这一下西德尼可彻底醒了，然后汤姆就开始嗷嗷地叫着，西德尼先是打了个哈欠，接着又伸了伸懒腰，一边低哼着一边用手肘把自己撑了起来。他看了看汤姆，汤姆继续呻吟着，西德尼说：

"汤姆！汤姆啊！"

没有人回答。

"嗨，汤姆！汤姆！汤姆你到底怎么啦？"西德尼一边说着一边摇他，焦急地盯着汤姆的脸。

汤姆呻吟道：

"哦，不要这样，西德尼，不要这么摇我。"

"怎么啦？汤姆，你怎么了啊？我去叫姨妈来。"

"不，不要这么麻烦，我一会儿说不定就好了，不要叫任何人。"

"但是我必须这样做啊！汤姆，你可不能再这么呻吟了，这可太难受了，你这样大概有多长时间了？"

"有几个小时吧，天啊，哦，不要动，你会要了我的命的。"

"汤姆，你怎么不早点把我叫醒啊？天啊，汤姆，别叫了，听得我毛骨悚然，汤姆，这到底是怎么了啊？"

"我什么都原谅你了，西德尼（呻吟着），不管你做过什么，我都原谅你了，西德尼，把我的窗扇还有那只独眼猫拿给镇上新来的女孩，告诉她——"

此时，西德尼已经套上衣服跑了出去，汤姆这会儿还真是比较难受，他总是能沉浸在自己超级厉害的想象之中，所以他呻吟的声音更加真实了。

西德尼飞奔下楼，喊叫着：

"天啊，波丽姨妈，快来啊！汤姆要死了！"

"要死了？"

"是啊，别站在那儿了，快点来啊。"

"你说什么瞎话呢，我才不信！"

虽然这么说着，她仍然飞奔上楼，西德尼和玛丽跟在她的后面。姨妈的脸变得惨白，嘴唇也在不住地发抖。当她跑到汤姆床边上时，她喘着气儿说道：

"汤姆，汤姆！你怎么啦？"

"啊，姨妈，我——"

"你怎么啦？孩子，你到底怎么了啊？"

"天啊，姨妈，我脚趾疼得厉害。"

这个老妇人一屁股坐在了椅子上，笑了好一会儿，又哭了一会儿，接着又哭又笑了一会儿，然后才恢复了平静，接着她说：

"汤姆，你真是把我吓坏了，现在你赶紧给我闭上嘴，快点从被窝里爬出来。"

呻吟声立马停止了，脚上的疼痛也消失了。这个男孩觉得自己有点傻，于是他说：

"波丽姨妈，它刚真是太疼了，我都受不了了，都忘记了我的牙也很疼。"

"你的牙疼？你的牙怎么啦？"

"一个牙松了，它疼得要死。"

"好吧，现在你可别再吼叫了。张开嘴，嗯，你的牙齿确实是松了，但是这才不会就把你疼死了。玛丽，给我拿针线来，再到厨房里拿一块烧红的炭。"

汤姆说：

"啊，姨妈，求你了，不要拔牙，我现在不疼了。我再也不胡闹了，姨妈，别拔啊，我可不想待在家里不去上学。"

"嗯？你不想？是吗？所有的这些不都是因为你想待在家里不去上学好去钓个鱼？汤姆啊，汤姆，我是疼爱你的，而你似乎要用各种手段，各种调皮来敲碎我的心。"

此时，拔牙所用的器具已经拿来了，老太太在线的一头儿做了个圈然后拴在汤姆的牙上，又将另一头儿拴到了床柱上。然后她抓住那块火炭，突然把它靠向这个小孩，都快烧到他的脸了，之后就看见一个牙齿吊在床柱上左右摇晃。

但是这所受的苦也给汤姆带来了好处，早饭过后，在汤姆去学校的那一路上，每个碰见他的男孩都很嫉妒他，因为他可以从牙上的那个缺口处，用一种新型的令人羡慕的方式吐吐沫，这可招来了好几个小孩儿跟在他的后面看他表演。有一个孩子因为切到了自己的手指而成为大家崇拜的中心，此时，他发现自己黯然失色，一个跟随者都没有了。他心里感到很沉重，于是他说像汤姆·索亚这样子吐吐沫根本没什么了不起，他说这话的时候，满腔的鄙视，可他自己却不这么觉得。然而，另一个男孩朝他说了句"酸葡萄"，这个男孩就像一个过气儿的英雄一样，灰头土脸地跑了。

不久，汤姆就碰到了村里的不良少年哈克贝利·费恩，他是镇上一个酒鬼的儿子。镇上所有的妈妈们都讨厌哈克贝利，因为他懒惰粗俗，无法无天，而且品行恶劣——还因为所有的小孩都很羡慕他，乐意看他做各种违规的事，孩子们恨不得也跟他一样。汤姆也像那些有教养的小孩一样，他羡慕哈克贝利四处流浪的生活，但却被严格要求不能和他一起玩。所以他一有机会就会去找他玩。哈克贝利总是穿着大人们不要的衣服，所以他总穿得花里胡哨的，这一条那一块的。他的帽子又大又破，帽檐呈新月形。他的外套，在他穿外套的情况下，几乎能拖拉到脚后跟处，背后的扣子一直扣到屁股后面。而且他的裤子只由一个背带撑着，所以裤裆就松松垮垮地低垂着，像个大袋子一样，但是袋子却是空的。他如果不把裤管挽起来的话，走起路来就会在地上蹭来蹭去，全是灰。

　　哈克贝利来去都很自由。天儿好的时候，他就睡在别人家门口的楼梯上，要是碰上阴天，就睡在空桶里。他不用去学校，也不用去教堂。不必叫谁先生也不必听谁的话，他想什么时候去钓鱼或游泳，以及去哪钓，全凭自己的意愿。没有人会阻止他打架，他爱什么时候起床就什么时候起，他总是春天里第一个打赤足的男孩，也是秋天里最后一个穿鞋子的男孩。他从来不用洗澡，也不用被逼着穿干净的衣服。他可以毫无顾忌地骂人，爱骂什么就骂什么。总而言之，就是生活里的舒服事儿都让这个男孩给占了。圣彼得堡每一个受折磨、受束缚的男孩都是这么想的。

　　汤姆跟这个潇洒的流浪儿打招呼：

　　"好啊，哈克贝利！"

　　"你好啊，瞧瞧这个怎么样？"

　　"这是什么啊？"

　　"一只死猫。"

　　"让我看看，哈克。天啊，它都这么僵硬了，你在哪搞的这个？"

　　"从一个男孩儿那买的。"

　　"你用什么买的？"

　　"我给了他一张蓝票，还有一个从屠宰场那弄的膀胱。"

"你从哪弄到的蓝票啊？"

"两个星期前我从本·罗杰那用一个铁圈钩换的。"

"好吧——这个死猫换来有什么用呢？"

"有什么用？它能治瘊子啊。"

"不是吧！这能治瘊子？我知道治瘊子效果更好的东西呢。"

"我敢打赌你不知道，什么能治？"

"我知道的，就是用仙水。"

"仙水！我看仙水才一文不值呢。"

"你不会这么觉得的，对吧？你用过仙水了吗？"

"没有，我是没有，但是鲍勃·坦纳用过了。"

"谁跟你说他用过了啊！"

"是他告诉杰夫·撒切尔，然后杰夫又告诉了约翰尼·贝克，接着约翰尼又告诉了吉姆·霍里斯，然后吉姆讲给了本·罗杰，本又告诉了一个黑小孩，那个黑小孩就跟我说了，就这样！"

"好吧，就这样？他们都在说谎，至少除了那个黑小孩其余都在说谎，我不认识那个黑小孩，但是我还从没见过不会撒谎的黑人，这群骗子！那你跟我说鲍勃·坦纳是怎么用的仙水啊？哈克。"

"好吧，他就是拿手蘸了点烂树墩子里的雨水。"

"是在白天的时候吗？"

"那是当然了。"

"他是面向着树墩子然后蘸的吗？"

"是的，至少我打赌是的。"

"他蘸的时候说什么了吗？"

"这我可不能打赌，我可不知道。"

"哈！他就是用这种愚蠢的方式来欺骗别人说他用仙水治瘊子的

啊！嘿，这可不管用。你得独自一个人到森林里去，走到森林正中央装着仙水的树墩子那里，然后你要在半夜的时候背靠着树墩，把你的手伸到水里，嘴里念着：

'大麦大麦，还有玉米麸子；

仙水仙水，帮我治好这些瘊子。'

说完这些，你得快速走上十一步，走的时候眼睛要闭上，然后转三圈，然后就赶忙回家，一句话都不能说，因为如果你说话的话，刚念的咒语就失效了。"

"嗯，这听起来像是个好办法，但鲍勃·坦纳可没这么做。"

"说的对，伙计，你完全可以打包票他没有这样做，因为他可是全镇长瘊子长得最多的人了，要是他知道怎么用仙水了他一个瘊子都不会长了，我用这种方法都已经除掉两只手上的几千个瘊子了，哈克，我老是喜欢玩青蛙，所以手上经常长瘊子，有时候，我还能用豆子除掉瘊子。"

"对啊，用豆子是挺不错的，我也用过。"

"是吗？你是怎么用的？"

"你要把豆子掰开，然后把瘊子戳开，好让它流点血，然后你把血涂到一片豆子上，接着你要挖一个洞，半夜的时候，在月亮的阴影下，把豆子埋在洞里。你就会发现这个有血的一半豆子就会拼命地吸啊吸，想要把另一半也吸过去，这样就能帮着治瘊子，很快瘊子就能好了。"

"对，就是这样，哈克——就是这样，你在埋豆子的时候还要说'下去吧豆子，走开吧瘊子，不要再来纠缠我'，这样会更有效的。乔·哈泼就是这么干的。他差不多所有的地方都去过，连库恩威尔都去过呢。那么你现在告诉我，你要怎么用死猫治瘊子呢？"

"让我告诉你吧，你把死猫拿上，差不多在半夜的时候跑到坟墓里——找个埋坏人的坟，在半夜的时候，恶鬼就会来，大概会来两个或者三个，但是你是看不见他们的，你只能听到类似于刮风这样的声音，或许你能听到他们讲话，当他们把那个坏蛋弄走的时候，你就把猫朝他们身后一扔，然后说'恶鬼跟着死尸，死猫跟着恶鬼，瘊子跟着死猫，我跟你一刀两断'这样的话，瘊子就被他们弄走了。"

"听起来不错，你这样试过吗，哈克？"

"没有，但是霍普金斯老太太跟我说这样就行。"

"好吧，我就知道是她跟你说的，因为大家都说她是个巫婆。"

"可不是嘛，汤姆，我早就知道她是个巫婆，她曾对我爸爸施过术，爸爸这么对我说的，有天他在路上走着，看到她正要向他施术，所以爸爸就捡起了一块石头，要不是她躲得快，他就砸中她了。呃，那天晚上当他喝醉的时候，他就从屋顶上滚了下来，摔断了胳膊。"

"天啊，这个真可怕，你爸爸怎么知道她要对他施术？"

"上帝啊，爸爸可以轻易地看出来，爸爸说要是别人两眼直直地盯着你，他们就是在向你施术，特别是如果他们还喃喃地说着什么的时候，因为他们正在倒背天主经。"

"嗯嗯，哈克，你什么时候打算用这只死猫？"

"今天晚上，我打赌那些厉鬼准要去捉霍斯·威廉姆老头儿。"

"但是他们是周六埋的他，他们不会周六晚上就把他勾走了吗？"

"你想啊，他们的咒文不到半夜怎么显灵啊？而且接下来就是周日，恶鬼在周日不会四处走动的，虽然我不能打赌他们一定不会走动。"

"我可从没想到过这个，不过确实是这样的，晚上让我跟你一起去可以吗？"

"当然可以——如果你不害怕的话。"

"害怕！这倒真不至于，那到时候你学猫叫好吗？"

"行啊——那你可得应声啊，如果你能逮到机会的话。上次，你让我学猫叫，我就一直喵喵地叫个不停，直到老海斯向我扔了块砖头还说'该死的猫'，所以我也朝他的窗户扔了一块石头——你可千万别把这说出去了。"

"我不会的，那天晚上我确实应不了声儿，因为我的姨妈一直都在看着我，但是今天晚上我会叫的，咦？那是什么？"

"没什么，就是一只虱子。"

"你从哪儿弄到的？"

"在林子里弄的。"

"你要用它来做什么啊？"

"我也不知道，我不想把它卖了。"

"好吧，这不过就是一只小得不得了的虱子。"

"噢，谁都可以诋毁一只不属于自己的虱子，我可对它很满意，它对我而言可是一只不错的虱子。"

"切，虱子到处都是，要是我想的话，我可以弄来一千只。"

"好吧，那你干吗不去弄呢？因为你清清楚楚地知道你弄不来。这只虱子出来的可是相当的早，是我今年看见的头一只呢。"

"噢，哈克——我用我的牙换这个怎样？"

"让我看看你的牙。"

汤姆掏出一团纸，然后小心翼翼地打开了纸团。哈克贝利瞅着它，表现出很想要的神态。这真是个很大的诱惑，最后他说：

"这真的是你的牙吗？"

汤姆扬起嘴角，把他牙床上的空缺显示给他看了看。

"嗯，那就这样吧，"哈克贝利说，"交易达成。"

当汤姆来到那个可怜兮兮的木板学校时，他迈起了轻快的步伐，看上去好像是急急忙忙奔过来的一样。他把帽子挂在钉上，然后就麻利地坐进了座位上。老师高坐在那个木夹板底子的扶手椅上，他正在这让人昏昏欲睡的学习气氛中打着盹。汤姆进教室的声音惊醒了他。

"汤姆·索亚！"

汤姆知道如果他被叫了全名，就意味着麻烦要来了。

"先生！"

"到这里来，小伙子，为什么你又跟平常一样迟到了呢？"

汤姆正要撒个谎逃过这一劫，但是当他看见了两条金黄色的辫子悬在一个女孩的背上的时候，他马上就被爱的电流击中了。汤姆知道在那个女孩旁边有一个空位，而且是女孩们旁边唯一的空位。所以他马上就说：

"我拦下了哈克贝利·费恩，然后跟他说了会儿话。"

老师被气得脉搏都要停了，他瞪着汤姆，不知道该说什么好。同学们读书的声音停了下来，大家都很怀疑这个傻瓜孩子是不是疯了。老师说：

"你——你做了什么？"

"我跟哈克贝利·费恩说了会儿话。"

"汤姆·索亚，这是我听过的最震惊的坦白，不打你几鞭真是不能弥补你所做的错事。把外套脱了。"

老师狠狠地打了汤姆，直到胳膊都打累了才停止了鞭打。接着老师命令道：

"现在，小伙子，去跟女孩坐在一起，当作是给你警告。"

教室里马上涌起了一阵窃笑，这看起来让这个男孩很窘迫，但是实际上这是他求之不得的好事，他是多么的爱慕那个不知名的偶像啊。他坐到了松木长椅的一头，然后这个女孩马上就往另一头挪了挪，她把头也偏到了另一边。教室里的同学们互相递起了眼色，互相推搡着，大家都在窃窃私语。但汤姆只是静静地坐在那里，他的手放在眼前的长桌上，看起来他正在专心地看书。

过了一会儿大家就把注意力转走了，教室里跟往常一样又响起了枯燥无味的读书声。这时这个男孩就开始偷偷地看这个女孩。女孩发现了，然后她朝他噘了噘嘴，把背对着他有一分钟之久。当她小心翼翼地又转了过来的时候，发现面前放了一个桃子。她把桃子推开了，但是汤姆又慢慢地把桃子推了过来，于是她又把桃子推开了，不过已经没有那么充满敌意了。汤姆耐心地把桃子推回了原位，然后她就没再理他了，于是汤姆就在他的石板上鬼画符般地写着："请收下吧——我还有很多呢。"这个女孩瞟了瞟石板上的字，但是没有说什么。接下来，这个男孩就在石板上画了起来，还用他的左手捂着不让别人看。有好一会儿这个女孩是没有搭理他的，但是她天生的好奇心马上就开始显露出来，虽然从表面上看不出来。女孩不露声色地想要看一眼，而汤姆此时也装作不知道，最后她只好投降了，然后犹犹豫豫地小声说道：

"让我看看吧。"

汤姆只把手收了一点，露出了画的一部分，他画了一个沉闷的房子，房子周围有两个三角墙，还画了一个往外冒着滚滚灰烟的烟囱。女孩开始津津有味地看着，把别的事都忘了。当汤姆画完的时候，她盯着画看了一阵，然后小声地说：

"要是能再画个人就更好了。"

于是艺术家神笔一挥，就在前院画了一个人，样子活像个起重机，一脚都能跨过整个房子。但是这个女孩并不吹毛求疵，她对这画出的怪物很满意，于是她说：

"这个男人画得真好看——快把我也画上吧。"

汤姆画了一个沙漏，一轮满月，他还给月亮画了几个支棱着的四肢，然后在那伸出的指头上加了一个矫揉造作的扇子。女孩说：

"这也画得很好——真希望我也能画。"

"这很简单，"汤姆低声说道，"我可以教你的。"

"是吗？你真的会教我？什么时候交？"

"中午的时候怎么样？你用回家吃饭吗？"

"你要是中午教我的话，我就留下来。"

"好啊——那就这样定啦，你叫什么呀？"

"贝琪·撒切尔，你叫什么呢？对啊，我知道的，你叫汤姆·索亚。"

"当我受罚的时候我才叫这名字。我没事儿的时候叫汤姆，你就叫我汤姆吧，好吗？"

"好。"

汤姆又开始在石板上写起了字，还不让这个女孩看见。但是她这回却没有因此退缩，她恳求他让她看看，于是汤姆说：

"呃，我没写什么。"

"你明明写了啊。"

"没有，我没写什么，你不会想看的。"

"我想看，我真的想看，快点让我看看吧。"

"你要跟别人说的。"

"不，我不会的——绝对绝对不会说。"

"真的，你不会想看的。"

"你怎么能这样呢，我就要看。"说着，女孩把她的小手按在汤姆的手上，他们推了一小会儿，最后汤姆假装推不过，手让开了一点，直到他写的字"我爱你"完全露出来。

"天啊，你这坏蛋！"然后她使劲儿戳了一下他的手，但脸上泛起了红晕，从她的神采间看得出她很开心。

就在这时，汤姆感觉到耳朵被人慢慢地重重地揪着，不觉地，他整个人都被拎了起来。他被死死地揪着耳朵在教室里转了一圈，然后在同学们尖锐的笑声中坐回了自己的位置。随后老师就站到了他旁边，让他十分痛苦地过了好一会儿，最后老师终于一言不发地回到了讲台上。尽管汤姆的耳朵刺痛不已，心里却乐开了花。

当快要放学的时候，汤姆才认认真真地想要学一会儿，但是他心里太急躁了，都学不进去。相反，当他在班上读书的时候，他读得一团糟，而且在地理课上他把湖认成了山，把山认成了河，还把河认成了洲，最终弄得一塌糊涂。在拼写课上，他把婴儿都能写对的字拼反了，直到他得了个倒数第一，还不得不交出了那块白镴奖牌，那可是他挂在脖子上炫耀好几个月的奖牌。

第七章

　　汤姆越是想努力地集中注意力看书，他的思想就越不集中。所以最后他叹了口气，打了哈欠，放弃了。他觉得中午的休息好像永远都来不了，周围都是死寂的空气，没有一丝活力，这可是最让人困倦的时候，二十五个学生边打着瞌睡边不停地读着书，听起来就像一群蜜蜂在嗡嗡地叫。远处炽热的阳光下，卡迪夫山青翠的山峦在闪着微光的热浪中染上了紫色的光晕。空中有几只鸟拍着懒洋洋的翅膀，除了几只母牛之外就再也看不到一只活物，这几只母牛还睡着了。汤姆的心里直痒痒，他很想早点下课，或者找点有趣的事来打发这乏味的时间。于是他把手插进兜里摸了一阵，脸上顿时放出光彩，喜形于色，只是他自己没感觉到。只见他偷偷地把那个装雷管的盒子拿了出来，然后把虱子从盒子中放了出来，接着便把虱子放到了长桌子上。估计此时这个虱子跟汤姆一样的暗自高兴，但是它高兴得过早了，因为当它满心欢喜地准备走开时，汤姆用大头针把它拨到了另一边，迫使它改变方向。

　　汤姆的密友坐在他旁边，跟汤姆刚才一样受罪，现在他立马就对桌上的玩物产生了浓厚的兴趣。汤姆的这个密友就是乔·哈泼，他们平时是铁哥们儿，但是一到周六就成了彻底的敌人。乔从翻领上也取下了一个别针，之后就开始训练这个狱中之囚。他们越玩越觉得有意思。很快汤姆说，这样玩的话都会干涉对方，两个人都玩不好，所以他把乔的石板拿到了桌子上，然后在板之间从上到下画了一条界线。

"现在，"汤姆说，"要是它爬到你那边，你就可以逗它，我就不会干涉你，但是如果你让它跑掉，跑到我这边的话，你就不能干涉，只要我能让它没法儿过界。"

"行啊，那你先来吧，发动游戏吧。"

这个虱子马上就从汤姆那逃开，跨过了边界。乔逮着它玩了一会儿，结果它也溜走了，又跑回到边界那边。游戏就这样进行了好几轮，当一个孩子带着浓厚的兴趣担心着虱子会跑到另一边的时候，另一个孩子也会饶有兴致地观看着，这两个小脑袋就紧紧地凑在一起俯在石板上，他们已经完全沉浸在自己的世界里了。最后看起来幸运女神是偏向乔这一边的，虱子往这边走走，又往那边跑跑，当然还会试试其他的路子，变得跟这两个孩子一样又兴奋又紧张，但是每次当虱子快要逃脱的时候，也就是汤姆的手痒痒得想要拨两下的时候，乔就会敏捷地拿针给它掉个头，让它继续在自己的地盘上。最后，汤姆完全受不了了，面前的诱惑实在是太大了。所以他把手伸了出去拿针去拨虱子，乔可就生气了。他说：

"汤姆，你不能插手啊。"

"我就只想玩一会儿，乔。"

"不行，哥们儿，这可不公平，快点让开。"

"去你的，我又不玩很久。"

"快让开，我警告你。"

"我凭什么让开。"

"你必须让开——它现在在我这边。"

"把话说清楚了，乔·哈波，这个虱子到底是谁的啊？"

"我才不管是谁的——它现在就是在我这边，你就不应该碰它。"

"好吧，这样的话我还就碰了，它是我的，我让它高兴它就高兴，"

让它死它就得死。"

于是乔就对着汤姆的肩膀猛捶了下去，在接下来的两分钟之内，只见两个男孩的夹克上尘土飞扬，而全班的学生都来围观看热闹。他们打得非常投入，直到老师轻手轻脚地来到了教室，并观赏他们打架。老师看了好一会儿，之后对他们拳打脚踢，为这场打架增加了新的花样。

当中午下课的时候，汤姆就飞奔到了贝琪·撒切尔的身边，在她耳边轻轻说道：

"戴上你的帽子，然后假装你在往家里走，当你走到那个拐角的时候，避开别人，顺着小路返回来，我会从另一条路上走，然后跟你一样返回来。"

于是他们各自都跟着一群同学走了，不一会儿，这两个孩子就在小路的尽头相遇了，当他们返回到学校时，这偌大的学校就只是他们两个人的世界了。他们并肩坐了下来，前面放了一块石板，汤姆给了贝琪一支铅笔，然后握着她的手，手把手地教着她画画，于是他们就又创造出了一座令人惊叹的房子。当渐渐画烦的时候，他们就开始谈心，汤姆幸福的感觉就像在蜜罐里游泳一样。他说：

"你喜欢老鼠吗？"

"不！我很讨厌老鼠！"

"好吧，我也讨厌它们——那些活生生的小东西。但是我指的是死老鼠，可以拿根绳子拴在尾巴上，然后在头上转着玩。"

"不喜欢！我对老鼠一点都不感兴趣，我喜欢吃口香糖。"

"是嘛，我早该问你这个的！我真希望我现在能有些口香糖。"

"是吗？我有一些，我会让你嚼一会儿，但是你必须要还给我。"

这可真是太让汤姆满意了，所以他们轮着嚼着口香糖，开心地坐在长椅上把腿荡来荡去。

"你看过马戏吗？"汤姆说。

"嗯，当我表现好的时候，我爸爸有时会带我去看。"

"我去看过三四回马戏呢——还可能更多。教堂可没马戏团那么有趣，在马戏团总有那么多的把戏可以看，我长大了就要去马戏团当一个小丑。"

"天啊，真的吗？这太好了，小丑们都那么可爱，全身都是花花绿绿的。"

"那当然啦，而且他们能挣好多钱——大部分情况一天能挣一块，本·罗杰就这么说的，贝琪，跟我说，你订过婚吗？"

"订婚是什么啊？"

"是什么！就是要结婚啊。"

"那可没有。"

"那你想吗？"

"我想会想吧，我也不知道，订婚是什么样子的？"

"什么样子？这可没有什么样子这一说。就是你告诉一个男孩，你除他之外不会再爱上别人，永远永远都不会。然后你亲一亲他，就是这样，任何一个男孩都会做这样的事。"

"亲一亲？为什么要亲一亲啊？"

"为什么？好吧，你知道的，就是——唉，反正他们就总这样做啊。"

"每个人都这样？"

"当然，每个相爱的人都这样做。你还记得我在石板上写过什么吗？"

"我——我记得。"

"是什么？"

"我不想跟你说。"

"那我跟你说好吗？"

"行——行吧，但是以后再说。"

"不行，现在就要说。"

"不行，现在不能说——明——明天再说吧。"

"天啊，不要，就现在说嘛，求你了，贝琪——我会轻轻地说的，轻轻地很快就说了。"

贝琪犹豫不决，汤姆满意地不作声了，然后用胳膊搂着她的腰，在她的耳际轻轻地，柔柔地说了出来，他的嘴唇贴近了她的耳朵，汤姆还补充说道：

"现在你也对我轻轻地说出来——就像我对你说一样。"

贝琪拒绝了好一会儿，然后说道：

"那你把头转过去，这样你就看不到了，然后我就会说，但是你不能告诉任何人——你会这样吗，汤姆？你不会的，对吗？"

"不，我绝对绝对不会，快说吧，贝琪。"他将脸转向了另一边。她害羞地弯下了腰，直到她呼出的气吹动着汤姆的鬈发，她说着，"我——爱——你！"

然后贝琪就跑开了，在桌椅之间不停地走着，汤姆在她后面追着，最后把她逼到了一个角落里，贝琪用白色的围裙捂住了羞红的脸，于是汤姆搂着她的脖子乞求道：

"贝琪，我们该做的都做了——就是剩下亲嘴了，你别害怕嘛——啥事都不会有，求你了，贝琪。"然后汤姆把她拉了过来抓住她的手。

贝琪一点点地退步，最后她放下了双手，她红通通的脸上写着挣扎，但是她还是屈服了，并靠了过来。汤姆亲了亲她红嫩嫩的嘴唇，说道：

"现在可算是都做完了，贝琪，你知道，这以后你就不能再爱上别的男生了，也不能再嫁给别的男生，除了我，永远永远都不能，你会做到吗？"

"嗯，除了你我不会再爱上其他任何人，汤姆，我也不会嫁给别人，除了你——你也不能娶别人，除了我。"

"那当然了，这可都是订婚的一部分，而且你要每天都来上学，我们放学回家的时候，你也要跟我一起走，当然是在没有人看到的情况下——而且在舞会上你要选我做舞伴，我也要选你，因为你订婚之后就是这样做的。"

"这真好，我以前可没听过。"

"天啊，这比你想象的还要好！我和艾米·劳伦斯——"

那双瞪大了的眼睛告诉了汤姆他犯了一个多大的错误，汤姆顿时不知道该怎么办。

"天啊，汤姆！我都不是第一个跟你订婚的人！"

这个小孩开始了哭泣，汤姆说道：

"别哭啊，贝琪，我再也不会在乎她了。"

"才不是呢，你在乎，汤姆——你知道你是在乎的。"

汤姆努力想要搂住她的脖子，但是她把他推开了，脸冲着墙，不停地哭。汤姆又尝试着搂她，嘴里还不停地说着情话，但是他又被拒绝了。于是他觉得自尊心受挫，就扭头走出了教室。汤姆在外面一动也不动地站了一会儿，心里不安极了，眼神时不时地瞥向门口，希望她能感到后悔，然后冲出来追他，但是她没有这样做。于是汤姆心里就难受极了，觉得这回是自己错了。现在让他往回走一步其实都很艰难，但是他鼓起了勇气，走回了教室。贝琪仍然站在教室的那个角落里冲着墙抽泣。汤姆的心被重重地打击到了，于是他走近了她，站在那里，不知道该怎么办，然后他支支吾吾地说着：

"贝琪，我——我真的只在乎你一个。"

没人理他——只有哭泣声。

"贝琪——"他祈求着喊道，"贝琪，你能说句话吗？"

她哭得更凶了。

汤姆掏出了他最心爱的宝贝——一个柴架上的铜把手，他把它举到她面前好让她看到，然后说：

"求你了，贝琪，你收下这个好吗？"

她一把就把它扔到了墙脚。然后汤姆就快步走出了教室，翻过了山，走了很远很远，那天他再也没回到学校。后来贝琪有点慌张，她跑到了门头，没有看见他，于是又飞奔到了操场里，结果他也不在那，然后她喊道：

"汤姆，回来吧，汤姆！"

她站在那努力听了一会儿，结果没有人回应她。此刻，只有寂静和孤单陪伴着她，所以她又坐了下来开始哭，并开始自责。这个时候，学生们都差不多回来了，她只好强忍住悲伤，让自己那颗破碎的心平静下来，整个下午她都像背了一个十字架似的，难受极了，没有一个人能够和她谈谈心，分享她的悲伤。

第八章

汤姆在小路上这儿躲一下那儿藏一下，直到他完全偏离了同学们走的那条路，这时，他才开始回味着悲伤，漫无目的地走着。他在一条小溪里来回了两三次，因为当时青少年之间流传着一种迷信，说是在水里过就可以摆脱追踪。一个半小时之后，他就消失在了卡迪夫山峦中的道格拉斯宅邸后面，学校的楼房隐匿在他身后的山谷中，已经模糊难辨了。他走进了一片郁郁葱葱的树林，选了一条人迹罕至的路抵达了森林深处，然后在一棵枝叶繁茂的橡胶树下坐了下来，他坐着的那块地上长满了苔藓。这里没有一丝风吹过；正午的酷热让鸟都不愿意唱歌；一切都让人想要昏昏欲睡，只有从远处传来的啄木鸟的笃笃声，时不时地会打破这种恍惚的状态。可这却更加突出了这林中弥漫着的寂静以及孤独。男孩的心沉浸在了忧郁之中，他的感觉跟周围的环境极其吻合。他静静地坐在那里，胳膊肘拄在膝盖上，手捧着脸，陷入了沉思。生活对于他而言仿佛就只有烦恼，他甚至都有一点羡慕那个才去世的吉米·霍吉斯。那一定很安详吧，他想道，永远都可以躺在无尽的黑暗中安睡，只有风沙沙地吹过树枝，抚摸着坟墓上的花草，永远都不会为任何事情惆怅或悲伤。如果汤姆在主日学校表现得好的话，他宁愿离去，守着那份安详。现在看看这个女孩，他曾做过什么对不起她的吗？什么都没有做，他本来抱着世上最美好的愿望，现在他却被当作一只狗来对待——真的就是一只狗。她总有一天会后悔的——也许那时已经太晚了，唉，除非他可以只暂时地死去！

　　当然一个年轻人的心是很有活力的，不可能长时间地受到束缚。汤姆不一会儿就慢慢地转向了生命意义的探究。如果他现在转头就走，神秘地消失了会怎么样？如果他就此离开——走很远很远，走到海那边的异国他乡，而且再也不回来又会有什么样的后果呢？她那时会有何感受！他又想到了要当小丑的想法，但只是感到很恶心，因为他现在正处在高贵而又庄重的精神世界，小丑的肤浅逗乐和斑点紧身衣自然是跟他现在的境界格格不入的。他才不要当一个小丑，他要当一名战士，还要身经百战，名扬四方之后衣锦还乡。不——还要比这更好，他要加入那些印第安人，与他们一起去捕野牛，深入崇山峻岭，跨过人迹罕至的大平原，身上插满了羽毛，涂满了让人惧怕的图腾，就这样昂首阔步走进主日学校，还应该是在一个昏昏欲睡的夏季的早上，大喊着战斗的口号，让人颤栗得血液都凝固了，那时他就能死死地抓住同学们充满无限嫉妒的眼球，但是这些绝对还不够，还有比这更加气派的事情。他要去当海盗！对，就是这样！现在，他未来的蓝图就在面前铺张了开来，闪烁着难以想象的光芒。那时他的名字将会响彻全世界，人们该多敬畏他啊！他将驾驶着那艘又长又矮的黑色赛艇——风暴之魂，穿梭在波涛汹涌的海面上，船头上插着那令人胆颤的旗帜在空中迎风飘扬，这该是多么的光芒万丈啊！在他声名鼎盛之期，他会突然出现在这个古老的乡镇，闯入教堂，饱经风霜的面庞闪烁着健壮的铜色，他穿着黑色丝绒紧身衣裤，脚蹬一双帅气的长筒靴，腰系一条深红色腰带，上面插满了马枪，身体一侧还要配一把血气润洗过的短剑，他那阔边帽子上的羽毛随风起舞，那面黑色旗帜迎风招展，上面还要印有一个骷髅头和两根交叉的大腿骨，那时他将满心欢喜地听人们悄声议论：“这就是汤姆·索亚大盗！——出没在西班牙海域的黑色复仇者！”

对，就是这样，汤姆决定了自己的未来。他将离家出走，来实现这个梦想。他会在明天早晨出发，因此他现在就要开始着手准备了。他必须要把自己所有的财宝收集到一起，于是走到附近的一个腐烂的树根下，开始用他那把巴洛牌小刀挖洞，很快他就凿到了树根，发出了空洞的声音。他把手放在那里，然后表情严肃地念道：

"没有到来的，快来！已经到来的，留下！"

然后他把土坷垃刨开，挖出了一块松木瓦。他将瓦块拿起，发现下面埋着一个四角都是松木瓦做成的精致小箱子，箱子里头有一个石头弹子，汤姆看到这非常吃惊！他困惑地挠了挠头，说道：

"好吧，我可没想到会是这种情况！"

于是他生气地将石头弹子撇在一边，在那里闷想着，原来这个迷信竟然不灵验，他和他的同伴们一直都相信的咒语竟然失败了。他们一直相信的就是，如果你埋下一个弹头，再念上几句咒语，让它埋个两星期，那么等你再去挖它的时候，你所有丢失过的弹头都会自己汇集在一起，不管它们曾经被丢了多远，它们都能自己再回来。但是现在，他彻头彻尾的失败了。汤姆所有的信念都从根基上被打垮了，他以前多次听说过成功的案例，从来没有见到它失败过，他没想到自己在这之前尝试了好几次，最后连埋在哪都找不到了。他困惑了好一会儿，最终想出应该是一些巫婆干扰了他的咒语，打破了这个法术。这个推断让他很满意，于是他四处寻找了一番，找到了一个小沙堆，沙堆中间有一个沙漏型的凹处，然后他跪在地上，冲着凹处喊道：

"小甲虫，小甲虫，告诉我我想知道的秘密！小甲虫，小甲虫，快点告诉我我想知道的秘密！"

沙堆有一点反应，不一会儿一只黑色的小甲虫钻了出来，但是又害怕地钻了回去。

"它不开口！肯定是一个巫婆捣的鬼，我就知道是这样。"

他知道对抗巫婆会是什么下场，于是他灰心丧气，不得不做了让步。但是他觉得自己还是应该把刚才扔掉的弹头收入囊中，于是他就耐心地到处搜寻那个弹头，但就是哪儿都找不到。于是他又回到了那个小宝箱旁边，然后小心翼翼地站在了刚刚扔弹头的地方，从口袋里掏出了另一个石弹头，接着也用同样的方式把这颗弹头扔了出去，口中还念道：

"好小子，快去找你的兄弟吧！"

他看着它掉到地上，然后过去捡，但是弹头扔得要么太远了要么太近了，于是他又试了两次，最后一次尝试时终于成功了。两个石弹头的距离不过一英尺。

就在此时，树林里的绿荫小道上隐隐传来了锡制玩具发出的声响，汤姆迅速脱掉上衣和裤子，把裤子的吊带做了腰带，接着他斩断了一片朽木后面的荆棘，找到了一个简陋的弓箭，一把木片剑，一个锡皮喇叭，不一会儿，他就抓起了这些武器飞奔在丛林间，赤着脚，身后挂着的外套随风飘拂。马上他就跳到了一棵大榆树下，吹了一声喇叭作为回应，然后蹑手蹑脚地四处张望，这边看看，那边瞧瞧，接着，他跟想象中的伙伴小心地说道：

"别急，伙计们，听我的口令再行事！"

这时，乔·哈泼出现了，他跟汤姆一样，全副武装，轻松上阵。汤姆喊道：

"站住，来者何人？竟擅自闯入我谢伍德森林！"

"我乃好汉吉斯朋，走遍天下，所向无敌，你是何方妖孽，竟敢如此——如此——"

"大胆!你竟敢口出狂言！"汤姆说道，他其实是在给乔提示词，因为他们都在背书上的内容。

"你究竟是何方人士竟敢如此猖狂？"

"我！我可是罗宾汉，你这小喽啰马上就能知道我的厉害！"

"这么说来，你真的是大名鼎鼎的绿林好汉？老子正想跟你决一雌雄，看看这林中宝地鹿死谁手，看剑！"

他们各持一把木片剑，把身上的包袱都扔到地上，两人脚抵着脚，做出格斗的架势，按照"两上两下"的打法，有模有样，小心翼翼地打了起来，过了一会儿，汤姆说道：

"听着，如果你真的有本事，那我们就痛痛快快地比一场！"于是他们就"痛快地"打了起来，打得两人气喘吁吁，大汗淋漓，后来汤姆就叫道：

"快倒下！快倒下！你为什么不倒下呢？"

"我才不会倒下！你为什么不自己倒下呢？你可是根本都招架不住了。"

"怎么可能，这点小伤算什么，我不可能败退的，书里可不是这样写的，书里还说'接着他反手一击，一把刺中了可怜的吉斯朋'，你应该转过身来让我刺中你的背部才对。"

确实没有理由违背书上白纸黑字的权威，所以乔转过了身，接了汤姆一剑，躺倒在地上。

"现在，"乔站起来说道，"你也应该让我刺一剑，这样才公平。"

"为什么？我可不能这样做，书里不是这么写的。"

"好吧，你可真是小气——就是这样。"

"好吧，听着，乔，你可以当塔克修士或者磨坊主的儿子马奇，拿着铁头木棒打我几下，或者我可以当诺丁汉郡长，你也当一会儿罗宾汉来杀我。"

这样可真是令人满意，于是他们继续进行了游戏。玩过之后，汤姆又当起了罗宾汉，遭到了那个修女的背叛，身受重伤，却无法医治，终于因失血过多而大伤元气。最后又由乔一人扮演所有的绿林好汉，哭哭啼啼地拖着汤姆前进，把他的弓箭塞进汤姆虚弱的手中，然后汤姆就说道："剑落之时，将可怜的罗宾汉埋在绿林之中。"说完，他就射出了手中的剑，身体向后倒，他本该就此辞世，但碰巧他躺在了一片荨麻上，于是他骤然跳了起来，那活蹦乱跳的样子一个死人是绝对做不出来的。

在这痛痛快快的打闹之后，男孩们穿戴好衣服，把他们的武器藏了起来，然后悲伤地离开了这里，从此就再也没有绿林好汉了，他们很想知道现代文明中有什么可以弥补这一切，他们说自己宁愿在谢伍德森林当一年的绿林好汉，也不愿意当一辈子的美国总统。

第九章

那天晚上九点半的时候，汤姆和西德尼像往常一样上床准备睡觉，他们做完了祷告后，西德尼很快就睡着了。汤姆清醒地躺在那里，焦躁地等着。当他觉得几乎都要到天亮的时候，听到了敲响的钟声，才十点！这可真是叫人绝望，他翻了个身，伸展伸展胳膊腿，但是又怕弄醒了西德尼，所以他只好静静地待着，盯着一片漆黑。所有的一切都笼罩在死寂中，在这片寂静中一些小小的，几乎听不见的动静开始慢慢地清晰可闻。首先听到的是滴答滴答的钟声，接着那老房子的屋梁也开始神秘地吱吱作响，楼梯也隐隐约约，嘎嘎地发出声音，很明显，鬼怪们出来活动了。从波丽姨妈的卧室里传来了一阵沉稳而又均匀的鼻鼾声，一只吵闹的蟋蟀乱叫着，让人分辨不出声音究竟是从哪里发出的。接下来，床头缝里一只小蛀虫发出的可怕声响让汤姆不寒而栗——因为这意味着某个人的时日已经不多了。紧接着，远处传来一只狗的长嚎，在漆黑的夜空上盘旋，更远一点的地方也响起了一阵嚎叫作为回应。汤姆害怕极了，最后他认定时间已经静止了，无尽的永恒已经来到，于是他不由自主地打起了瞌睡，时钟敲响了十一点，但是他没有听到。最终，在迷迷糊糊的昏睡之中他好像听到了一阵猫儿叫春的凄惨声音，邻居家打开窗户的声音打断了猫叫，只听到一阵咒骂："死猫，见鬼去吧！"接下来一只空瓶砸到他姨妈的木屋顶上的声音惊醒了汤姆，片刻之间，他已经穿好了衣服，他从窗口爬了出去，顺着屋顶慢慢地爬行着，他小心翼翼地"喵喵"叫了一两回，然后跳到木屋顶上，接着下到地上。只见哈克贝利拿着他的死猫站在了那里，男孩们匆匆走掉，消失在了黑暗之中。半个小时之后，他们就穿行在了坟包中长长的杂草间。

这是一个西部的旧式坟场，它坐落在一个小山上，离村子大概有一英里半之远。它的四周围了一圈歪歪扭扭的栅栏，有的栅栏板向前倾着，有的向外斜着，就是没有能好好伫立着的。杂草在墓地里肆无忌惮地生长着，所有的坟墓都塌陷下去了，在这里，没有一块墓碑，有的只是圆突突的生虫了的木板牌无依无靠地斜插在坟墓上。木板上还印着"纪念某某某"之类的字样，但是即使在有月光的情况下，大多数的字迹都已经难以辨别。

一阵微风吹过了树梢，汤姆害怕这会是鬼魂对他们的抱怨声，抱怨他们的打扰。男孩们几乎没说什么话，就算说话，也只敢压着气息悄悄地说，因为此时这周围只有一片死寂，让他们从灵魂深处感到压抑。他们找到了那座刚建的新坟，便将自己隐藏在了离坟几英尺远的大榆树下，这是三棵根长到一起的大榆树。

然后他们静静地等了似乎有很长时间，此时，只有远处猫头鹰呜呜的叫声打破这一死寂的状态。汤姆实在是受不了这种压抑了，他必须找点话说，于是他小声说道：

"哈克，你觉得那些死去的人会喜欢我们在这吗？"

哈克贝利也轻声说着：

"我倒希望我知道啊，这可真是安静得可怕，不是吗？"

"我觉得也是。"

此后就是相当长的一段沉默，孩子们都在心里各自思索着，之后汤姆小声说：

"嘿，哈克——你觉得霍斯·威廉姆能听到我们讲话吗？"

"他当然能听到，至少他的魂魄能听到。"

这话让汤姆顿了好一会儿，之后他说：

"我刚才得说威廉姆先生才对，但是我不是故意要那么说的，大家都叫他霍斯。"

"死人是很在意人们是怎么说自己的，汤姆。"

这句话一说出来，就又是死一样的寂静。

过了一会儿，汤姆抓住伙伴的胳膊叫了声：

"嘘！"

"怎么啦，汤姆？"这两个小鬼的心开始怦怦直跳。

"嘘！他又来了，难道你没有听到吗？"

"我——"

"听着！你快听听。"

"天啊，汤姆，他们来了！他们真的来了，我们要怎么办？"

"我不知道，你觉得他们会看见我们吗？"

"天啊，汤姆，他们在晚上都能看清楚，跟猫一样，我真希望我今天没来。"

"啊，不要害怕，我不认为他们会找我们的麻烦，我们可没打算做什么坏事，如果我们就静静地待在这里，也许他们就根本不会注意到我们。"

"我会努力不出声的，汤姆，但是天啊，我浑身直哆嗦。"

"看！快看那！"汤姆悄悄地说，"那是什么？"

"那准是鬼火，啊，汤姆，这可真是糟透了。"

一些依稀可辨的身影在黑暗中穿行，手里还晃动着几个老式的锡皮手提灯，灯光照在地上，一闪一闪的，过一会儿，哈克贝利害怕地低语道：

"肯定是鬼，而且是三个！天啊，汤姆，我们死定了，你会祈祷吗？"

"我会试着祈祷，但是你别害怕，他们不会伤害我们的。'此时我已躺下睡着，我——'"

"嘘！"

"怎么了，哈克？"

"那都是人！至少有一个是人，那是老穆夫·波特的声音。"

"不会吧，怎么可能呢？"

"我保证我听出来是他的声音，你可别动，他十分机敏，准会察觉到我们的。他又跟以往一样喝醉了——这见鬼的老头！"

"好吧，我会一动不动的，现在他们不动了，看来没找到东西，他们又来了，现在他们又动起来了，又停下来了，又动起来了，这下他们走得真快，这回可是找对路了！嘿，哈克，我听出来了另一个人的声音，是那个印江·乔。"

"可不是嘛——那个杀人不眨眼的野兽！我情愿遇到鬼也不愿看见他，他们要做什么呢？"

现在男孩之间的私语声戛然而止了，因为有三个人逼近了坟墓，在孩子们的藏身处站了好一会儿。

"就是这儿，"第三个人说道，说着他举起了提灯，灯光下显现出年轻医生鲁宾逊的面庞。

波特和印江·乔正推着一个手推车，车上放有一根绳子和两把铁锹。他们卸下家伙，就开始挖墓。医生将提灯放在了坟墓的顶上，然后靠着一棵榆树坐了下来，他跟男孩们离得太近了，孩子们几乎都能伸手摸到他。

"快点，伙计们！"他低声说："月亮随时都会出来。"

他们用低沉的声音回应了他，然后继续挖着墓地。好一阵儿的时间，四周只能听到铲子铲起土块和石头的嚓嚓声，听起来十分枯燥。最后，一把铁锹铲到了木棺材，发出沉闷的呜呜声，接着不到一两分钟，他们就将棺材从土里撅了出来。然后他们用铁锹揭开棺材盖，将尸体从棺材里拖出来，粗鲁地把尸体扔到了地上。月光从乌云后露了出来，照亮了地上那张苍白的脸。他们把车又推了过来，将尸体放到车上，然后用毯子盖住，再拿绳子把它捆好。波特拿出了一把很大的弹簧刀，将绳子的剩余部分剪掉，接着他说：

"现在这该死的东西已经处理好了，大夫，你必须再出五块钱，否则我们就把它扔这儿。"

"没错！"印江·乔也说道。

"你们这是什么意思？"医生说："你们说要提前付费，我已经付给你们了啊。"

"是的，你做的还不仅仅是这些呢，"印江·乔边说着边逼向已经站起来的医生，"五年前的一个晚上，当我来讨点吃的的时候，你将我从你父亲的厨房里赶了出来，而且你还说我去厨房没好事，从那时候起，我就发誓我就是花上一百年也要整倒你，你父亲把我当作无赖关进牢里，你觉得我是忘了吗？我们印江人的血从来不会白流。现在你已经在我手里了，你可要乖乖儿地听话！"

他把拳头在医生的面前抢着，以此来恐吓他，而这回，医生突然向他猛击，把这个恶棍扑倒在地。这时波特扔掉了他的刀，吼道：

"嘿，你竟敢打我兄弟！"于是他一把上去把医生扯了过来，他们两个就这样使出浑身解数斯打在一起，在草地上翻滚，脚跟处扬起一片灰尘。印江·乔此时攥紧了拳头，眼里迸射出仇恨的光芒，拎起波特的刀子，悄悄地向他们两个靠近，像猫一样，走走停停，在他们两人周围转来转去，寻找机会。突然，医生挣脱了出来，抄起威廉姆坟上的那块笨重的木板对着波特的头打了下去，一下就把波特打倒在地——与此同时，那个嗜血的野兽找到了下手的机会，于是他抽出刀子一把刺进年轻人的胸膛。医生晃着倒了下去，他的身体一半伏在了波特的身上，鲜血溅红了波特的身体。就在这时，乌云遮住了这可怕的场景，两个吓坏了的孩子飞奔着消失在了黑暗中。

不一会儿，月亮就又露出了光芒，印江·乔站在这两个人的身边，凝视着他们。医生艰难地吐出来几句话就大喘了几口气死去了，于是这个杂种就嘟囔道：

"你欠我的还清了——你这该死的。"

接着他又搜了搜尸体，之后把那把杀了医生的刀放到了波特张开的右手中，然后就坐在了打开的棺材上，就这样，三四分钟过去了，波特开始动弹并呻吟着，他的手抓住了那把刀，于是把它举起，看了看，顿时波特感到无比害怕，刀就从手中无力地滑落了，接着他坐了起来，将医生的尸体从身上推了下去，盯着它看了好一会儿，然后他又不解地四处张望，他的目光就碰上了乔的目光。

"天啊，这是怎么了，乔？"他问道。

"这下可真的糟糕了，"乔一动也不动地说着，"你为什么要这样做呢？"

"我！这不是我干的！"

"看吧！这就是洗不掉的证据啊。"

波特害怕得抖了起来，脸色苍白。

"我以为我还是清醒的呢，我今晚本来不该喝醉的，我现在脑袋都还晕乎乎的——比我们来的时候更糟糕，我现在完全处在混乱当中，我什么都记不起来了啊，乔，伙计，说实话，我到底做了吗？乔，我真的不是故意的——天地良心，我从来都没想过要这样，乔，告诉我这是怎么回事，乔，这真是太糟糕了——他是多么的年轻而又前途无量啊。"

"怎么回事？你们两个厮打在了一起，他用一块木板打了你的头，然后你就倒下了，接着你又晃晃悠悠地站了起来，一把夺过刀子，刺进了他的身体，这时他又给了你一棒——于是你就躺在这儿了，直到刚刚都还像死了一样躺在这儿。"

"天啊，我都不知道我到底干了些什么，如果我真的做了，我希望我现在就去死，都是因为那瓶威士忌的作用，让我那么冲动，我发誓。我这一生可从来没动过家伙，乔，我打过架，但是从来没有抄过家伙，这一点大家都是知道的，乔，你可不能把这说出去了！你不会的是吗？乔——你可是个好伙计。我总是那么喜欢你，乔，还总是帮你，你不记得了吗？你不会说的，是吗，乔？"这个可怜的家伙跪倒在这个残忍的凶手面前，攥紧了双手乞求他。

"我不会说的，你总是对我那么好，穆夫·波特，我不会出卖你的，我能说的就是这么多了啊。"

"天啊，乔，你真的就是个天使，只要我活一天，我就会为你祝福的。"波特说着就开始了哭泣。

"哦，行啦，已经够了，现在可不是哭的时候，你从那边走，我从这边走，快点行动，可不能在路上留下什么痕迹。"

于是波特就一路小跑着，后来就大跑起来，那个杂种站在那里看着他嘀咕道：

"他喝得烂醉，又挨了一击，看他那样子不跑到老远是不会想起他的刀子的，就算他想起来了，也一定不敢一个人再回来取——真是个孬种！"

两三分钟以后，只有月光照亮着那个被害者，那个用毯子裹着的尸体，那口掀开的棺材以及那个打开了的坟墓，一切又笼罩在了死寂之中。

第十章

这两个孩子一路朝向村子跑啊跑，害怕得一句话也说不出来。他们时不时地还回头向后看看，很显然，他们是怕自己有可能被跟踪。路上遇到的每一个树桩都好似一个人，一个敌人，吓得他们气都不敢喘，当他们经过村子旁边的农舍时，几只看门口的狂吠让他们脚底生风。

"真希望我们能一口气跑到老制革厂那儿去！"汤姆在换气的瞬间小声说道，"我这样跑不了多久。"

哈克贝利什么也没有说，孩子们都望着他们希望的目标奋力地跑着，目标渐渐地在向他们靠近，最后，他们大喘着气冲进了开着的大门内，疲惫而又庆幸地瘫倒在能够隐藏自己的阴影里，过了好一会儿，他们的心跳终于缓和了下来，这时汤姆轻声说：

"哈克贝利，你觉得这事儿会怎么样呢？"

"如果鲁宾逊医生死了的话，我觉得会举行绞刑。"

"你确定？"

"为什么不呢，我了解这，汤姆。"

汤姆思索了良久，说道：

"谁去告发凶手呢？我们吗？"

"你在说什么啊？如果有什么事情发生了，印江·乔没有被判绞刑怎么办？他准会杀了我们的，而我们是逃不掉的。"

"我也是这么想的，哈克。"

"要是有人去告，那就让穆夫·波特去告好了，只要他够蠢，他每天喝那么多，准会蠢成这样。"

汤姆什么也没有说——继续着自己的思考，过了一会儿，他说：

"哈克，穆夫·波特什么也不知道，他怎么去告发呢？"

"他为什么不知道？"

"因为当印江·乔做的时候他已经昏过去了，你不觉得他什么都没看到吗？你不觉得他什么都不知道吗？"

"正经说还真是这么回事，汤姆！"

"而且除此之外，你想想，他一击有可能已经把他打死了！"

"不会的，汤姆，我看得出来他只是喝多了，他总是这样的，当我爸喝醉的时候，你就算是把一座教堂扔到他头上他都不会醒，他自己都是这么讲的，所以穆夫·波特当然也是这样的。但是如果一个人是很清醒的，那我想那一击准会把他撂倒。"

汤姆又沉默地想了一会儿，然后他说：

"哈克，你能保证你不把这事说出去吗？"

"汤姆，我当然可以保证，这你是知道的。那个印江恶鬼弄死我们就像弄死两只猫一样简单，如果我们说漏了这事儿，而他们又没把他绞死，他准会这样做。汤姆，我说咱们互相发誓吧——我们以前就是这么做的——发誓谁都不说。"

"我同意你说的，这是最好不过的了。你把手举起来，然后发誓说我们——"

"不不，这次不能这么做，那种方式只适合平常的小事——特别是跟姑娘们发誓，因为她们随时都能跟你翻脸，她们要是生气了的话就会把事情说出去——像这回的这种事情就应该写下来，还要用血书。"

汤姆真心觉得这是个妙主意，夜色正黑，四周非常深沉而又恐怖，时间，环境，还有周围的气氛都跟这一举动非常和谐。他借着月光从地上捡起了一个松木板，从口袋里掏出了一小节红化石，映着月光写了起来，他使劲儿一笔一画地写着，写到向下的笔画时，用牙齿咬紧舌头努力地刻着，写到向上的笔画时，则轻轻地一抬手一气呵成：

哈克贝利和汤姆·索亚发誓他们将恪守这一秘密，如不守约，则当场毙命。

哈克贝利觉得汤姆写得很漂亮，语言也很帅气，心中钦佩万分。他立即从衣服领上取下一个别针，就准备扎进肉里，但是汤姆阻止道：

"先别慌！不能这样做，如果别针生锈了的话，它上面可是会有铜绿的。"

"铜绿是什么？"

"铜绿是有毒的，它就是这样厉害，只要吞下去一点，你就能知道它的厉害。"

于是汤姆从自己的针线上取下一根针，两个男孩都各自往大拇指上戳了一下，然后挤出一滴血。最后，在挤了好几次之后，汤姆才用小指作为笔在木板上签上了自己姓名的首字母。接着他又教哈克贝利如何来写一个H和F，做完了这之后，立誓就算完成了。在举行了庄严的仪式以及念了几句咒语之后，他们就将松木板埋在了墙脚里。做完这件事之后，他们觉得锁住自己口舌的锁也被埋了进去，因此不用去找钥匙了。

这时，一个身影从这破楼的另一头的缺口处悄悄地溜了进来，可他们什么也没有注意到。

"汤姆，"哈克贝利小声问道："我们这就真的永远不会把秘密说出去了是吗？""当然了，无论发生了什么，我们都不会将秘密说出去的，要不我们会暴毙的——你不知道吗？"

"当然，我当然是知道这的。"

他们继续说了一会儿悄悄话，就听见外面传来了一只狗凄凉的长嚎——离他们不过十英尺远。孩子们突然抱在了一起，害怕极了。

"他在冲我们谁嚎？"哈克贝利倒抽着气说。

"我不知道——你从缝里看一眼，快点！"

"不，你去看，汤姆！"

"我不能——不能去看，哈克！"

"求你了，汤姆，它又在叫。"

"天啊，谢天谢地！"汤姆小声说道，"我听出了它的声音，它是布尔·哈比森。"

"真的啊，那太好了——跟你说，我都害怕得要死了，我还以为是只野狗呢。"

那只狗又开始长嚎，男孩们的心又一次沉了下去。

"天啊，上帝，那不是布尔·哈比森，"哈克贝利小声说道，"去看看吧，汤姆！"

汤姆吓得直发抖，但是还是走了过去，将眼对准缝隙瞅了过去，"天啊，哈克，真的是条野狗！"汤姆用低得几乎听不到的声音说道。

"快点，汤姆，快点看清楚！它到底在嚎谁？"

"哈克，他肯定是在嚎我们两个——我们是在一起的啊。"

"天啊，汤姆，我觉得我们准完了，我知道我是什么下场的，我这么坏。"

"真是自作自受啊，谁叫我在学校时老旷课，又总是干坏事，我要是好好表现的话，也能像西德尼那样的优秀，但是我没有好好干。要是我这次能侥幸活了下去，我发誓我会在主日学校里好好表现！"说着汤姆就开始抽泣了起来。

"你还算坏？"哈克贝利也开始了抽泣，"算了吧，汤姆·索亚，跟我这种人比起来，你什么都算不上。天啊，上帝，我的上帝，上帝啊，我能有汤姆一半的机会来改过自新就好了。"

汤姆这时停止了啜泣，小声说道：

"快看，哈克，快看！它转了个身背对我们了。"

哈克看了看，心里高兴了起来。

"真的耶，它真的背对着我们，它之前是不是也一直都是这样的？"

"对啊，真是的，我真是太傻了，竟然没有想到这一点，这真是太好了，你觉得它是在朝谁叫呢？"

嚎叫停止了，汤姆竖起了他的耳朵。

"嘘！你听到了吗？"他小声地说。

"听起来像——像猪在哼哼。不——是有人在哭，汤姆。"

"对，就是这样，在什么地方啊，哈克？"

"我觉得应该是在楼房那头，至少听起来像是在那头。爸爸有时候会睡在那里，他跟猪睡在一起，但是我的个老天啊，他要是打起呼噜来能把房顶都掀翻，而且我打赌他今天晚上也不会再回镇里来。"

于是孩子们想再去碰碰运气。

"哈克，要是我带路的话，你敢去吗？"

"我不是很想去，汤姆，有可能是印江·乔啊。"

汤姆犹豫了，但是不一会儿他们的好奇心就引诱他们想要再试一次，他们达成了一致，只要呼噜声一停，他们就赶紧跑。所以他们蹑手蹑脚地悄悄逼近，一个孩子跟在另一个孩子后面。当距离打呼噜的人不到五步之遥的时候，汤姆踩到了一个树枝，发出了清脆的响声，地上的男人呻吟了起来，微微挪动了几下，他的脸暴露在了月光下，此人竟是穆夫·波特。当这个男人挪动的时候，男孩们吓得心都不跳了，心中的希望也都破灭了，但是现在，他们又不再恐慌了。接着他俩轻手轻脚地从挡风板的缺口处溜了出去，走了几步就分手道别了。他们转身时，看见那个陌生的狗站在离波特几步远的地方正冲着波特长嚎。

"嘿，我的老天，原来是在嚎他啊！"两个男孩异口同声地惊呼。

"我说汤姆——大概在两个星期前的一个午夜，人们说有一只野狗绕着约翰尼·米勒家的房子不停地嚎叫，那天晚上还有一只夜鹰也飞了过来，停在栏杆上叫个不停，但是并没有人死去啊。"

"是啊，我是知道这个的，尽管没有人死，但是在接下来的周六，格雷西·米勒不还是掉到了厨房的火里，烧得很惨吗？"

"是的，但是她又没死，而且，她现在是越来越好了啊。"

"好吧，你就等着看吧，她早晚是要死的，就跟穆夫·波特一样是要死的，这是那些黑鬼们说的，他们对这些事情再了解不过了，哈克。"

说完这些，他们就分道扬镳了，分开的时候还都在想这个问题。当汤姆从窗户爬进自己的房间时，晚上都差不多过完了。他轻手轻脚地脱去衣服，睡着的时候还暗自庆幸没有人发现他偷偷溜了出去，他根本没注意到那个轻轻打呼的西德尼是醒着的，而且醒了有一个小时了。

当汤姆睡醒的时候西德尼已经穿好了衣服出去了。从亮堂堂的光线可以看出来他睡过头了，汤姆感到非常吃惊，为什么没有人叫他呢，往常应该有人来折磨他一直把他弄醒才对啊？他想着就觉得不太对劲，不到五分钟他就已经穿戴好，下了楼，他觉得不太舒服，昏昏欲睡。大家都还在桌子旁，但是他们都已经吃过早饭了，没有人训斥他，但是谁都不去看他，大家都保持着沉默，这种沉默让汤姆的心凉了半截，他坐了下来，竭力地想要表现得快乐一点，但都是无用功，没有人对他微笑，没有人回应他，于是他只好安静了下来，心沉到了谷底。

早饭过后姨妈把他叫到了一边，汤姆想着自己又挨一顿鞭子就好了，因而心里有些开心，但是事实并非如此，姨妈对着他哭了起来，问他为什么非要这样做，让她如此伤心，后来姨妈又说了顿气话，叫他接着去闹，接着去把自己毁了，接着让她在这满头白发的年纪徒添悲伤，伤痛到死，因为她再努力也没有用了。姨妈的这番折腾比打他一千遍还要难受，汤姆现在心里比肉体更加痛苦不堪，他号啕大哭，乞求姨妈的原谅，保证自己再也不胡闹了，姨妈最后还是接受了他的道歉，但是汤姆觉得她还是没有完全原谅自己，心里还是半信半疑的。

　　他悲伤地离开了，连报复西德尼的心都没有了，所以西德尼赶紧从后门溜走的举动实在是不必要。他就这样悲伤地把自己拖到了学校，跟乔·哈泼一起挨了鞭子，因为昨天下午他们都逃学了。汤姆心里装满了太多的苦楚，这种鞭打对他来说都不算什么了，于是他走回到了座位上，胳膊肘撑到桌子上，双手托着下巴，默默地盯着墙，内心的痛苦已经到达了他能承受的极限。此时，他的胳膊肘抵到了什么硬的东西，过了好一会儿，他才缓过神来，悲伤地换了个姿势，拿起桌上的这个东西，叹了口气。东西包在纸里，他把纸打开，接着就又重重地叹了口气，他的心彻底碎了，纸里面的是他的那个铜把手！

　　就像谚语中所说的那样，这最后的小小羽毛竟然压塌了骆驼的背。

第十一章

临近中午时，整个村子都突然间笼罩在那个可怕的消息制造的雾霾中。这一消息根本都用不着通过当时想都没想过的电报公布，就一传十，十传百，家喻户晓的速度丝毫不亚于电报的效果。当然校长给学生们放了半天的假，要是他不这样做的话，镇上的人会觉得他很怪的。

在死者身旁发现了一把血淋淋的刀，有人认得那是穆夫·波特的东西——于是消息不胫而走。有人还说，晚上一两点的时候，一位深夜回家的居民曾看到波特在小河里洗澡，见有人来，波特马上就逃走了——这真是太令人怀疑了，特别是波特从来没有在河里洗澡的习惯。人们还说城镇已经开始搜寻这个谋杀犯了（公众细查证据，达成裁决的速度是非常迅速的），但是哪儿都找不到波特。骑手已经被派遣从各个方向沿着条条大路搜查，治安官很有信心在夜幕降临之前抓到他。

镇上的人们都向墓地涌去，汤姆也没空去管伤心事了，他也加入了大家的队伍，这倒不是因为他有千万个理由不去别的地方，而是因为有一种很恐怖但又很巨大的力量在吸引着他。当他到达那个可怕的墓地时，他那小小的身体从人群中挤出来，看到了那恐怖的场景。对他而言，再次来到这里好像已经隔了一个世纪那么久。有人拉了拉他的胳膊，他转过身去，对上了哈克贝利的眼神，他们不约而同地四处观望了一下，怀疑着是否有人在他们的观望中察觉到了什么。但是每个人都在说话，专注在眼前这一可怕的场景当中。

"可怜的家伙！""可怜的年轻人！""这对盗墓者应该是个教训！""要是他们抓住了穆夫·波特，他就应该被绞死。"人们都这样说着，于是牧师说道："这就是天意！"

现在汤姆全身都在发抖，因为他看到了印江·乔冷漠的脸。这个时候，人群开始蠕动，人们在高呼："就是他！就是他！他竟然自己来了！"

"是谁？是谁？"人群中有二十个声音叫道。

"穆夫·波特！"

"啊，他停了！小心，他在转身！别让他跑了！"

汤姆头顶上的树杈里坐着的人还说他不是想跑，他只是有些迟疑和困惑。

"真是该死的！"一个看热闹的人说道，"他竟然想来看看自己的杰作，我打赌他没想到会有这么多人都来了。"

人们分散开让出了一条路，治安官威武地领着波特走了过来，这个可怜人脸色憔悴，眼神中充满了恐惧。当他站在死者面前时，便像中风了一样，捂着脸失声痛哭了起来。

"我没有杀他，老乡们，"他抽搐着说道，"我发誓我从来都没有干过这个。"

"谁控告你杀人了？"一个声音喊道。

这一喊似乎给事情带来了转机。波特扬起了脸，满眼委屈而又无助地向四周望了过去，他看见了印江·乔，于是说道：

"噢，印江·乔，你答应过我你绝不——"

"这是你的刀子吗？"治安官一下把刀子扔到他的面前。

要是没有人搀扶他的话，波特可能就倒在地上了，于是他说：

"我的直觉告诉我必须要回来把它拿走，要是不拿的话——"他颤抖了起来，然后无力地挥了挥手，说道，"告诉他们吧，乔，都告诉他们吧，现在不说也没用了。"

于是哈克贝利和汤姆就呆呆地站在那里，看着他们，听着那个铁石心肠的骗子说着大堆的谎话，他们无时无刻不在期待着老天显灵，能有一个晴空霹雳劈死这个大骗子，又不清楚到底要等多久才会实现。最后当乔说完的时候，他仍然神气活现地站在那里，他们本想打破誓言去救那个遭受背叛的可怜家伙，但这种冲动此时已经消失不见了，因为这个恶棍肯定早已卖身给了撒旦魔鬼，而和魔鬼的力量做斗争是必死无疑的。

"你怎么不离开呢？你还来这里干什么？"一些人说道。

"我也不知道——我就是无法控制自己，"波特喃喃地说，"我想逃跑，但是我除了这不知道还能到哪。"于是他又开始了啜泣。

几分钟后，开始验尸，乔又发了誓，又把刚才说的话平静地重复了一遍，男孩们看到仍然没有晴天霹雳，于是非常确信他真的把自己卖给了魔鬼。他现在已经变成了孩子们所感兴趣的事物当中最为恐怖的一个，他们对他十分着迷，简直无法把眼球从他身上挪开。

孩子们心里暗暗决定要连夜看着他，想看看能不能有机会可以看一眼他那凶狠的主人。

印江·乔帮着把尸体抬到了马车里运走，惊恐的人群中窃窃私语到，尸体还在流血！男孩们想到这是个绝好的机会引领人们走向正确的判断道路，但是他们非常失望，因为不止一个村民叫道：

"穆夫·波特杀他的时候，距离近得不足三英尺呢。"

汤姆那可怕的秘密以及良心不断地谴责让他在接下来的一个星期都无法睡个好觉，一天早上吃早饭的时候，西德尼说：

"汤姆，你晚上翻来覆去的，还一直说梦话，简直让我都睡不着觉。"

汤姆听到后脸都发白了，他低着头不敢看他们。

"这可不是个好事，"波丽姨妈严肃地说道，"你脑子里在想什么呢，汤姆？"

"什么都没想，我什么都不知道。"但是这个孩子的手抖动太厉害了，以至于他手里的咖啡都溅了出来。

"你还说着这样的事呢，"西德尼说，"昨天晚上你说：'是血，是血，就是血！'你说了一遍又一遍，你还说：'不要这样折磨我——我说！'你说什么？你要说什么啊？"

汤姆眼前模糊了起来，很难说马上会发生什么，但是幸运的是，波丽姨妈脸上担心的神色马上消失了，她接下来的话让汤姆松了一口气，她说道：

"一定是那个可怕的杀人犯，我也每天都做梦梦到这，有时候我还梦到是我自己杀了他呢。"

玛丽说她自己也是同样的感觉，西德尼好像已经不再怀疑了，于是汤姆飞快地从这里溜了出去，在这之后的一周，他都抱怨牙疼，每天晚上都把下巴用绷带包起来，他从来都不知道西德尼每天晚上都守在那里盯着他，还经常把他的绷带卸下来，挂着胳膊肘看上好一阵子，之后又会把他的绷带缠回原处。汤姆受压抑的精神慢慢地好转了过来，但是牙却疼得越来越厉害，汤姆却不去理会。就算西德尼从汤姆的嘴里听出了点门道，他也只能自己闷着。

汤姆的同学们似乎从来不会对死猫失去兴趣，而这又老是勾起他不好的回忆。西德尼注意到汤姆现在从来不去当验尸官，尽管他以前总是变着花样想新主意。也还注意到，汤姆再也没去扮演过证人，而这是非常奇怪的，他还发现汤姆对这些询问显示出十分厌恶的表现，他还千方百计地避免被询问，西德尼感到困惑不解，但是却什么都没说。庆幸的是审问这种游戏最后也不再流行了，这种对汤姆良心上的折磨也就停止了。

在汤姆感到很痛苦的这段时间里，每隔个一两天，他就会瞅着机会跑到监狱那儿，透过小小的窗户把自己能弄到的小宝贝送给那个"杀人犯"做安慰。监狱就是一个由一堆红墙砌成的小屋子，就在村头的一片湿地里。根本就没有给监狱配备警卫，而实际情况是，它很少关过犯人，这种情形让汤姆的良心好过多了。

村民们很想把印江·乔全身涂满柏油，插上羽毛，因为这是对盗墓者的惩罚，但是一想到他那凶狠的性格，就没有人愿意牵头做这件事，所以这也就慢慢被放下了。他在两次验尸的时候都认真交代了他们的打斗，但都没有供认之前的盗墓行为，所以大家都一致认为，不要再纠缠此案才是最明智的举措。

第十二章

汤姆的心思从他那个烦恼的秘密移开的一个原因就是他的心又发现了另一件重大的事情。那就是贝琪·撒切尔没有来上学。汤姆跟自己的自尊心苦苦挣扎了好几天，他想让她的事随着风吹散了，但是他做不到，他开始天天晚上到她爸爸的房子外面转悠，每天心情都很糟糕。她生病了吧，要是她死了怎么办！想到这他就心烦意乱，他对战争再也不感兴趣了，就算是当海盗也没兴趣了。生命的意义已经消失了，没有了心爱的人就真的什么都没有了。他把铁环和棒球都抛到了脑后，他再也对这些提不起兴趣了，姨妈不禁担心起来，千方百计地开始找药给他医治，姨妈是那种对治病的药很着迷的人，对各种复杂的治病方法都很痴迷。在寻找各种强身健体药方面，姨妈可谓是做实验做上瘾了。当她得知有什么新奇的方法时，就会马上疯狂地实验起来，当然不是在她自己身上实验，因为她从来不会生病，她会把身边近在咫尺的人当作实验对象。她订阅了所有的"健康杂志"和各种骗人的颅骨相学之类的书，这些东西都仅仅写一些愚昧无知的话，在她却视为无上至宝。其中所描写的谬论包括如何做好通风啦，怎样上床睡觉啦，如何起床啦，吃什么喝什么啦，要做多少锻炼啦，还有怎么保持心情舒畅啦，以及穿什么样的衣服都是她心目中的福音啊，她从来都没有发现她这个月订的健康之书经常会全盘否定上个月书上所推崇的一切。她就是个头脑简单，质朴单纯的女人，因此她是个非常容易上当的人。她把她的那些江湖医术还有药方都收集到了一起，用比喻的话说就是，她已经骑上了那匹灰马，拥抱着死亡，身后还跟了一群魔鬼。但是她从来没有怀疑过自己根本就不是什么救人观世音，也不是来解救大家的在世华佗。

水疗法现在比较时兴，于是情绪低落的汤姆就成了她的摆弄对象。她每天早上天一亮就把他叫到外面，让他站在木棚屋里，接着就劈头盖脸地给他浇一阵冷水，然后就像在使锉刀一样，拿块毛巾给他从上到下使劲地擦，想让他缓过来神，接着就会用湿床单将汤姆裹起来，再盖上毯子，让他出一身大汗，把灵魂净化一下，用汤姆的话来说就是"要让肮脏的东西从他的每个毛孔里出来"。

但是这种治疗的效果一点也不明显，这个男孩只是越来越虚弱，越来越忧郁了。于是她又使用了热水浴、坐浴、淋浴以及浸水浴等疗法，但是这个男孩仍然像要死了一样糟糕，于是为了配合水疗的功效，她开始给汤姆灌稀燕麦粥，还给他涂治水泡的药膏，她还像估量一个陶罐的容量一样算算每天汤姆能接受多少的用量，每天都会给汤姆灌这些灵丹妙药。

汤姆开始变得对这些折磨不再上心了，这可让这个老太太的心感到惊慌失措，她决定不惜一切代价改变汤姆的这种漠视。这回她头一次听来了止疼药的这种疗法，于是她一次性地买了一大堆来，她尝了尝，高兴得欢天喜地的。于是她就放弃了水疗法等一切治疗方式，将全部希望都倾注在她的止疼药上。她喂了汤姆一勺之后，就满心焦急地审视着药效。她心中的忧虑马上就得到释放了，她的心又平静了下来，因为汤姆的这种低落情绪被打破了，这个男孩又活蹦乱跳的了，就算是她把他架在火上烧，他也不会比这再兴奋，再兴致勃勃的了。

汤姆觉得是时候该醒醒了，如今的生活在他备受折磨的情况下，虽然称得上是很有情趣的，但是这已经发展到姨妈对他的关心成分很少而各种花样不断的程度了。所以他想了无数的计划来逃脱姨妈的摆弄，最后他还是觉得假装喜欢止疼药比较好。他老是去问姨妈要，姨妈已经觉得他很碍事了，于是姨妈叫他自己去拿，别来找她要了。如果他是西德尼的话，她的心里肯定是纯粹的高兴，不带一点担心，但是因为他是汤姆，所以姨妈不得不看着点药罐子，她发现止疼药确实是渐渐减少了，但是她没想到这个男孩拿着这种灵丹妙药去塞地板缝了。

一天当汤姆拿着止疼药塞着地板缝的时候，他姨妈的黄猫走了过来，咕噜噜地叫着，渴求地盯着汤姆的药勺，乞求尝一尝，汤姆说：

"不要要这个，除非你真的想要，彼得。"

但是彼得表示它真的很想吃。

"你最好确定你真的想吃。"

彼得非常确信它真的想要。

"好吧，既然你要吃，那我就给你吧，我可不是个小气鬼，但是你如果发现你不喜欢吃，那你就只能怪你自己去。"

彼得同意了他，所以汤姆就把它的嘴掰开，给它灌了勺止疼药。结果彼得一下子蹦起几码高，然后大叫着，在屋子里到处乱窜，不是撞到家具，就是撞到花盆，把家里掀了个底朝天。接着它又用两条后腿站立起来，高昂着头，那欢快的叫声就证明了它那无法抑制的快乐。然后它又在屋子里大闹了一番，在身后留下一片狼藉，波丽姨妈进来的时候刚好看到它翻了几个筋斗，发出最后一声幸福的欢叫，就从大开的窗户跳将了出去，还把窗台上仅剩的一盆花也带翻了。老太太惊讶地呆站在那里，从她那副眼镜中努力地看着，汤姆早已躺在地板上乐得不行了。

"汤姆，那只猫到底怎么了？"

"我不知道，姨妈。"这孩子喘着气说道。

"天啊，我从来没见过这种事情，它究竟是怎么了会变成这样？"

"我真的不知道，波丽姨妈，猫开心的时候总是会那样的。"

"是这样，真的是这样吗？"姨妈的话语里带着让汤姆感到不自在的语气。

"是的，就是这样的，我认为它们就会这样。"

"你认为？"

"是的。"

这个老太太弯下了腰，汤姆好奇又不安地看着她，他发现她的目的时已经太晚了，床帷子底下的药勺已经暴露了出来，波丽姨妈捡起了它，把它高高举起。汤姆往后畏缩了一下，并且闭上了眼睛。波丽姨妈用平时老揪他的手将他拎了起来——揪着他的耳朵——用顶针在他脑袋上敲得梆梆作响。

"现在，先生，你那样对那只可怜的猫是为什么呢？"

"我是因为同情它才这样做的——因为它没有姨妈。"

"没有姨妈！你这个木瓜脑袋，它有没有姨妈跟这有什么关系？"

"当然有关系了，要是它有姨妈的话，它姨妈保准会给它灌药，肯定会把它的肠子都灌出来，会把它当个人一样对它毫不留情。"

波丽姨妈突然感到一阵自责，这对她而言是个新想法，可是对猫而言就可能是很残忍的，对一个男孩而言也有可能是这样。她的心开始软了下来，她感到有些内疚，眼眶也有点湿润了，然后她把手放到汤姆的头上温柔地说：

"我的本意是很好的，汤姆，而且汤姆，这对你有好处。"

汤姆一本正经地盯着姨妈的脸，严肃的眼神中透露出一丝闪闪的光芒。

"我知道你是对我好的，姨妈，我对彼得也是这样的，这对它也有好处，我从没见过它如此的开心——"

"嘿，汤姆，在你又惹怒我之前快自个儿走开吧，你该试试能不能做个乖孩子，这样你就再也不用吃任何药了。"

汤姆提前到了校，这一惊人的举动在接下来的每一天都发生了，现在，跟以前习惯了迟到一样，他已经习惯了在大门口晃悠，而不是跟他的同伴们玩耍。他说他病了，他看起来也像是病了。他努力地让自己看起来是在到处张望，但实际上他是在看学校前面的那条路，不一会儿杰夫·撒切尔就出现在了视线内，汤姆的脸马上容光焕发，他盯了他好一会儿，又悲伤地转身走了，当杰夫到学校时，汤姆在他身边转个不停，想引导着他讲一讲贝琪的事情，但是显然这个呆瓜根本没察觉汤姆的这一目的，汤姆瞅了又瞅，看了又看，希望着什么时候就会有一个活蹦乱跳的小姑娘出现在他的视线里，一看到出现的女孩不是她，汤姆就恨起她们来。最后不再有女孩出现了，汤姆失望地垂下了头。他走进了空空的教室，坐在那里受着煎熬，突然一个女孩的身影进了大门，这让汤姆的心猛跳了一阵。转眼间，汤姆就已经跑了出去，像一个印第安人似的登台亮相了。他叫着，笑着，追着男孩子们，冒着生命危险从栅栏上跳了过去，翻着筋斗，倒起了立——做着所有他能想到的英勇举动，他还不时地瞥向贝琪，看她是不是在看自己。但是她看起开根本都没有在意，她一直也没有看他一眼。会不会是因为她不知道自己在这儿呢？于是他马上跑到她跟前耍起把戏，他一路高叫着，抢走了一个男孩的帽子，到处翻腾，还把自己摔到贝琪跟前，这几乎都要把她惹恼了，于是她转身，昂起头就走，他还听到她说："哼，有些人总以为自己很聪明，总是会炫耀自己。"

汤姆羞得满脸通红，于是他爬了起来，灰溜溜地跑了。

第十三章

汤姆现在已经下定决心了，他又悲伤又绝望。他说自己是个被抛弃，没有一个朋友的孩子，没有人喜欢他，当人们发现把他逼成这样的时候，他们会很后悔的。他已经尽力想要做好，跟他们和睦相处了，但是他们不让他干，既然人们一心想要摆脱他，那就随便吧，让他们为以后要发生的事说他好了——他们干吗不这么做呢，一个没有朋友的人有什么权利去抱怨呢，是的，是他们逼他这么做的：他要过充满犯罪的一生，除此之外再无他法。

此刻他已经在芳草巷上走得很远了，学校那催人快点的铃声在他耳边叮叮地响了起来。他现在抽泣了起来，一想到他永永远远都听不到这熟悉的铃声，他就非常难过，但是既然他被驱逐到一个冰冷的世界，他就只好这么做了，他只能听天由命，但是他原谅了人们，接着他的呜咽声变得凝重而急促起来。

就在这时，他遇到了他的密友乔·哈泼——他眼神坚定，很显然他的心里在谋划着什么不好的事情。现在在这里就聚集了两个小鬼，但是他们心里打着同样的主意。汤姆用袖套擦了擦眼，开始哭着向他的朋友诉说着怎样远离这受苦受难而又没有温暖的家，他要流浪到异国他乡再也不回来了，他最后还希望乔不要忘了他。

但是凑巧的是，乔本来也就想着要说服汤姆这么干，他来找他就是为了这个。乔的妈妈冤枉他说他偷喝了奶油，但是他压根就没有尝过，而且都不知道还有这玩意儿，很显然她是对他厌烦了而且希望他就此离开，如果她真是这么想的话，那他就只好去流浪了，他希望她可以因此而开心起来，而且永远不要后悔把她这可怜的孩子赶到外面冰冷的世界去受难，一步步走向死亡。

这两个孩子一边悲伤地往前走，一边立了一项新的誓言，那就是他们要永远团结在一起，做一对好兄弟，永远不分离，直到死亡将他们从苦难中解脱出来。接着他们就开始展开他们的计划，乔本来想要做一个隐士，住在遥远的洞穴里靠吃面包皮维持生命，就这样慢慢死去，死在冰冷、渴求还有悲伤中。但是听了汤姆的话，他觉得过一个充满犯罪的一生也非常不错，所以他立志要当海盗。在圣彼得堡下面三英里处的一块地方，密西西比河面只有一英里宽，这里有一片狭长的小岛，岛上面郁郁葱葱，在岛的前方有一块很浅的沙洲，这是个流浪绝好的去处。这里没有人居住，离河对面也很近，并肩坐落在它旁边的是一片人迹罕至的浓密森林，所以杰弗逊小岛就成了他们的不二之选。他们当时并没有想到当了海盗到底要去劫谁，而且他们找来了哈克贝利·费恩，马上哈克就加入了他们，因为对哈克而言，他干什么都一样，没有什么分别。不一会儿他们就分开了，他们决定在一个绝好的时间，也就是午夜时分，在村子上头两英里的河岸边的一处孤地上见面。他们打算将那里的那只小小的长竹筏占为己有，每一个孩子都会带上钩子、绳子这样的工具，这可以让他们用最阴险而又神秘的方式把东西偷到手，就像强盗们的做法一样。下午结束之前，他们都沉浸在快乐之中，因为他们三个为在村子里散播"要出大事了"的消息而感到非常自豪，所有听到这个消息的人都被叮嘱要"管好自己的嘴，耐心等着"。

大概在午夜时分，汤姆拿着一个煮过的火腿和一些零碎的东西来到了悬崖下的一片灌木丛中，从这里可以俯瞰到他们约好的地方。天上星星闪烁，周围都是静静的，那条大河像一片静谧的海一样缓缓地淌着。汤姆竖着耳朵听了一会儿，但是什么声音都没有听到，于是他发出了一声低沉而又很明显的口哨，悬崖下面当即就有人回应他，一个警惕的声音说道：

"谁在那里？"

"汤姆·索亚，西班牙海上的黑色复仇者，报出你的名字。"

"我乃阴辣杀手哈克贝利·费恩，这位是海上恐怖者乔·哈泼。"这两个称谓都是汤姆从他最喜欢的书里挑出来送给他们的。

"非常好，请对口令。"

两个嘶哑的声音在皓白的月光下，异口同声地悄悄说出了同样恐怖的字眼：

"血！"

说罢之后，汤姆就将他的火腿扔下悬崖，自己也跟着它滚了下去，这一折腾把他的衣服刮坏了，还蹭破了点儿皮。在悬崖下面本有一条很明显而又舒服的小路可以走，但是这样对于海盗而言，就缺少了他们所看重的困难艰险了。

海上恐怖者带来了半个熏猪肉，他为把这带来，路上都快要累死了。阴辣杀手偷来了一个煎锅和一些还没有全干的烟叶，他还拿来了一些做烟斗所用的玉米棒子。但是只有他一个海盗会吸烟，会嚼烟叶。西班牙海上的黑色复仇者说要是不弄点火出来就不算开始，这倒是个聪明的想法。在那些时候，火柴可不是很常见，他们看见在百米之外有一个木筏冒着烟，于是他们就偷偷地溜了过去弄了点炭来。他们去弄火的时候，还把这当成一场威风的冒险，嘴里不时地说着"嘘！"还突然停下来，将手指竖在嘴唇前，想象着手里拿着短剑在移动，并不时地小声下令"敌人"一旦有动静，就要"用剑刺死他"，因为只有死人才不会泄露他们的秘密。他们其实很清楚木筏上的人早已在村里的商店里闲逛，或者已经在那儿自在享乐了，但是他们还是要采取这种海盗们的方式来行动。

不一会儿，他们就撑着木筏离开了，汤姆指挥着他们行进，哈克站在队尾，乔打头。汤姆站在船的中间，神色凝重，两手抱在胸前，用低沉而又坚定的声音下达着命令：

"转舵，顺风行驶！"

"是的，长官！"

"稳住，稳——住——"

"已经稳住了，长官！"

"稍稍外转舵！"

"已经转了，长官！"

随着孩子们平稳而单调地划着木筏驶向河流正中，很明显可以看出这些命令只是一种"形式"，实际上他们什么都没有做。

"船上挂有什么帆？"

"大横帆、中桅帆、飞身三角帆，长官。"

"把上桅帆升起来！升到桅顶！你们六个！将前桅的中桅升起来！动作迅速点，快！"

"遵命，长官！"

"拉出第二桅帆！使用脚索和转帆索！快点，伙计们！"

"遵命，长官！"

"风暴就要来了，快点左转舵！坚守住迎风行驶！左转，左转！快点，伙计们！使劲转！稳住！"

"稳住了，长官！"

竹筏已经驶过了河流的正中央，孩子们把船头调正，接着就使劲儿地划起桨。河水并不深，流速只有两三英里，在接下来的四十五分钟之内，大家都在奋力前行，谁都没有多说什么话。现在竹筏已经驶过了那远方依稀可见的城镇，它正安详地沉睡在波光粼粼的河水旁，根本没有意识到正在发生什么惊天动地的大事，只有隐约闪烁的两三盏微弱的灯光诉说着它的位置。黑色复仇者双手交叉着站在船上，他正在"看最后一眼"这个之前充满快乐现在又充满了痛苦的城镇，并希望"她"现在能够看到他，看到他现在正漂泊在异国波涛汹涌的大海上，勇敢地面对着一切的艰难险阻、死亡威胁，嘴角挂着冷酷的笑迎接他命中注定的人生。他可是只使用了一丁点儿的想象力，就把杰弗逊岛移到一个视野之外的地方，于是他就这样带着一个既千疮百孔又满意十足的心"看了他的最后一眼"。其他的海盗当然也在看他们的最后一眼，他们都看了很久，这一看差一点让他们被河流冲出驶向小岛的航道，还好他们及时发现了危险，又把船头调正了。大概在晚上两点钟的时候，木筏在岛前两百多码的沙滩上搁浅了，于是他们就在水里蹚了好几回，把货物从船上都运了下来，这个小竹筏上原本带着一块旧帆布，于是他们就把它拿下来铺到了角落里的一堆灌木丛中，为他们的物品做一个遮风挡雨的帐篷。但是海盗们自己在天好的时候是露天睡觉的，因为成为强盗就是要这么干。

他们在距离森林中心二三十步远的地方生起了火，火堆靠着一个巨大的树干，然后用煎锅做了一些熏猪肉作为晚餐，还把他们带过来的玉米饼吃了一半，在这种还未被探索过的原始森林以及人迹罕至的小岛上，毫无拘束地吃着晚餐在他们看来是非常荣耀的，而且他们还说自己永远都不会再回到人类社会中了，火苗照亮了孩子们的脸庞，也映红了那用树干架起的林中圣殿，给树叶添上了光泽，给藤蔓砌了流彩。

在吃掉最后一条熏猪肉和最后一口玉米饼之后，孩子们躺在草地上伸起了懒腰，内心满足极了，他们本可以找个更凉快的地方睡觉，但他们不愿意远离这种浪漫的环境，比方说睡在营火旁。

"今天真美好，不是吗？"乔说。

"当然了！"汤姆说，"如果村子里的男孩们看见我们这样会说什么呢？"

"说什么？嘿，他们准是巴不得能来这——对吧，哈克！"

"我也这么觉得，"哈克贝利说道，"管它呢，反正我是觉得这儿挺好的，能一直这样就再好不过了，平时我可连顿饭都吃不饱，而在这儿他们没法来抓我或者那样欺负我。"

"我想要的就是这种生活，"汤姆说，"每天早上你都不用非要起床，你也不用去学校，不用洗碗，不用被骂是个蠢蛋，乔，你看当一个海盗在岸上的时候，是什么都不用干啊，要是去当一个隐士，他每天都要做很多祷告，而且生活那么无聊，总之就是每天孤独的一个人。"

"对啊，就是这样，"乔说，"但是我之前没有想过那么多，这你是知道的，现在尝试过了，我倒宁愿当个海盗。"

"这下你知道了吧，"汤姆说，"现在当隐士可没多大好处，不像古时候那样，但是一个海盗可是一直都受人们尊重的啊，而且一个隐士要睡在最坚硬的床上，头上要披着粗麻布，还要撒上灰，就那样站在雨里，还要——"

"他为什么要披着粗麻布还要撒上灰呢？"哈克问道。

"我也不知道，但是他们必须这样做，隐士总是这样的，要是你是个隐士你也得这么做。"

"我神经了才会这么做呢。"哈克说道。

"好吧，那你要干吗？"

"我不知道，但是我才不会那样做。"

"噢，哈克，你必须要这么做的，你要是不这样怎么能行呢？"

"怎么不行，我就是受不了这样，我会逃跑的。"

"逃跑！好吧，那你就成了最懒最懒的隐士了，你将成为一个耻辱。"

阴辣杀手没有再接话了，因为他忙活着别的事去了，他已经把一个玉米棒子掏空了，现在他往棒子里插了一根苇秆作为烟斗柄，然后又在里面塞上了烟草，接着他拿一块炭点着了烟草，深吸了一口，吐出一团喷香的烟云来——他已经沉浸在一种奢侈的满足之中，其他的两个海盗都很羡慕他伟大的举动，私底下都打定主意尽快将这一招学到手。接着哈克说道：

"海盗们都做什么呢？"

汤姆说：

"这个嘛，他们的日子可真是痛快——先是抢船，再烧船，接着把钱捞过来，然后再埋到自己岛上一个很恐怖的地方，那里将会有鬼怪来看守这些钱财，最后还要将船上的人都杀掉——逼着他们走跳板。

"而且他们还会把女人都带到岛上，"乔说，"他们是不会杀女人的。"

"是这样的，"汤姆赞同道，"他们不会杀女人——他们太高尚了，而且还因为女人们总是很漂亮的。"

"他们穿的衣服不也都是顶好的吗？啊，不！应该全是金银做的，而且还镶满了钻石。"乔充满激情地说道。

"谁们？"哈克说。

"当然是海盗们啊。"

他说完后哈克满脸愁苦地审视了一下自己的衣服。

"我觉得我这么穿是当不了一个海盗了，"他用悲怆而又懊恼的口气说道，"但是我就只有这些衣服啊。"

但其他两个男孩都对他说，在他们开始冒险之旅之后，很快就能穿上好衣服。他们还设法让他明白，尽管海盗们在进行第一次冒险时已经有漂亮衣服穿了，但是他从这身破烂衣服开始也是没有问题的。

渐渐地他们不再说话了，睡意袭来，这几个小东西困得眼皮都睁不开了。烟管从阴辣杀手的手中滑落在地，他就这样困倦地睡去了，丝毫没有受到良心的谴责。海上恐怖者和西班牙海上的黑色复仇者却花了些工夫才能入睡。他们躺着默默地做了祷告，因为现在没有人命令他们跪在那里然后大声地背诵。他们本有一丝不情愿去做祷告，但是他们都害怕要是不这么做的话，他们会突然遭受晴天霹雳。很快他们就迷迷糊糊地要睡着了——但是又一个入侵者到来了，这回是良心这个东西来捣乱，让他们不能安然入睡。他们开始感到有点害怕，觉得离家出走这件事是不是做错了，他们还觉得自己不应该从家里偷肉，接下来的才是真正的折磨。他们试图将这种想法从脑袋里挤走，于是他俩提醒良心，说他们以前都偷过好几回蜜饯还有苹果了，但是良心根本无法满意这种似乎有理的辩解。最后，在他们看来好像真的没有什么能改变这个铁生生的事实，那就是拿蜜饯只不过是"顺手捞的"，而从家里拿走熏猪肉、火腿以及其他的东西则是真真实实的偷盗——而这是《圣经》要求人们严戒的罪行之一。所以他们在内心里挣扎很久，最终他们决定他们海盗的生涯再也不能被偷盗行为给毁了。于是良心就放了他们一马，这两个好奇而又善变的海盗就安静地进入了梦乡。

第十四章

当汤姆早上醒过来的时候，他已忘记了自己身在何方。他坐了起来，揉了揉眼睛，朝四周张望了一番后就明白自己在哪儿了。此时天刚蒙蒙亮，空气十分清凉。森林里的一切都笼罩在安然的睡意和平静之中。没有一片叶子在飞舞，没有一丝声音打破大自然的沉思。晨露正挂在树叶和小草上，火堆已经烧成了一层白灰，一缕蓝色的烟雾在空气中萦绕，乔和哈克依然沉浸在梦乡。

远远的，一只鸟清脆地叫着，其他的鸟也回应起来。不一会儿就听到了伐木工人捶打树木的声音。渐渐地，天空褪去了那熹微的晨光，清凉也渐渐淡去，森林中的声音不断多了起来，生命又回归到最具活力的状态。大自然从沉睡中醒来，准备将无尽的神奇展现给这个惊呆了的孩子。一条小青虫从还挂有露珠的叶子上爬了过来，时不时地把大半个身子抬起来到处嗅一嗅，接着又前行——汤姆说它这是在探路，当这只小虫子主动向他爬来时，他坐在那里一动也不动，小虫子一会儿像是要径直地爬向他，一会儿又像是要爬向别处，弄得他一会儿满怀希望一会儿又情绪低落。最后它弓起身子挣扎了好一会儿才意志坚定地爬上汤姆的腿，开启了爬过汤姆的路途，汤姆心里乐开了花，因为这意味着他将要得到一套新衣服，毫无疑问会是一套华丽丽的海盗服。此时不知从哪儿又冒出来了一队蚂蚁，它们正辛勤工作着，一个干劲十足的小蚂蚁钳着一只有它五倍大的死蜘蛛，正奋力地往树上拖，一个棕色的斑点瓢虫爬到了一片叶子的尖端，于是汤姆弯下身子凑近它说道："花大姐，花大姐，快点飞回家吧，你家房子着火了，你家娃娃一个人。"说罢这个瓢虫就展开翅膀飞走查看情况了——男孩对它的反应一点都不吃惊，因为他知道瓢虫很容易相信火灾的传言，他已经耍过这种笨蛋不止一回了。接下来又飞来了一只屎壳郎，它正奋力地滚着一个粪球，于是汤姆把它戳了一下，就看到它把腿缩到身子底下装死。鸟儿们正在叽叽喳喳地乱叫，一只猫鹊——一种北方的学舌鸟，飞到了汤姆头顶上的树枝上，然后用它那颤抖的声音学着旁边的鸟叫，它学得极其欢喜，接着一只松鸦尖声叫着飞了下来，身影宛如一条蓝色闪电，它飞落到一条细枝上，孩子们几乎都能碰到它，此刻它正高昂着头，饶又兴趣地盯着这些陌生人看，远处又匆忙地跑来了一只灰色的松鼠和一只类似于狐狸的大家伙，它们一会儿坐在那打量着孩子们，一会儿又冲着他们嘎嘎直叫，这些原始动物估计在此之前没有见过人类，所以它们都不知道要害怕。现在大自然的所有生物都已完全清醒，活跃了起来。阳光如一支支长矛透过浓密的树叶刺了进来，散落了一地，近处、远处，都沐浴在暖暖的日光里，几只蝴蝶鼓动着翅膀恍恍惚惚地飞舞在这晨光中。

汤姆摇醒了其他两个海盗，他们都大声叫喊着跑开了，一两分钟的工夫他们就脱光了衣服，跑到那白色沙洲上的清澈溪水中去了，追逐着，互相泼水嬉闹着，开心极了，在这欢快的溪水中他们已经忘记了那远方沉睡的小村庄。不知是由于河水中的一阵湍流还是河水涨潮了，竹筏已经被冲走了，但是这只让他们更加的开心，因为竹筏一被冲走他们与文明社会之间的桥梁就被斩断了。

他们又跑回了大本营，神清气爽，满心欢喜，但也饥肠辘辘了。于是他们很快就又生起了营火，哈克在附近找到了一股清冽的泉水，孩子们将橡树皮或者山胡桃叶做成杯子，狂饮着那甘甜的泉水，这种天然的野物可比咖啡要好多了。当乔正切着熏猪肉做早饭时，汤姆和哈克叫他先等一会儿，他们跑到河边，挑了一个不错的隐蔽处向河里扔进了钓鱼线，很快就有鱼儿上钩了。还没等到乔不耐烦的时候，他们已拿着几条肥大的石首鱼、两只鲈鱼和一条小鲶鱼回来了，这些鱼足够喂饱一家子了。他们将鱼和熏猪肉放在一起炸了炸，结果简直出人意料，因为他们似乎从未吃过这么美味的鱼。其实他们不知道一只活鱼在抓起来之后越早被放到火上烤，其味道就越鲜美，而且他们也没想到在露天睡觉、在户外玩耍、在河里洗澡都会让人觉得饥饿而胃口大增。

吃罢早饭他们就胡乱躺在了树荫下，哈克吸了一阵烟，然后大家就又往森林里探险去了，他们开心地散着步，跨过腐枝败叶，穿过了缠绕在一起的灌木丛，行进在神圣的森林王国中，周围的树冠都穿着葡萄藤做的盛装，时不时地他们还会走过一些温暖舒适的角落，那里铺着青草做的毯子，缀着鲜艳的花朵，好似一颗颗闪闪发光的宝石。

他们发现很多东西都很有趣，但没发现什么能让他们大吃一惊的。这个小岛有三英里长，四分之一英里宽，最近的地方和河岸不过隔着一个不到两百码的狭窄河道。他们大约每个小时都要去游会儿泳，所以等回到营地的时候差不多都是半下午了，而此时孩子们饿得连鱼都不钓，就着冰冷的火腿就是一顿狼吞虎咽，吃完之后他们都瘫倒在树荫下聊了起来。但是不一会儿就找不到什么话题好聊的，渐渐地就说不起来了。森林中弥漫着静谧和肃穆，一阵孤独感侵袭着这几个男孩，他们开始想着心事，一种说不清楚的渴望爬上心头，马上就给他们的心田涂上了灰色——这种感觉就是初露头角的思乡啊。连阴辣杀手哈克贝利都幻想着回到了他睡觉的门阶上，还有那空着的大桶。但是他们都为自己的这种软弱感到羞耻，没有人有勇气将想法说出来。

有一阵儿的时间，孩子们隐隐约约地听到了远处有什么声音在响，就像你有意无意地听到了摆钟的嘀嗒声一样。但是这种神秘的声音越来越明显，逼着他们不得不弄个清楚。孩子们互相望了望，然后每个人都摆起了认真辨听的架势，此时空气中弥漫着死一般的寂静，然后就听到一阵低沉的隆隆声从远处滚了过来。

"那是什么？"乔屏住呼吸问道。

"我也纳闷儿呢。"汤姆小声说。

"那是雷声啊，"哈克贝利充满敬畏地说道，"因为雷——"

"你们快听！"汤姆说道，"听着——别说话。"

他们就这样等着，仿佛等了一个世纪，接着同样隐约的声响划破了这沉闷的寂静。

"咱们去看看吧。"

他们飞也似的跑到了能看到镇子的岸边，拨开岸边灌木丛，从河面上向远方张望着。有一只渡船在村子下方一英里的河里顺着流水行驶，甲板上好像站满了人。有很多小艇在渡船附近行驶，划来划去的，但是孩子们分辨不出人们到底在那儿做什么。不一会儿，从渡船的一边骤然冒出了一行白烟，它腾空弥散开来，像一朵懒散的云一样，同时孩子们又听到了和刚才一样的低沉隆隆声。

"我知道了！"汤姆叫道，"有人淹死了！"

"对，就是这样！"哈克说道，"去年夏天比尔·特纳掉到河里时，他们就是这样干的，他们朝水里发射了一个大炮，让他的尸体浮上来，对，他们还往河里扔大块的面包，还把里面塞上水银，让面包漂在水面上，这样不管尸体在哪都会浮上来停在那里。"

"是的，我也听过这个，"乔说，"我还纳闷儿为啥要扔面包呢。"

"噢，估计不是面包那么神奇，"汤姆说，"我猜他们在扔之前说了什么才会这样的。"

"但是他们在扔的时候什么也没说呀。"哈克说,"我看过他们做这个,但是他们什么也没说。"

"好吧,那还真有趣,"汤姆说,"但是有可能他们在心里默念来着,他们肯定是在默念,这是显而易见的。"

其他两个孩子同意汤姆说的有些道理,因为他们觉得要是没被下咒语的话,单凭几片面包自己是不可能这么漂亮地完成这一重大任务。

"说真的,我真希望我现在也在现场。"乔说。

"我也希望啊,"哈克说,"要是能让我知道到底是谁淹死了,我宁愿拿东西去换。"

孩子们就这样听着炮声看着人们忙来忙去,突然汤姆脑袋里闪过一道灵光,于是他说:

"孩子们,我知道谁淹死了——是我们啊!"

他们立刻觉得自己成了英雄,无比的成功,因为这证明有人还念着他们,有人在为他们哀痛,有人为他们心碎,有人为他们洒泪,一想到曾对这些失踪的孩子那么不好,他们的良心就会受到折磨,他们还要永远做着徒劳的忏悔,沉浸在自责中,最棒的一点就是,全镇的人都一定在谈论这几个淹死的人,而只要人们都还在关注这件名扬天下的事,村里的男孩们都会嫉妒他们到眼红,这真是再好不过了,总而言之,当海盗真是太值了。

暮色将近之时,那只渡船回到了正常作业的岗位,小艇也都回去了。海盗们回到了大本营,他们正为自己所创的伟业以及给村子带来的大麻烦而感到满心欢喜。孩子们又抓了鱼,做成晚饭吃,然后开始谈论村子里的人们该如何想他们,又该如何议论他们。他们描绘着人们为他们的死而悲恸欲绝,心里满意极了——当然仅仅是他们自己的想象。但是当夜色渐浓时,谈话逐渐停止了,孩子们坐在那里,凝视着篝火,思绪不知又飘向了何方。现在他们已经不再那么兴奋了，汤姆和乔就忍不住回想起家里的某些人，他们可不会像自己一样面对这种过火的玩笑，开心不已。于是不安涌上心头，他们开始觉得烦恼，觉得不开心，不经意间，他们还叹了一两口气。后来乔胆怯地兜着圈子，试探着另外两个海盗，看看他们对于返回文明社会有什么看法——不是现在就回，但是——

汤姆嘲弄了他一番，打消了他的这种念头。哈克虽然表面上没承认，但是现在是站在汤姆这边的，于是这个动摇者赶忙解释起来，他竭力让自己脱离这种思乡的胆小鬼形象，最后摆脱了困境。这场暴动此时终于平息了下来。

随着夜色更加浓重，哈克开始打瞌睡，不一会儿就打起了呼噜。接下来乔也打起了呼噜，汤姆用胳膊肘支着头，一动也不动地趴在那里，他专心地盯着两个同伴看了好一会儿。最后他跪起来，小心翼翼地起了身，到草丛里和篝火中寻了一番，篝火中火星点点地飞舞着。他在草丛里搜捡起了几片半圆形的白色梧桐树皮，最终只挑选了似乎是最适合他的两片。然后他跪在了篝火旁，努力地用他的红化石在树皮上写了些什么，之后他把一片卷起来放进口袋里，然后把另一片放到了乔的帽子里，还把帽子从乔的身边移远了点。他还在帽子里放进了几个小学生心目中价值连城的宝贝——一段粉笔、一个橡皮球、三个钓鱼钩还有一个算得上是"真水晶"等级的白石子。做完这些后，他就轻手轻脚、小心翼翼地走出了林子，等他觉得他们不会听到自己的脚步声时，就立马改为小跑朝着沙洲的方向飞奔了过去。

第十五章

　　几分钟之后，汤姆就踏进了沙洲上的浅水里，朝着伊利诺伊那边的河岸蹚了过去。在水齐腰的时候，他已经蹚了一半的路途了，随后湍流涌来，情况不允许他再蹚水过了，所以他鼓足了信心想要游过剩下几百码的距离。他全力以赴地逆水游了起来，但是水流比他想象的还要急，直把他往下游冲。最后他终于到达了河岸，接着又在水里漂了一会儿，然后找到了一个水势较低的地方，爬上了岸。他将手放进了外套口袋里，发现他的树皮仍然安安全全地待在那儿。接着他就钻进了树林中，浑身湿漉漉地沿着河岸走去。十点过了不久，他就来到了村子对面的一片旷地上，看见渡船正停在高高的河堤下的树荫中。天上群星闪烁，大地万籁俱寂。他从高堤上爬了下来，睁大了眼睛看着这一切，然后他潜到水中，游了三四下，接着就爬到了船尾的备用小艇，躺在横甲板上，喘着气等待着。

　　不一会儿船上的铃叮叮地敲响了，一个声音下命道："开船。"大概一两分钟后，小艇的头部就被掀起的排浪高高抬起，直抵到船身，航行就开始了。汤姆对自己的成功潜入感到很开心，因为他知道这一趟出行是今晚的最后一次了。在行进了十五到二十分钟之后，渡船停了下来，于是汤姆就溜下了小艇，在黑暗中朝岸边游去，为了避免碰到可能认识的人，他又向下游多游了五十码。

　　他跑到了平时不常走的小路上，不一会儿就发现他来到了姨妈的栅栏后。于是他爬过了栅栏，进了厢房，向起居室的窗户里望去，因为那儿还点着灯。他看见波丽姨妈、西德尼、玛丽还有乔·哈泼的妈妈正坐在一起谈论着。他们坐在床旁边，床摆在他们和门之间。汤姆走到了门口，小心翼翼地拉开了门闩，接着轻轻地推了一下，于是门就漏了一个小缝出来。他继续这样谨慎地推着门，只要门发出嘎吱的声音，他就吓得发抖，直到他估摸着自己可以跪着爬进去时，他就战战兢兢地开始先将头挤进去。

"烛光怎么摇得这么厉害呢？"波丽姨妈说。

汤姆赶紧加快往里爬。"噢，肯定是因为门在开着，肯定是这样的，现在真是怪事不断，西德尼，快去把门关上。"

此时汤姆刚好爬到了床底下藏了起来。他躺在地板上，喘了好一会儿，然后爬到几乎能碰到姨妈脚的地方。

"但就像我一贯说的那样，"波丽姨妈说道，"他并不是个坏孩子，可以说他就是淘气些，就只是有些浮躁，有些冒失，这你是知道的啊。他还不过是个没长大的孩子，可他从来都没有坏心肠，他是我见过的最心地善良的孩子了。"姨妈说着就哭了起来。

"我的乔也是这样啊——总是一肚子坏主意，总是那么淘气，但是他一点都不自私，也是那么善良——啊，我的老天啊，我还不分青红皂白地责备他偷吃了奶油，就压根没有想起来是因为奶油已经酸了，我自己给倒掉了，我再也无法在这世上看见他了，再也不会，再也不会，再也不会了，我可怜的受尽虐待的孩子啊！"哈泼太太说着也啜泣了起来，好像她的心已经碎了一样。

"我希望汤姆现在过得很好，"西德尼说，"但是要是他以前也能好一些的话——"

"西德尼！"尽管汤姆看不见，但是他可以感觉到这时老太太愤怒的眼神，"不许再说我的汤姆一句坏话，他已经走了，老天会照顾好他——你可别自找麻烦，先生！噢，哈泼太太，我简直都不知道如何忘记他！我真是不知道如何不惦记他！尽管他总是折磨我这颗苍老的心，但他对我是巨大的安慰啊。"

"上帝把孩子赐予我们，现在又把他们收回——愿上帝与我们同在！但是这真是太残忍了——天啊，这真的是太残忍了！就在上个星期六，我的乔还活生生地在我眼前放了一个鞭炮，我还把他揍趴在地上，我真没想到，这么快就——天啊，要是能重来的话，我定会一把抱过他，夸他做得好。"

"是啊，是啊，是啊，我真地了解你现在的感受，哈泼太太，我完全了解。不久前，也就昨天中午吧，我家汤姆还给猫灌了一勺止疼药，我当时还认为它会把家给掀个底儿朝天。哦，上帝原谅我吧，我当时还拿顶针敲了汤姆的头，可怜的孩子，我那可怜的短命孩子啊，不过他现在总算是远离烦恼了，我最后听到他说的话就是责备我——"

这些痛苦的回忆对这个老太太来说已经太多而难以承受了，她放声地大哭了起来。汤姆现在也正抽着鼻涕——与其说他在同情别人，还不如说他是在同情自己。他听到玛丽也在哭，时不时地还为他说几句好话，他瞬时觉得自己比以前还要伟大。而且他被姨妈这悲恸欲绝的样子深深感动了，他真想从床底下冲出去，一把抱住姨妈给她个惊喜，况且他本身就喜欢制造一些富有戏剧性的场面，但这回他控制住了自己，躺在那里一动不动。

他继续听着，根据一些零零碎碎的信息明白了，原来一开始人们以为孩子们是游泳的时候淹死的，但他们又发现一只小竹筏不见了，而且有些孩子还说这几个失踪的小孩儿曾对他们说村子里不久就要"出大事"，村子里头脑好使的人们将这些零七八碎的信息整合到一起，推断出孩子们应该是乘着竹筏逃跑了，不久就会在村子的下游出现，但是快半晌的时候，人们发现竹筏搁浅在了村子下游五六英里的密西西比河岸——于是大家的希望就落空了，他们肯定是淹死了，要不然的话，光是饿着肚子就能把他们在日落之前逼回家。人们觉得没有打捞到他们的尸体是因为孩子们肯定是在河当中被淹死的，要不这几个游泳好手肯定早跑到河岸上了。今天是星期三的晚上，如果到周日为止都还没有发现尸体的话，就不会再继续进行打捞工作了，周日早晨的时候便会在教堂举行葬礼仪式。汤姆听到这些，惊得汗毛都立了起来。

哈泼太太哭哭啼啼地道了声晚安就准备走了，突然这两个失去亲人的女人感到一阵激动，紧紧扑到对方怀里大哭了一场，然后才分手。波丽姨妈跟西德尼和玛丽道晚安的时候，声音变得异常的温柔。西德尼也抽泣了一阵，玛丽则痛心地大哭了起来。

接着，波丽姨妈跪了下来，虔诚地为汤姆做了祷告，她哀求地说着，话语间充满了无限的爱，她那苍老的声音颤抖着，于是还没等姨妈说完，汤姆又泣不成声了。

在姨妈上床以后，他还静静地趴在那里，因为姨妈时不时还心碎地喃喃说上几句，翻来覆去地无法入睡，但最后她还是睡着了，偶尔还会在睡梦中呻吟一两下。于是汤姆轻轻地爬了出来，从床边慢慢地站了起来，他右手挡着烛光，站在姨妈面前凝视着她。他心里难过极了，于是便从口袋里掏出了那张皱皱巴巴的树皮，然后放到了灯台旁边。但是他又想到了一些事，表情犹豫了起来。最后他又眼前一亮，找到了一个完美的解决方法。于是他匆匆地将树皮放回了口袋，弯下了腰，轻轻地吻了一下姨妈苍白的嘴唇，接着就径直地溜了出去，走时还把门闩给插好了。

他绕着道儿回到了渡船码头，发现周围没有人看守，于是就大胆地走上了船，因为他知道船上除了一个看船的之外，就再也没有其他人了。而那个看船的总是在睡觉，睡起来就像个雕塑一样，纹丝不动。他将船尾的小艇卸了下来，钻了进去，不一会儿就小心翼翼地往上游划去了。当他在村子上方划过一英里的时候，他斜转船身，全力以赴地奋力前划。他很利落地靠上了另一边的河岸，因为这对他而言简直就是雕虫小技。这时他正打着主意想把小艇占为己有，理由是这完全可以被当成个大船，而海盗们打击大船是再正常不过的了，但他也知道人家丢了船肯定会大搜一番，这样的话事情反而会弄巧成拙，所以他丢下了船上了岸，走到树林里去了。

进了树林之后，他就坐了下来，休息了好一会儿，强打起精神不让自己睡着，接着又小心翼翼地朝大本营走去，此时夜已将尽，而当他走到小岛的沙滩上时，天已大亮。他又坐下来休息了一会儿，直到日头高挂，阳光已在河面上镶上了一道金边，接着他就一头扎进了河里。一小会儿之后，他已经浑身湿漉漉地站在了营地门口，这时他听到乔说：

"不是的，汤姆是个讲信用的人，哈克，他会回来的，他肯定不会食言。他知道要是食言的话对于海盗而言会是个多大的耻辱，汤姆的心那么高，必然不会因为这种事儿食言。他肯定是忙活什么事儿去了，我真想知道是什么。"

"好吧，不管怎么说，现在这些宝贝是我们的了，对吧？"

"可以这么说，但是也不完全，哈克，这上面写着，要是他在早饭前还没有回来的话，才归我们。"

"他就在这儿呢！"汤姆叫道，说着他昂首挺胸地大步走进了营地，营造出一种很好的戏剧效果。

不一会儿，一顿丰盛的鲜鱼加熏肉的早餐就做好了，他们一边狼吞虎咽地吃着早餐，一边听汤姆滔滔不绝地讲他的冒险之旅，汤姆边讲还不忘边添油加醋。吃完后汤姆就瘫倒在一片树荫底下睡起大觉来，一直睡到了晌午，另外两个海盗忙着准备去钓鱼和探险。

第十六章

吃过中午饭以后，所有的海盗都动身到沙滩上找乌龟蛋。他们拿树枝往沙子里戳，当戳到松软的地方时，就跪在那里，用手来掏。有时能从一个洞里掏出五六十个乌龟蛋，这些蛋是白色的，而且都圆不溜秋，比英国胡桃稍小一点。当晚他们就美美地吃了一顿炸乌龟蛋，在周五的早上又享用了一番。

早餐过后，孩子们欢呼雀跃地跑到了沙滩上，互相追着跑了一转儿又一转儿，边跑还边甩着衣服，直到他们都脱了个精光。接着又跑到沙滩上的浅水中嬉闹，他们笑着，闹着，直到湍急的河流渐渐没到腿部，而这湍急的流水却也大大增加了他们的趣味。有时他们围成一团，哗哗哗地掀着水向对方脸上泼去，后来大家越靠越近，都把脸扭到一边防止被那让人透不过气的水花击中，最后扭到了一起，你拍着我，我抓着你，直到最能干的一个把另一个按到水里，于是他们都纷纷摔倒在水中，露出白花花的大腿和胳膊，接着便摇摇晃晃地爬了起来，嘴里还喷着水，他们哈哈地笑着，并急促地喘着气。

等到玩累了之后，孩子们就从河边跑开，四脚朝天地躺在又干又热的沙滩上，还拿沙子把全身都盖住。过一会儿，他们又冲进了河里，愉快地打起了水仗。最后他们突然想到，可以把自己那赤裸的皮肤当成肉色的紧身衣，于是他们在沙滩上画了一个圈，开始上演马戏活动，谁也不愿意在这个最值得骄傲的角色上输给对方。

接下来他们将石子掏出，玩起了"滚弹子""打弹出圈"和"扣弹子"这三种弹子玩法，直到玩腻了。然后乔和哈克又下去游了一会儿泳，而汤姆则不想再去冒险了，因为他发现在抖裤子的时候，把脚踝上的一串响尾蛇尾巴上的响环给抖没影儿了，他此时正纳闷儿，没带这个神秘的护身符玩了那么久，既然没有出事。在没找到它之前他是不敢再去冒险了，这会儿另外两个男孩都已经累了，准备回来歇一歇。于是他们渐渐地各自坐在那里出神，一句话也不说了，都向那宽广的河对岸望去，村子这时已经在柔和的阳光之中打起了盹。汤姆发现他用大拇脚趾在沙子上写了"贝琪"两个字，他赶忙把它抹掉，并对自己的软弱十分懊恼。可是一会儿他又写起了这个名字，他实在是控制不住自己了。于是他又一次地把字擦去，接着为了让自己逃脱这种诱惑，他拉来了其他两个孩子一起玩耍。

但此时乔已经完全没有了兴致，他现在非常想家，根本都忍受不了想家的痛苦了。眼泪顺着他的脸流了下来，哈克现在也沉浸在悲伤之中。汤姆此刻也心情低落，但是他竭力地控制住自己不表现出来，他有个秘密还没有准备好跟大家说，但要是这种低迷的情绪不能很快被打破的话，他就不得不吐出秘密。于是汤姆做出兴致高昂的样子说：

"我想这个岛上肯定有海盗居住过，孩子们，我们将再次探寻，海盗们在岛上藏了财宝，我说，当你找到一个烂箱子，里面装满了金银财宝的时候，该是什么感受呢？"

但是这没有激起大家一丁点儿的热情，两个伙伴都没有搭理他。汤姆又试着拿别的事情引诱他们，但也没有任何起效。乔坐在那儿一个劲儿地拿树枝戳着沙子，看起来很伤心，终于他说：

"噢，伙计们，我们放弃吧。我想回家，这样太孤单了。"

"噢，不，乔，你以后就会好起来的，"汤姆说，"想想吧，在这可以钓鱼。"

"我才不管能不能钓鱼呢，我要回家。"

"但是乔，没有比这更适合游泳的地方了啊。"

"游泳对人又不好，而且我现在对这也不感兴趣，不知道为什么，要是没人老命令我不准去游泳，我就不想游了，我就是想回家。"

"切！小屁孩！你就是想回去找你妈。"

"是啊，我就是想见我妈妈——要是你有妈妈，你也想见她，我跟你一样，才不是什么小屁孩。"说着乔吸起了鼻子。

"好吧，我们就让这个小屁孩回家找妈妈吧，对吧？哈克，可怜虫，不是想找妈妈吗？那就去啊，你是喜欢这儿的，对吧，哈克？我们俩待在这儿，是吧？"

哈克不带任何感情地说着："是——是的。"

"我这辈子都不会再跟你说话了。"乔提高了音调说，"绝不！"说完他就生气地走开了，开始穿衣服。

"谁在乎哦！"汤姆说，"才没人想跟你待一块儿呢，回家去吧，准备接受嘲笑去吧，呵，你真是个不错的海盗，哈克和我都不再是小毛孩了，我们要待在这儿，是吧，哈克？他要想走就叫他走好了，没有他我们也准能过得很愉快。"

但是汤姆此时心里却很不安，他吃惊地看到乔还气呼呼地倒腾着他的衣服。哈克正用渴望的眼神望着忙忙乎乎的乔，而且还一直保持着沉默，这可不是个好兆头。不一会儿，乔连句分别都没说，就朝着伊利诺伊河岸快步走了过去。汤姆的心开始下沉，他瞥了一眼哈克，哈克此时承受不了汤姆的眼神，于是就垂下了头。接着他说：

"我也想走，汤姆，反正待在这儿也挺无聊的了，乔走了就会更无聊，我们也走吧，汤姆。"

"我才不走！要走你走吧，我是要待在这儿。"

"汤姆，我还是想走。"

"好吧，那你也走吧，谁也没拦着你。"

"汤姆，我希望你也能来，你再好好想想吧，等我们到了河对岸时，我们会在那儿等着你。"

"好吧，那你们可是要等死了，还有啥好说的。"

哈克也伤心地走了，汤姆站在那儿盯着他的背影，内心里跟他的自尊心苦苦斗争着，他也很想抛开自尊，跟他们一起走。汤姆忽然觉得四周变得孤单、冷清起来。他又跟自尊心做了最后一次斗争，然后边去追着他的同伴们边喊：

"等一下！等一下！我要告诉你们一个秘密。"

这两个同伴都停了下来，转过了身子。当汤姆跑到他们面前时，他开始向他们吐露自己的秘密，同伴们心情糟糕地听着，但当他们弄明白汤姆是要干什么的时候，又欢呼雀跃了起来，连呼："真是太妙了！"还说要是汤姆能早点告诉他们的话，他们就不会走了。汤姆编了一个貌似有理的理由，但实际上他是害怕这个秘密不能让他们在岛上再待一段日子，所以他必须要等到迫不得已的时候才能使出这个杀手锏。

于是这几个孩子又高高兴兴回到了营地，一个劲儿地感叹汤姆的计划是多么的妙，还不停地表达对汤姆的羡慕，不断赞美他竟能想出这么精妙绝伦的点子。在享用了一顿乌龟蛋加鲜鱼之后，汤姆说他想学抽烟。乔说他也想学，于是哈克就做了几个烟管，然后在里面塞满了烟叶。这两个新手之前就抽过葡萄藤做的雪茄，那种雪茄抽起来让人舌头发麻，而且叫人看上去一点也不男人。

现在他们用胳膊肘支着身体，侧躺在草地上，小心翼翼地尝试着喷烟云，心里实在是没底儿。一口下肚，味道真是不怎么样，不一会儿他们就觉得要窒息了。但汤姆却说：

"哈，这可真是简单！要是我知道抽个烟这么简单，我早就学会了。"

"我也这么认为，"乔说，"这根本没什么。"

"对吧，我见人们抽烟见过很多次，还想着要是我也会抽该多好，但是我从没想过我还真会抽。"

"我也是这么想的，是吧，哈克？你肯定听我这么说过，是吗，哈克？要是我骗人的话，我就卖给哈克，让他说了算。"

"是的——他说多好次了。"哈克说。

"好吧，我当然也这么说过啊，"汤姆说，"唔，准说过几百次。有次是在屠宰场，你还记得吗，哈克？当时鲍勃·坦纳也在那，约翰尼·米勒还有杰夫·撒切尔都在那儿，你还记得我这样说过吗，哈克？"

"没错，你真这样说过，"哈克说，"那天我刚丢了一个白弹子，不对，是在那天之后我才丢的白弹子。"

"对吧——我就这么说过，"汤姆说，"哈克也记得。"

"我真希望我能一整天都抽这种烟，"乔说，"我一点也没觉得恶心。"

"我也没有，"汤姆说，"我倒是能吸上一整天，但是我打赌杰夫·撒切尔不能。"

"杰夫·撒切尔！算了吧，让他抽个两口他就能呛晕，不信让他试一试，保准抽一回都不行了。"

"我也觉得，还有约翰尼·米勒——我真想看看他抽上一口是啥样儿的。"

"唔，我也想看呢！"乔说，"嘿，我敢跟你打赌他干这事儿最逊，一小口就能把他熏个半死。"

"准是这样的，乔，唉，我真想那些小子能看到我们现在的样子。"

"我也是。"

"嘿——伙计们，不用再多说什么了，下次等他们在场的时候，我就走到你跟前说：'乔，有烟吗？我想抽一口。'然后你就满不在乎地说——就像这算不了什么一样，'有啊，我一般都用我的老烟斗，唔，这儿还有一个，但是我的烟叶子不怎么好。'然后我就会说：'没事儿的，够劲儿就行。'然后你就掏出烟斗，然后咱们慢悠悠地点上火，你就瞅着他们那嫉妒的样儿吧。"

"真是不错，那简直是美极了，汤姆！我真想现在就能看看。"

"我也是！当我们告诉他们我们是在当海盗的时候学的抽烟，他们准巴不得自己也跟我们一起来了呢。"

"哈，他们准会的，我敢打赌他们准会这样的！"

谈话就这样继续着，但是不一会儿他们就说不下去了，谈话开始变得断断续续的了。继而沉默占了上风，他们开始不停地吐痰。孩子们腮边的每一个毛孔都像正在喷涌的泉眼一般，舌头底下就像被大水淹没的地下室一般，任他们多么努力地去舀水，也无济于事，水还是源源不断地滚了出来。不管他们怎么抑制，痰还是从嗓子眼儿喷了出来，他们不停地干呕着。现在两个孩子看起来都很虚弱，也很悲惨。此刻乔的烟斗已从他无力的手中滑落，汤姆的烟斗也是这样。两个孩子的泉眼都喷薄不断，他们又像是两个小泵一样，奋力地往外吐着痰。接着乔虚弱地说：

"我把小刀弄丢了，我觉得我最好该去找找。"

汤姆颤抖着嘴唇，结结巴巴地说：

"我去帮你，你从那条路上走，我去到溪水边瞅瞅，对了，哈克你不用来，我们可以找到。"

于是哈克又坐了下来，他一直等了一个小时，等得他实在是太孤单了，于是他去找他的两个伙伴去了。只见这两个伙伴都在林子里，但是相隔很远，他们看上去都很苍白，昏昏欲睡。但是直觉告诉他，他们刚刚很难受了一阵儿，不过现在已经好了。

晚饭的时候，他们并不似以往那么说个不停。他们看上去都很脆弱，饭后，哈克又拿出了烟斗准备抽烟，当问及需不需要给他们也弄烟叶的时候，这两个男孩称自己不舒服而拒绝了，他们说是晚上不知道吃了什么，让他们这会儿有些难受。

半夜的时候乔睡醒了，于是他叫醒了其他两个孩子。空气中有种沉闷的声音似乎在预兆着什么。尽管周围无比沉闷，热得让人都要窒息了，但是男孩们还是紧紧地围在篝火旁，想从中寻找些友好的氛围。他们静静地坐在那里，屏住了呼吸等待着即将发生的事情。沉闷依旧掌控着大局，除了篝火之外，每个地方都笼罩在死一般的寂静和黑暗中。不一会儿，远处的天空中划过一道亮光，照亮了树叶，马上就又消失了。又过了一会儿，天空中又闪过一道更强的光，接着又是另一道。紧接着从森林的树木中传来了一阵隆隆声，孩子们感觉到脸颊旁拂过微微的气息，他们以为是夜神身边的精灵们从这儿走了过去，一个个吓得直哆嗦。一阵短暂的平静过后，一道恐怖的闪光照亮了整个夜空，孩子们脚下的每一片叶子都能看得清清楚楚，同时你也能看见三张惊恐发白的脸。轰鸣的雷声隆隆地响着，从空中滚过，又消逝在远方。一阵凉风袭来，叶子都沙沙作响，篝火中的灰烬被吹得飞舞了起来，接着又是一道闪电照亮了森林，继而又响起了隆隆雷声，好像要把孩子们头顶上的树枝劈断一般。随后又是无尽的黑暗，他们害怕地抱成了一团，几个豆大的雨点噼里啪啦地拍在了树叶上。

"快点！孩子们，快点到帐篷里去。"汤姆说。

于是他们一下子就跳了起来跑开了，黑暗中还被树枝和藤蔓绊得踉踉跄跄的。他们吓得摸不着方向，大家朝着不同的方向跑去了。一道刺眼的闪光在树林中划过，闪电所到之处，万物都在震动，一道接着一道，一声雷鸣接着一声。片刻，倾盆大雨就滚泻而下，雨水劈头盖脸地泼到地面上，被狂风刮成了一片片雨幕。孩子们朝对方喊着，但是他们的声音淹没在了这呼啸而过的狂风和电闪雷鸣之中。不过，最终他们陆陆续续地抵达了营地，个个都又冷又怕，浑身都被雨淋透了，在这悲惨的境遇之中能彼此做伴也算是不幸中的万幸了。他们无法听到彼此说话，因为那块旧帆布在风雨中噼啪作响，声音太大了，就算没有其他的吵闹，这声音也足够淹没他们的话语。狂风越刮越大，不一会儿这块旧帆布的固定绳就被吹断了，把帐篷一卷而飞。孩子们手拉着手飞奔了起来，身上溅了很多泥巴，他们在风雨中摔得鼻青脸肿的，终于跑到了河堤旁的一棵大橡树下躲雨，此刻正狂风乱作，雷电之战正猛烈地进行着，在电光火石之中，森林中的万物都被照得清晰可见：弯曲的大树，白浪滚滚的河流，飞舞翻腾的泡沫，对岸高耸的悬崖那黑咕隆咚的轮廓，都在漂浮的云雾和倾泻而下的大雨中隐约可见。每隔片刻就会有大树在这场交战中败下，伴着断裂声倾倒在小树丛中。惊雷不断袭来，震耳欲聋，那场景真是难以名状。最后风暴更加汹涌，好像要把小岛撕裂，还要将它烧毁，让水淹没树梢，再将它吹走，把岛上所有的生物都彻底地震聋震傻。这一夜对这几个无家可归的年轻人来说简直是一场噩梦。

好在最后风暴总算过去了，风雨声渐平，所有的一切又归于平静。孩子们筋疲力尽地回到了营地，营地真是一片狼藉，可他们还是发现有值得感恩戴德的，因为在这场灾难之中，他们的床已被惊雷劈毁了，但当时他们并不在营地里。

营地的一切都被雨水淋湿了，营火也没有幸免。毕竟是个孩子，他们跟同龄人一样，做事情不会做周密的考虑，根本没有为避雨准备过什么。这会儿他们又湿又冷，懊恼极了。此刻他们真是灰心丧气，但是不一会儿就又发现，篝火已经烧到了当初靠着的木头（在它向上翘起，而离开地面的地方），而且烧得很深，然后他们发现了一块巴掌大的干木，所以他们耐心地挖着，终于从原来挡风用的木头上弄下来了一些碎木头和树皮，接着便小心翼翼地拨弄着，终于又点着了火。然后他们又往火堆里添了很多树枝，直到火焰熊熊地燃了起来大家才恢复愉快的心情。在这之后，他们把火腿煮了煮，然后烤干，好好享用了一番，接着就坐在了篝火旁，夸耀着他们这一晚上的冒险经历直到天明，因为到处都是湿的，没有一块地可以睡觉。

太阳冉冉升起的时候，睡意袭上了这几个孩子的眼皮，于是他们都躺到沙滩上睡觉去了。不一会儿就被晒得通红通红的，于是他们无精打采地去准备早饭。吃过饭后，孩子们感到目光呆滞，浑身困倦，并又一次地想回家了。汤姆看出了大家想回家的迹象，于是便开始卖力地鼓舞其他两个海盗。但是他们现在对白弹子、杂耍或者游泳之类的任何事都没有兴趣了。于是他提醒大家别忘了那个秘密计划，顿时所有人都又兴致盎然。趁着这个秘密还在起效，他又将大家的兴趣转移到了另一个事上，这件事就是暂时不当海盗，先当一会儿印第安人换换心情。大家都被这个主意吸引了，所以不一会儿他们就脱光了衣服，在身上糊了很多泥巴，就像好几个斑马一样——当然他们全都是酋长——接着便呼啸地穿梭在林中，袭击一个英国殖民地。

后来他们又变成了三个敌对的部落，从埋伏处吼叫着出来攻向对方，杀掉对方，剥下敌人的皮，牺牲者数以千计，这可真是一场血流成河的征战，当然也是最令人满意的一场。

晚饭时分，他们聚集了起来，尽管饥肠辘辘但却十分开心。但眼下一个新问题又产生了——敌对的印第安人要是事先不讲和，是不能坐在一起吃饭，同分一杯羹的，而讲和的前提是要抽一袋烟，他们可没听过别的讲和方式。三个当中的两个野蛮人真希望自己还当海盗，但是现在可没有别的办法，所以他们竭力地表现出非常欢喜的样子，向哈克要了烟斗，按规矩轮流抽了烟。

瞧，他们正为当了野蛮人而感到高兴，因为他们从中又找到了收获。他们发现自己可以抽上一小会儿，而不用出去找丢了的小刀。感觉是有些恶心，但还没到很难受的地步，既然现在有可能学会抽烟，他们才不会就此罢休呢，不会的，在晚饭后，两个孩子又小心翼翼地练了起来，成果很明显，于是他们喜气洋洋地过了一晚上。他俩为自己新学的技艺感到骄傲和开心，这比把六大部落的人全都剥皮还要值得令人感到骄傲。我们就让他们吸会儿烟，好好地自吹自擂一番吧，暂时是用不上他们了。

第十七章

　　但是就在这静谧的周六晚上，小镇里却没有欢声笑语。哈泼一家和波丽姨妈一家都被悲伤所吞噬，淹没在眼泪之中。尽管同平常一样安静，一种不同以往的气氛却笼罩在这小镇，揪着每个人的心。村民们跟以往一样地干着事，但却心不在焉的，而且大家都很少说话，倒是时不时地叹着气。对孩子们而言，周六这个放假的日子无疑是个沉重的日子，他们无心玩耍，最后都玩不起来了。

　　下午的时候，贝琪·撒切尔在校园的操场上忧郁地闲逛，觉得糟透了，但是她找不到可以聊以慰藉的方法，她自言自语道：

　　"哦，真希望我能再一次得到那柴架上的铜把手！我现在连个纪念他的东西都没有了。"她说着强忍住了泪水。

　　过了一会儿，她停住了脚步，自言自语道："就是在这儿，哦，要是能重来的话，我决不会那样说了，怎么样也不会那样说了，但是现在他已经不在了，我永远，永远，永远都不能再见他一面了。"

　　想到这里，她的心都要碎了，于是她漫无目的地走开了，眼泪止不住地从脸上滑落。这时有一大群小孩儿——都曾是汤姆和乔的玩伴，走了过来，他们向栅栏那边看过去，还用虔诚的口吻讲着他们最后一次见到汤姆时他都干了些什么，还有乔曾说过的这样或那样的琐事。（每件事情都孕育着危险，而他们现在很容易就看穿了！）每个人说话的时候都能明确指出当时这些失踪的孩子站过的地方，而且他们还在讲话中添油加醋，说道："而且我就那么站着——就是我现在站的位置，要是你是汤姆——我当时跟他距离那么近——他就这样冲我笑，我就像浑身被电了一样，就像——天啊，太可怕了——我当然没想过那是怎么回事，但是我现在算是明白了。"

然后孩子们争起了到底谁是最后一个见过汤姆的人，很多孩子都为了这件不好的事争夺荣誉，抢着列举了各种证据，而且基本上都被证人篡改过了，最终，当轮到决定是谁最后一个见过那些失踪的男孩，最后跟他们讲过话时，那些幸运得到肯定的孩子便立刻脸上增光，觉得自己的地位大增，其他的孩子则目瞪口呆地看着他们，羡慕极了。一个小家伙儿摆不出什么证据来，于是他就相当骄傲地回忆道：

"唔，汤姆·索亚曾经揍过我一回。"

但是这却没什么值得骄傲的，大部分的孩子都能这样说，所以他这么一说就自降身价了。最后这群小孩又游荡到别的地方去了，他们边游荡还边回忆那几位逝去的英雄，无不骄傲。

第二天上午，主日学校放学时，没有像平常那样响铃，而是敲响了丧钟。在这个非常安静的主日里，丧钟的声音似乎跟大自然的寂静协调一致。村民们开始聚集起来，人们在门厅处逗留了一会儿，到处都在小声议论这一悲痛的事情。但当人们进了教堂之后，就停止了私语。只听到穿着丧服的女人们坐到座位上时，裙子发出的沙沙声。没人记得小教堂如此座无虚席的时候是多少年以前的事了。后来教堂里便鸦雀无声，人们都沉默了，期待着即将发生的事情。接着波丽姨妈走了进来，后面跟着西德尼和玛丽，再后面是哈泼一家，所有的人穿着素净的黑色。这时全场起立，包括年迈的牧师都站了起来，直到丧亲家属在前排就座。接着又是一阵的沉默，时不时地会有人捂住脸抽泣，打破这一寂静。牧师摊开了双手，做了祷告。接着人们唱了一首动人的圣歌，还说道：

"我乃重生，我乃生命。"

随着丧礼的进行，牧师描述了逝者的美德和他们吸引人的魅力，以及他们美好的前途，每个到场的人听完后都暗自认可，都觉得自己之前真是执迷不悟，只能看到这些可怜鬼的缺点，才会那样对待他们，心里懊悔极了。牧师还讲了这些孩子的其他一些闪光点，这都展示了孩子们天真可爱，慷慨大方的本性。人们现在可以很容易地看出那时这些小鬼是多么的高尚和美丽，但他们也悲痛地回忆起当时竟把孩子们当作流氓一样用皮鞭抽打。随着牧师的动情演说，人们越来越受感动，直到最后整个人群都心痛不已，跟着丧亲家属一起号哭起来，这极其痛苦的哭声汇成了一曲大合唱。牧师自己也深受感动，在圣坛上哭了起来。

这时走廊里有些窸窣的声响，但是没人注意到，片刻以后，教堂的门被推开了，牧师拿开手绢，抬起迷离的双眼，站在那里惊呆了！接着一双又一双的眼睛顺着牧师的目光看了过去，接着全体人员几乎一齐站了起来，瞪大了双眼，看着这三个死去的孩子大摇大摆地从过道走了进来。汤姆打头走着，乔紧随其后，哈克穿着一身破烂衣服，不好意思地跟在最后，他们一直都藏在无人的走廊里，听着自己的悼词！

波丽姨妈、玛丽还有哈泼一家立刻扑向了这几个复活的孩子，不停地亲着他们，又谢天又谢地的，让他们直喘不过来气。只有可怜的哈克窘迫地站在那里，满身不自在，此刻他不知道该做什么，也不知道要藏在哪里才能躲开这么多不欢迎他们的眼神。他站在那踌躇了一下，想着要溜走，但是汤姆抓住了他，说：

"波丽姨妈，这不公平，也应该有人欢迎哈克回来才对。"

"你说得对，我真高兴看到哈克也回来了，可怜的没娘孩子！"说完波丽姨妈就扑向了哈克，给了他无尽的关怀，这却让他比刚才更不自在了。突然，牧师高声说道："赞美上帝，所有的人都会被救赎——唱起来吧！——用心去歌唱！"

于是人们就唱了起来，大家满怀激情地高声大唱，歌声里充满了胜利的喜悦。就在歌声响彻教堂的时候，汤姆·索亚大海盗扫视了一眼那些满眼嫉妒的小孩，他暗自窃喜，这该是他一生最骄傲的时刻了。

到场的人们走出教堂的时候还说要是还能听到这么动人的老百首，他们愿意再被捉弄一次。

汤姆那天得到了比平时一年都还多的巴掌和亲吻——这要根据波丽姨妈时好时坏的心情而定，他几乎都搞不清楚哪种是在表达对上帝的感谢，哪种是对他的怜爱。

第十八章

这就是汤姆的大秘密——和他的海盗兄弟们一起返回家乡，参加自己的葬礼。他们那时坐在一个大木头上划着水到了密苏里州的岸边，那时候已经是周六的傍晚了，他们在村子下方五六英里的地方上了岸。然后在村头的树林里几乎睡到了天明，接着顺着小路偷偷溜到了教堂里，教堂正七零八落地放着一堆椅子，一切正处在混乱中，于是他们就躲在长廊里睡了个够。

周一早晨吃早饭的时候，波丽姨妈和玛丽对汤姆无微不至，什么要求都满足他，说的话也比平常多，在谈话中，波丽姨妈说道：

"喂，汤姆，我可不觉得这是个好把戏，你们是好好玩了一番，我们却痛苦了一个星期，而且你真的如此狠心让我这么难过，你都能坐着一根木头回来参加你的葬礼，你为什么不能回来给我点暗示好让我知道你没有死，只是跑出去了呢？"

"是啊，你本可以这样做的啊，汤姆，"玛丽说道，"我相信你肯定也想到过这。"

"是吗，汤姆？"波丽姨妈问道，脸上一副渴求的表情，"说吧，要是你想到的话，你会回来吗？"

"我——呃，我不知道，这会毁了一切计划的。"

"汤姆，我原以为你会这么爱我，"波丽姨妈说，话语间充满了悲伤，让汤姆感到十分不安，"要是你当时想到回来看看的话，就算你没做，那也还是不错的。"

"姨妈，别这么想，这没什么关系，"玛丽替汤姆说着好话，"汤姆就是这么冒冒失失的——他总是这样毛手毛脚，做个事儿从来不考虑那么多。"

"这样说的话，就叫人更难受了。西德尼就会想到要回来看看的，而且他也会这么做。汤姆，总有一天你会后悔的，到那时一切都晚了，你会后悔在能关心我的时候，没有尽到孝心。"

"噢，姨妈，你是知道我真的在乎你。"汤姆说。

"要是你能做得好点，我就更相信你是在乎我的。"

"现在我希望我当时那么想过，"汤姆用后悔的语调说道，"但是不管怎么说，我梦到过你了，这总能证明我在乎你，对吧？"

"这可没什么——一只猫也会做做梦呢——但是这总比什么也没有强啊，你梦到什么了？"

"哦，星期三的晚上我梦到了你坐在床边上，西德尼就坐在木柴箱上，玛丽坐在他旁边。"

"好吧，我们确实是这样坐的啊，我们一贯都是这样坐的。真高兴你在梦里还这样为我们费心。"

"我还梦到乔·哈泼的妈妈也来了。"

"唔，她当时确实来了！你还梦到什么了？"

"噢，我梦了很多啊，但是现在记不大清了。"

"好吧，试着回忆一下嘛，好吗？"

"不知道怎么回事，我好像记得风——风吹灭了——吹灭了——"

"努力想想，汤姆！风确实吹灭了什么，快想！"

汤姆将手指贴在脑门上，焦急地想了一会儿，说道：

"啊，我想起来了！我想起来了！风把蜡烛吹灭了！"

"天啊，快接着说，汤姆，接着说呀！"

"好像你还说了'咦，我觉得门——'"

"快说呀，汤姆！"

"让我想一会儿，就一会儿。啊，对了，你说的是我觉得门开了。"

"我当时就像现在这样坐着，我确实这样说的！对吧，玛丽！快接着说吧！"

"接着——接着——我真的记不太清了，但是好像你让西德尼去——去——"

"去哪儿？去哪了呀？我让他去干什么了，汤姆？我让他去干什么了啊？"

"你让他——你——噢，你让他去关上门。"

"天啊，我的天啊！我这辈子从没听过这样怪的事！再也别说梦里都是假的了，我马上就去跟塞伦尼·哈泼讲讲，我要看看她这回怎么说我迷信，接着说呀，汤姆！"

"噢，现在我全都想起来了，记得清清楚楚了，接着你又说我不是个坏孩子，只是有些淘气，有些冒失，并不是不负责任，——嗯，你好像说我还是个小毛孩儿，反正就是诸如此类的话。"

"我真是这样说的！噢，我的老天爷啊！你说得一点也没错啊！接着讲吧，汤姆！"

"接着你哭了起来。"

"我是哭了，我真的是哭了，不过这也不是第一次哭了，后来呢？"

"后来哈泼太太也开始哭，她说乔也是这样的孩子，她说自己真希望没有为奶油的事责备他，因为其实是她自己把奶油倒掉的——"

"汤姆！你真是神灵附体了啊！你简直就是个预言家！你说得一点也没错！真是老天显灵了，继续讲，汤姆！"

　　"接着，西德尼他说——他说——"

　　"我不认为我说过什么。"西德尼说。

　　"你说了的，西德尼。"玛丽反驳他说道。

　　"闭上你的嘴，让汤姆接着说！他当时说了什么呀，汤姆？"

　　"他说——我好像记得他说希望我在另一个世界里过得很好，但是要是我在世的时候，能表现好一些——"

　　"哎，都让你知道了！跟他当时说的真是一个字都不差！"

　　"你还让他闭上嘴。"

　　"我确实这么说的！当时肯定有个天使在旁边，肯定有个天使藏在某个地方！"

　　"还有，哈泼太太还谈到了乔用一个鞭炮吓她的事，你跟她讲了彼得和止疼药的事——"

　　"完全正确！"

　　"然后你们还讲了要去河里打捞我们，还有周日葬礼的事，接着你和哈泼太太就相拥而泣了，然后她就走了。"

　　"真是这样的！当时真的是这样的，我说汤姆，就算你当时亲眼所见，你都不一定能说这么准确，后来又怎么了？说呀，汤姆！"

　　"后来我梦到你为我做了祷告——我能听到你说的每一个字，接着你就上床睡觉去了，我当时很难过，于是我拿出了一个梧桐树皮，在上面写道：'我们没有死——我们只是在当海盗。'然后我把树皮放到了桌上的蜡烛旁，当时你躺在那里熟睡着，看起来很美，我想我该走了，于是我弯下腰亲了亲你的嘴唇。"

　　"真的吗，汤姆，真的吗？要是真的话，我什么都能原谅你！"说着她一把抱过这个男孩，紧紧地搂住他，搞得汤姆觉得自己是个十恶不赦的坏蛋。

"这真好，尽管只是个梦。"西德尼自言自语道，他声音小得都快听不见了。

"闭上嘴，西德尼！一个人要是醒来就会按照梦里发生的去做。汤姆，这是我特意给你留的大苹果，打算找到你的时候给你，现在快去上学吧，感谢仁慈的上帝把你带了回来，这回的事对于那些相信上帝，并且按上帝旨意做事的人而言，既是一场磨炼，又是一种慈爱，尽管对上帝而言我并不配他施与我恩慈，但要是只有配受他佐佑的人才能得到他的庇护，那么没有几个人死之前会瞑目，也没几个人能去他身边安息了。跟西德尼和玛丽一起上学去吧，汤姆——快走吧，你们已经耽误了我不少时间。"

于是孩子们都上学去了，老太太就去找哈泼太太，想用汤姆活生生的梦来说服她。西德尼从家离开时，对汤姆的话心里暗自忖度了好一番，他显然不太相信汤姆的梦，他认为："这么长的一个梦，竟然没有一点纰漏，这显然不可能！"

汤姆现在可成了大英雄！他再也不像以前那样蹦蹦跳跳地走路了，现在他走起路来，大摇大摆，非常自信，俨然是个万众瞩目的海盗。事实上也是如此，他刻意让自己看起来没有在注意别人的眼光，没有在听别人的议论，但其实这样的场景却是他日日渴求的。小一点的孩子都跟在他屁股后面，他们觉得能跟在汤姆后面非常值得骄傲，况且汤姆也不觉得他们烦，这架势看上去就像他是仪仗队打头的鼓手，或者是进城耍马戏的领头象。跟他一般大的孩子们表面上装出不知道他走失的事儿，心里却嫉妒得眼都红了。要是能有汤姆现在这黝黑的皮肤，又能像他一样受人敬仰，他们真愿意用一切来换，但就是拿马戏团来换，汤姆也是不愿意的。

在学校里，孩子们都十分仰慕汤姆和乔，大家看他们的时候，眼神里充满了羡慕，这两个英雄很快就开始显摆起来。他们开始给如饥似渴的听众们讲自己的冒险之旅——但他们光讲开头，因为这种故事显然不会很快结束，像他们这种想象力丰富的人，很容易就能在故事里添油加醋，讲个不停。最后他们拿出烟斗，优哉游哉地抽起烟时，众人崇拜的眼光已将他们推入最光辉的殿堂。

汤姆现在觉得自己离了贝琪·撒切尔也能活，有荣誉就已经足够了，他愿意为荣誉而活。既然他现在已经如此显赫，那她可能非常想要重归于好。呵，才不管她了呢，她会发现自己跟其他人一样一点都不在乎她了。不一会儿，贝琪就来了，汤姆假装自己没有看见她，于是他走到另一组孩子那儿说个不停。过了一会儿他发现她正开心地跑来跑去，面色通红，眼神飞舞。她正假装追着其他的孩子，爽朗地笑着，但是他注意到她每抓到的同学都在他的附近，而且她总是朝自己这个方向瞟来瞟去。这一发现大大满足了汤姆的虚荣心，所以贝琪不但没有讨汤姆欢心，反而让他更趾高气扬了，让他更努力地克制自己，装作不知道她就在旁边。过了一会儿，贝琪不再欢呼雀跃了，她犹豫不决地走来走去，边走边叹了一两口气，她惆怅地偷看着汤姆，结果发现汤姆跟艾米·劳伦斯说的话特别多，她顿时觉得痛苦极了，于是变得不安了起来。她很想走开，但是她的脚就是不听使唤，反倒让她走近了那些孩子。她走上去装出很开心的样子跟一个小女孩说话，这个女孩几乎就站在汤姆边上，她说：

"嘿，玛丽·奥斯汀！你这个坏孩子，怎么没来上主日课呢？"

"我来了啊，你没看到我吗？"

"是吗，没有啊！你当时坐在哪儿啊？"

"我平时都在彼得老师班里坐着，我看见你了呢。"

"是吗？嘿，真是有趣，我竟没看见你，我想跟你说一下野炊的事。"

"噢，这太有趣啦，谁要请啊？"

"我妈妈说让我请同学们一起去。"

"太好了，真希望她能让我参加。"

"当然，她当然会同意的，野炊是为我举行的，我想让谁来，她就会同意谁来，我希望你来。"

"这真是太好了，什么时候去啊？"

"晚些时候就会去，可能在暑假的时候。"

"哈，真是太棒了！你会请所有的同学吗？"

"嗯，凡是我的朋友或者想跟我成为朋友的人都可以去。"她说着偷偷瞥了一眼汤姆，但是他正滔滔不绝地跟艾米·劳伦斯讲小岛上那场可怕的风暴以及闪电是如何将那棵"离他不到三英尺远"的梧桐树劈成两半。

"噢，我能参加吗？"格蕾丝·米勒说。

"当然。"

"我呢？"莎莉·罗杰问。

"你也可以呀。"

"那我呢？"苏珊·哈泼问道，"还有乔能不能也去？"

"可以啦。"

就这样，除了汤姆和艾米，其他的孩子都得到了邀请，高兴地拍手欢呼。这时，汤姆冷冷地带着艾米走了，贝琪气得嘴唇发抖，眼里包着泪水，她强颜欢笑，继续跟同学们聊着，但是她现在对野炊已经没有心思，对什么都不感兴趣了。于是她立马走开了，藏在一个角落里，用她们女人的话来说就是要"大哭一场",然后她悲伤地坐在那里,自尊心大大受伤,直到铃响了以后她才站了起来,眼神中充满了报复,把两条辫子一甩,说知道自己要干什么了。

休息的时候,汤姆得意地继续跟艾米调情,他还不时地走来走去让贝琪看见,好用自己的表现伤她的心。最后他发现了她,但是他立刻就没了神气。因为他看见贝琪惬意地坐在教室后面的小长凳上,正在和阿尔弗雷德·坦帕尔看着画画书呢,他们看得如此着迷,两个小脑袋都要凑到一起了,根本没注意到其他人。汤姆顿时就嫉妒得血脉贲张,他开始恨自己,白白浪费了贝琪给他和好的机会,他骂自己是个傻子,把各种骂名都安到自己头上,他这会儿恼火得都想哭。艾米还在他旁边叽叽喳喳地说着,因为她心里正乐开了花,但是汤姆的舌头好像已经麻木了,他根本都听不见艾米说了什么,每次她满怀期待地停下时,汤姆都只能结结巴巴地表示赞同,而且还总是牛头不对马嘴。他不住地往教室后面看,看到他们恨得眼珠子都要掉下来了,但他控制不住自己不看,这让他快要发疯了,因为他们那亲密的样子让他觉得好像贝琪根本都不知道这个世上还有汤姆这个人。但是毫无疑问,贝琪看见了汤姆气急败坏的样子,她知道这回是她赢了,看见他跟刚才的自己一样痛苦,她高兴极了。

艾米开心地说个不停,这让汤姆难以忍受。他暗示她自己还有事要做,事情是必须要做的,时间不等人啊。但是这个女孩还是没有停止讲话,汤姆想道:"唉,真是烦,我可怎么把她弄走呢?"最后他说自己必须要去办事儿了,不能陪她了,她还天真地说放学后会等着他,于是汤姆赶忙走了,怕她还缠着自己。

"除了他哪个男孩都行!"汤姆想,此时他恨得咬牙切齿,"除了那个从圣路易斯来的自以为是的家伙,其他任何人都行,他以为自己穿得好就是个贵族了！哼，很好，在你第一次见到这个镇子的时候，我就揍过你一顿，小子，我还会再揍你一顿！你就等着碰上大爷我吧！我可就——"

于是他对着想象中的男孩拳打脚踢——对着空气一阵乱舞，又是抓来抓去，又是挖眼戳鼻的，"噢，你求饶了，求饶了是吧？还叫！现在求饶不求？哼，好吧，这回算是个教训！"说完后，这场想象中的架就算打完了，他满意极了。

中午的时候，汤姆跑回了家，他的良心再也受不了看到艾米那开心激动的样子，他的嫉妒之心再也无法承受更多的折磨。贝琪又和阿尔弗雷德看起了画画书，但是时间一分一秒地过去了，她再也没看见汤姆来接受折磨，于是她的胜利感开始挫败，她顿时对看书就失了兴趣，接着她变得心情沮丧，心不在焉，最后她伤心了起来，有两三次，一听到脚步声她就赶忙竖起了耳朵，但是每次希望都落空了，汤姆没有再来。最后她的心情已经跌到了谷底，从内心里希望自己没把事情做到这么过分。当可怜的阿尔弗雷德看到她对和他在一起看画画书不再感兴趣时，他不知道怎么办才好，于是他叫了起来："嘿，这个图真好看！你快看看呀！"贝琪此时已经没了耐心，于是她说："哦，不要烦我！我根本就不在意这些！"说完她就哭了起来，然后起身走开了。

阿尔弗雷德放下书跟了上来，他想安慰她，但是她说：

"走开，让我一个人待会儿，行不行啊！我讨厌你！"

男孩呆呆地站在了那里，不知道他到底做错了什么——她说过一个中午都想跟他一起看画画书——贝琪继续朝前边走边哭，于是阿尔弗雷德傻傻地走进了空无一人的教室。他这会儿又没面子又生气，因为他已经猜到了事实的真相——这个女孩就是借他来报复汤姆·索亚。当他想到这些时，对汤姆也恨之入骨了，于是他暗自欣喜地走上了讲台，打开了下午要检查的作业本，然后他在汤姆的本上泼了墨水。

恰巧此时贝琪正从窗户外向教室瞥了一眼，看到了他的行为。但她没有暴露自己，而是继续朝前走。她开始朝家的方向走去，想要找到汤姆然后告诉他这件事，这样汤姆就会对她充满感激，然后他们就能重归于好了。然而还没走到一半的路时，她就改变了主意。她回想起了自己在宣布野炊的时候汤姆的样子，不由得又气得发羞。于是她决定要让他受到惩罚，并想着要恨他一辈子。

第十九章

汤姆闷闷不乐地回了家，他姨妈见到他说的第一句话就让他觉得，他带着的一身悲伤将无处寄托了。

"汤姆，我真想剥了你的皮。"

"姨妈，我又做什么了啊？"

"好吧，你做得够多了，我还像个大傻子似的跑到哈泼家，还想着用你的梦让她无话可说，当我去了才发现，乔早把你那天晚上回来偷听我们谈话的事告诉她了。汤姆，我不知道一个小孩子家家的怎么会做这样的事。一想到你让我那样子去哈泼家，如此地戏弄我还一句话也不说，我就觉得伤心。"

汤姆没有想到事情会这样，他还觉得早晨耍的小聪明是个巧妙的玩笑，但是现在看起来又自私又愚蠢。于是他抱着头，不知道说什么好，过了一会儿他说：

"姨妈，我希望我没有这么做——但是我没想过。"

"噢，孩子，你从来都没想过，你除了自己从来都没想过别人。你那晚从杰弗逊岛上回来就是想看我们的笑话，而且你觉得用一个梦来戏弄我很好玩，但是你从来没想过同情我们，让我们不那么伤心。"

"姨妈，我知道现在这看起来很自私，但是我不是故意这样的。我真的不是，真的，而且那天晚上我回来也不是要笑话你们的。"

"那你是回来干什么的啊？"

"我就是要回来告诉你们别为我们担心，因为我们没有淹死。"

"汤姆，汤姆，要是我能相信你有这么好的心，那我就是这个世上最感激上帝的人了，但是你知道你从来都不会这样——而且这我是知道的，汤姆。"

"真的，我真的是这样想的，姨妈——要是我没这样想就天打雷劈。"

"噢，汤姆，别撒谎了——别说了，这只会让情况糟糕一百倍。"

"我没有撒谎，姨妈，我说的都是真的。我就是不想让你那么悲伤来着——就是因为这，我才回来的。"

"你就是说破天我也不信，要不我就该忽略那么多的错误了，你离家出走，又表现这么差劲，我难道应该高兴？这也太不讲理了，因为，你倒是告诉我啊，孩子？"

"好吧，你瞧，当你们在说葬礼的时候，我脑子里尽是想要藏在教堂里的想法，我真不愿意破坏这一计划，所以我又把树皮塞回口袋里了，没有告诉你。"

"什么树皮？"

"就是那个我在上面写着我们在当海盗的树皮，我现在真希望，当时我亲你的时候，你能醒过来，真的，我说的都是真话。"

听到这，姨妈脸上皱起的眉头渐渐舒展开了，她的眼里溺着温柔。

"你亲过我，汤姆？"

"当然啦，我亲了你一下。"

"你真的亲过我，汤姆？"

"真的，姨妈——我肯定我亲过你。"

"你为什么要亲我呢，汤姆？"

"因为我很爱你啊，你躺在那里呻吟，我真是难过极了。"

这话听起来不假，于是这个老太太忍不住颤抖地说道：

"再亲亲我吧，汤姆！——现在快去上学去吧，再也别烦我了。"

他刚一走，姨妈就跑到了衣橱前，拿出了那件汤姆当海盗时磨得不像个样的外套，然后她停住了，手里拿着外套，自言自语道：

"不，我不敢，可怜的孩子，我觉得他在说谎——但是这是个美丽的谎言，美丽的谎言，听着真让人舒心。我希望上帝——我知道上帝会原谅他的，因为他是好心才这样说的，但是我不愿发现这是个谎言，我不会看的。"

说罢，她又把外套放到了一边，站在那里待了一分钟。然后又把外套拿到手里，但她又一次地后退了。于是她又试了一次，这回她自我鼓励道："这是个美丽的谎言——是个美丽的谎言——我不会伤心的。"然后她摸了摸外套口袋，片刻之后，就读到了汤姆在树皮上写的字，于是她老泪纵横，说道："现在就是他犯了一百万个错儿，我也原谅他了。"

第二十章

　　姨妈亲了亲汤姆，这一举动将他低落的心情一扫而光，他又开心自在起来了。然后他准备去上学，碰巧在芳草巷头遇到了贝琪·撒切尔，汤姆总是用心情决定行为的，于是他毫不犹豫地跑向贝琪对她说：

　　"我今天的行为真是很不好，贝琪，我真的很抱歉，我再也不会，再也不会那样了，只要我活着我就不会那样，我们和好吧，好吗？"

　　这个女孩停住了脚步，轻蔑地看着他的脸说：

　　"托马斯·索亚先生，请你别再缠着我了，谢谢，我再也不会跟你讲话了。"

　　说完她一甩头就走了，汤姆呆站在那里没有意料到这一结果，他甚至连说一句"谁在乎你啊，自以为是的小姐"都忘了，当反应过来的时候，人家已经走了。所以他什么也没说成，他现在十分愤怒，于是他就这样恼闷地走进了学校，边走边想着要是她是个男孩就好了，那样他就能揍她一顿了。不一会儿，他在学校碰见了她，于是他路过她的时候说了句尖酸的话，而她也用同样尖酸的话回敬了他，这下他们俩是彻底决裂了。贝琪现在迫不及待地想要看到汤姆因为泼了墨的拼写本而受罚，她本来还想着要不要揭发阿尔弗雷德·坦帕尔干的坏事，但是汤姆刚刚伤人的话语让她彻底打消了这个念头。

　　可怜的小女孩，她还不知道大祸就要降临了。杜宾斯先生已经人到中年了，但却还壮志未酬。他梦想做一名医生，但是贫穷的家境让他只能做到小村子里的老师。每天他都从桌子里拿出一本神秘的书，然后当没课的时候就会专心致志地看起来。他每次总把书锁起来，拔下钥匙，学校里的每个捣蛋鬼都想看看书里写的什么，但是从来没有得手过。每个孩子都能说出书的内容，但是没有一个版本相同，而事实上没有办法知道真正的内容到底是什么。现在贝琪正路过那个挨着门的桌子，她注意到钥匙竟然还插在锁上！这真是千载难逢的好时机，于是她朝四周望了望，发现就自己一个人，紧接着她就把书拿到手了，书的扉页上写道"某某教授的人体解剖学"，她对于这几个字没有一点概念，于是她翻开了书本，映入眼帘的是一张精致的彩色刻画——一张人体图，赤身裸体。就在此时，一个阴影落在了书页上，汤姆·索亚走了进来，看见了这幅图画。贝琪一把将书合住，但不幸的是，她不巧撕掉了图画的一半，于是她把书扔到了抽屉里，插上了钥匙，然后又羞又恼地哭了起来。

"汤姆·索亚，你真是卑鄙，偷看别人在看什么。"

"我怎么知道你在看什么东西？"

"你应该为自己的行为感到惭愧，汤姆·索亚，我知道你会去告发我，天啊，我该怎么办，我该怎么办呢！我会被鞭打的，我在学校里从来没被打过。"

接着她急得跺着小脚说：

"你真是太卑鄙了！我知道有事会降临到你头上，你就等着瞧吧！讨厌鬼！讨厌鬼！讨厌鬼！"说完她就哭着冲出了教室。

汤姆静静地站着，被她这劈头盖脸的臭骂搞得有些懵了，过了一会儿，他自言自语道：

"女孩还真是又傻又好笑，一会儿这样，一会儿那样。从来都未挨过打！去你的吧，挨打算得了什么！女孩们总是这样——脸皮薄，胆小怕事。话说回来，我当然不会去向老杜宾斯告发这个可怜的小东西，因为有的是法子治她，用不着这么卑鄙，但是这件事会怎样呢？老杜宾斯肯定会问是谁撕了他的书，没人会回答，然后他就会像往常一样——一个接一个地问，到时候不用别人告状，他一走到这个女孩面前就能明白谁撕的，女孩们的表情总能出卖她们。她们都是些意志不坚定的人。她会被惩罚的，贝琪·撒切尔这回是插翅难逃了。"汤姆暗自把这事忖度了一番，然后他补充说道："好吧，既然她想看我的笑话，那我也让她自作自受好了！"

之后，汤姆跑出去跟伙伴们一起玩耍嬉戏，稍过了一会儿，老师就来了，同学们赶忙进了教室，开始上课了。汤姆对他讲的课没有什么兴趣，每次他朝女孩们那儿望一眼，贝琪的脸色都让他觉得不安，想想之前所有的事情，他也就不想再同情她了，而且他也无计可施，但他心里一点也不开心。不一会儿，汤姆就发现了拼写本的问题，于是有一段的时间里，他只顾惦记自己的事了。贝琪这下不再无精打采，饶有兴趣地关注着事态的发展。她觉得就算汤姆说那不是自己泼的，也不可能取得老师的信任，事实果真如此，汤姆的否认只能让事情更加糟糕。贝琪觉得自己应该开心才是，但是她发现自己并不开心，当事情变得糟糕时，她本想立即站起来揭发阿尔弗雷德，但是她强力地控制着自己，逼着自己坐在那里，因为她心里一直认为"汤姆会说出我撕书的事，所以我什么都不能说，不能救他"！

汤姆受了惩罚，然后回到座位上了，心里一点也不悲伤。因为他想着有可能自己没注意的时候，就把墨汁洒到拼写本上了，可能是和别人疯打的时候。他否认是自己弄的只是一种形式，因为这是惯例，死不承认是一种做事原则。

一个小时过去了，老师在椅子上打起了瞌睡，教室里一片嗡嗡读书声让人昏昏欲睡。过了一会儿，杜宾斯先生坐直了起来，打了个哈欠，然后打开了抽屉锁，把书拿了出来，但是他犹豫着是该把书拿出来还是放在那。大部分的学生都耷拉着眼皮抬起头瞥向他，但是其中有两个人正紧张地注视着他。杜宾斯先生心不在焉地在抽屉里摸着书本，接着他把书拿了出来，在椅子上坐定，然后就读了起来！汤姆望了一眼贝琪，她看上去就像一只被追捕的无助的兔子，而枪已经瞄准了兔子头部。他马上就忘记了跟她的争吵，快——要做点什么！还要立刻马上就做！但是这回汤姆干着急，却想不出法子。对了——他突然来了灵感！他想冲过去一把抓出书，然后夺门而逃。但是他犹犹豫豫地刚想了一会儿，就错失了良机——老师已经将书打开了。要是能再有个机会多好啊！但此时已晚，他也无力回天了。紧接着，老师就瞪着学生们，大家都不敢看他的眼睛。他的眼神是如此的凶狠，就连最无辜的人都不禁害怕起来。教室里立刻鸦雀无声，这一安静持续了足足十秒钟——老师正满腔的愤怒，于是他问道：

"谁把这本书给撕开了？"

没有人回答，此时掉一根针你都能听到声音，教室里仍然是一片安静。老师一张脸又一张脸地审视着，想找出犯罪痕迹。

"本·罗杰，是你撕的吗？"

她否认了，接下来又是一阵沉默。

"乔瑟夫·哈泼，是你吗？"

他也否认了，在这种慢节奏的审问之下，汤姆变得越来越紧张。老师扫视了所有的男孩，思考良久之后，将目光转向了女孩：

"艾米·劳伦斯？"

她摇了摇头。

"格雷丝·米勒？"

她也摇了摇头。

"苏珊·哈泼，是你干的吗？"

他又得到了一个否定的答案。接下来就轮到贝琪·撒切尔了。汤姆从头到脚都激动得颤抖了起来，他觉得这会儿情况非常绝望。

"贝琪·撒切尔，"（汤姆看了看她的脸——此时她已经吓得脸色发白）"是你撕的吗？——不行，要看着我的脸。"（她要举起双手求饶）——"是你撕了书吗？"

说时迟那时快，汤姆脑中闪过一个想法，他跳了起来，叫道："是我干的！"

同学们都困惑地看着汤姆，觉得他愚蠢至极，简直是难以置信。汤姆站了一会儿，好让自己镇定下来，接着他走上前去接受惩罚，此刻可怜的贝琪眼神里充满了惊讶，继而又转为感激和敬佩，汤姆觉得哪怕挨上一百鞭都值了。他也被自己的义行深深地感动了，于是在接受杜宾斯先生有史以来最残酷的鞭打时，他没有叫喊一声。而且在被宣判放学后要在外面站两个小时时，汤姆表现得毫不在乎，因为他知道谁会在外面等着他，一直等到他受完罚。所以这两个小时的无聊也算不了什么。

汤姆那天晚上上床的时候还想着要怎么样报复阿尔弗雷德，因为贝琪又羞又后悔地把所有的事都告诉了他，甚至连她的背叛都跟汤姆讲了。不久汤姆又沉浸在一些甜蜜的事上，连报仇都抛在脑后了。他最后迷迷糊糊地进入了梦乡，耳边还萦绕着贝琪对他说的最后几句话：

"汤姆，你怎么会这么伟大呀！"

第二十一章

就快要放暑假了，而这种时候校长总会比往常更加严厉，更加苛刻。因为他想让同学们在考试那天有个好表现。他手里的教鞭以及戒尺很少处于空闲的状态——至少在低年级同学中是这样的。只有一些高年级男孩或者十八、二十岁的姑娘们才能逃离此劫。杜宾斯先生的责罚也比之前更凶猛了，尽管在他那顶假发下面是一个光亮光亮的脑袋，但他才刚刚步入中年，肌肉仍然结实有力。随着考试的临近，他暴君的本性也暴露无遗，就算学生犯了一个微不足道的小错，他也会鞭打学生，趁机享受报复学生的快感。结果就是小一点的孩子们白天总是在恐惧中度过，而晚上则会策划各种报复行动。他们从不浪费可以给校长添乱的机会，但是校长总是占上风。因为在每次报复成功之后，随之而来的是更为残忍，更为彻底的鞭打，孩子们只得伤痕累累地败下阵来。最后，他们聚在一起密谋，想出了一个绝对能取得辉煌战果的策略。他们把画广告牌那家的儿子也拉来入伙，把计划告诉他，想请求他的鼎力相助。这个孩子也很高兴可以参战，他当然有他的理由，因为校长曾借住在他家，这可没少让他吃苦。过几天校长的太太就要去乡下走亲访友，这可是个绝佳的机会来实施计划，而且校长在重大场合到来之前总是会喝得酩酊大醉，于是画广告牌那家的儿子说在大考那天晚上，等到老师在椅子上坐定，他就"趁机下手"，接着会设法把他在合适的时间弄醒，赶去学校。

晚上八点，这个有趣的时刻终于来到了。教室里张灯结彩、花团锦簇。校长安坐在了高高的讲台上的那把椅子上，其背后就是一块大黑板。他看上去喝了不少，教室两边各摆三排长椅，校长的面前也摆了六排，长椅上坐着镇里的显赫人物以及学生家长。左侧长椅的后面搭建了一个临时大讲台，上面坐着今晚将要参加表演的小学者们，一排一排小男孩们穿着干干净净的衣服，感觉浑身不自在，一排排大男孩呆头呆脑地坐着，一排排雪白雪白的小姑娘、大姑娘们穿着上等细麻布和平纹麻布做的衣服，不住地在意着自己裸露的胳膊。她们还老是去看身上佩戴的从祖母那儿留下来的老式饰品，不停地留意衣服上花花绿绿的绸缎以及头上插的花朵。整个教室还坐满了不用参加表演的小学者们。

考试正式开始了，一个很小的男孩起立，胆怯地背了起来，"你们很难想象像我这样小的孩子可以站在台上讲话……"他背起了诸如此类的话，——不时僵硬地做些动作，虽然这些动作很准确，但是他做起来僵硬得就像一个机器一样——还是个出点问题的机器。最后，他虽然很胆怯，但还是顺利背完了，当他机械地深鞠一躬，然后坐下时，台下响起了一阵热烈的掌声。

又一个害羞的小女孩站了起来，口齿不清地背诵了《玛丽有只小绵羊》，背完后她恭恭敬敬地行了个屈膝礼，赢得了一片掌声，然后她红着脸，开开心心地坐下了。

接下来汤姆·索亚十分自信地走上前去，背起了那经久不衰的名篇《不自由，毋宁死》，他背得慷慨激昂，手舞足蹈，但是背到一半突然卡壳了，这时他变得怯场了起来，他的腿开始发抖，憋了半天也没说出来一句话。显然，教室里的人都对他充满了同情，但教室里也一片寂静，这对他来说比受到同情更糟糕，校长皱起了眉头，想赶快结束汤姆的演讲。于是汤姆在上面犹豫了一会儿，只好以失败告终了。台下发出一两下微弱的掌声，但是这掌声也马上就消失了。

接下来的是《那男孩站在燃烧的甲板上》，再接着就是《亚述人走来了》等一些其他的名篇。接下来还有朗诵比赛，还有拼写比赛。寥寥几人的拉丁语班满怀骄傲地诵读了起来，最后上来的是那天晚上的重头戏——一些年轻姑娘自编自演的原创。每一个孩子在轮到自己读的时候，都会向前走到舞台边上，清清嗓子，然后拿出手稿（用彩色的绸缎扎起来的），专心致志地念了起来，并且特别注重情感的传递和诗节的停顿。她们所咏颂的主题在她们母亲那辈已经朗诵过了，甚至在她们祖母那辈也用过，毫无疑问这可以追溯到她们母系方面所有的祖先，直到十字军时代。"友谊"就是这亘古不变的主题之一，还有"往日的回忆""历史上的宗教""乐岛""文明的益处""各种政体的比较和对比""哀愁""孝道"和"心愿"，等等。

这些文章中普遍存在的一个特点就是基调悲伤，另一个特点是喜欢用一些华丽的辞藻，再一个就是老用一些耳朵都能磨出茧子的陈词滥调，这些文章还都带着一种刻意而为的怪异特点，那就是在每篇文章结尾处都要有一堆说教之词，一个个听起来就像一条尾巴断了一截，还在不住地摇摆一样，令人难受。不论是什么主题，她们都绞尽脑汁地把它扯到道德或宗教方面，让那些专家可以从中悟出点道道。这些说教之词粗制滥造，但尽管如此，这却是当时学校里崇尚的写作方式，当今社会又如何不是呢。也许只要这个世界没被毁灭，它们就会永远流行。在这个国家里，没有一个学校的女孩们会觉得自己不应该用一顿说教结尾。你会发现学校里最不相信宗教的女孩们所创作的文章反倒是说教最长，最虔诚的，朴实真诚的话反倒变得无味了。

让我们回到大考试吧，第一个要被诵读的文章的题目是《这就是生活吗？》，也许读者们，你们可以忍受其中的一小段节选：

"在日常生活中，年轻人是以怎样高兴的心情翘首企盼一些节日场景的啊！他们正用飞舞的想象描绘出玫瑰般绚丽的喜悦场景，拜倒在时尚裙下，那骄奢淫逸的追随者们发现在想象之中看见自己正置身于欢腾的人群中，成了所有人们膜拜的巨星。她举止优雅，身穿雪白长袍，在人们曼妙的舞姿中旋转，她的双眸像太阳般明亮，她的步伐轻盈灵动，在这欢乐的人群中无人可及。"

　　"时间在这些美妙迷人的梦幻中总是悄然划过。她进入极乐世界的时间来临了，这可是她梦寐以求的。于是她眼前的一切就像被施了魔法一样，如仙境一般！风景如画，一处胜似一处。但是片刻之后，她发现在这无与伦比的美丽之下，全是人的虚荣。那些曾经令她心花怒放的甜言蜜语此刻已经显得无比刺耳。舞厅顿时失去了曾经的光彩，她身心俱疲，于是她悄然转身，因为她相信世俗之乐是无法满足人们对灵魂的渴望！"

　　等等诸如此类的话，说个不停。在她朗读时，人群中不断发出满意的啧啧声，不时地还有人轻声喊道"多么美啊！""口才真好！""多么逼真啊！"等这样的赞美，最后，文章在令人极其痛苦的说教中结束，刚一读完，观众们就热情地鼓起了掌。

　　接下来一个瘦弱而悲伤的女孩站了起来，她那苍白的脸色十分引人注意，那是长期服药和消化不良的结果，她读了一首"诗歌"，这里我们听两个诗节就够了：

　　"密苏里少女告别阿拉巴马

　　再见了，阿拉巴马！

　　我是那么爱你！

　　可我即将和你暂别！

　　你悲我亦痛，

回忆在胸中燃烧！

我曾在你万花丛中徘徊；

我曾在你达拉波莎溪水旁读书、漫步；

我曾在达拉西湍急的河边聆听你的流淌；

我曾在库莎山上伫立，迎接黎明的曙光。

我心有惭愧，岂敢领受你沉甸甸的内心，

含泪回首，我无怨无悔。

我必须和这片熟悉的土地道别，

离开亲友，我长长叹息。

这里欢迎我，这里给了我家，

可我还是要远离你幽幽的山谷、耸起的高山。

倘若有一天，我不再热切想念你，

亲爱的阿拉巴马，那时，我已远离人世。"

没有几个人明白她其中有个词的意思，但是这首诗毋庸置疑还是令人很满意的。

接下来出场的是一个皮肤黝黑的姑娘，她的眼睛和头发都是黑的。她上场先是站了一会儿，接着显示出一种很悲伤的表情，然后用一种庄严而又悲戚的语调朗诵了起来：

"一个幻想。

"这是一个一片漆黑，风雨交加的夜晚。深不可测的天空中没有一颗星星在闪烁。但是低沉的闷雷在耳边吼叫，可怕的闪电怒气冲天，刺穿乌云，划破夜空，似乎在嘲弄借用自己力量而闻名的富兰克林！甚至连全体暴风都从它们神秘的家咆哮而出，似乎要给这电闪雷鸣的夜晚增加自己的威力。

"就在这一时刻，在这又黑又可怕的时刻，我的灵魂在为人类同情地哀叹，但是就在此刻，'我最亲爱的朋友，她是我的参谋，我的安慰，更是我的引导者——是她在我悲伤的时候给了我快乐，比我这快乐更加让人快乐'，来到了我的身边。在浪漫的年轻人想象的伊甸园中，她摇摆轻盈的身姿，行走在金灿灿的阳光下。她是美丽的化身，她的美超凡脱俗。她的步伐轻盈灵动，走起来无声无息。若不是她和其他仙女一样，温柔地抚摸人间，让人为之兴奋，她就会悄然离去，不见踪影，更不会被人追寻。她指向外面毫无止境的争战，要我沉思他们都象征着什么，这时，一种奇怪的忧伤落入她的脸庞，恰如冬神长袍上结冰的朵朵泪花。"

这噩梦一般的演讲足足有十页之长，最后还朗读了一段让非长老派成员都彻底丧失希望的说教辞令，而她也因此得了一等奖。此篇文章被认为是今晚写得最好的作品。镇长在给该文作者颁奖时热烈致辞道，这是迄今为止他听过的文章中最虔诚的一篇，连丹尼尔·韦伯斯特本人都有可能为此感到骄傲。

顺便提一下，在文章中频繁使用"美丽"一词，而且总把人生经历比作"人生的一页"的人，像以往一样的多。

此刻校长因为喝醉了反倒显得很和蔼，他将椅子抽到一边，背对着观众，开始在黑板上画美国地图，为考地理作准备，但是他由于喝醉了，所以手拿不稳粉笔，于是在黑板上根本画不直线条。这时教室里大家都憋着笑，不时发出咻咻声。校长知道他们在笑什么，于是他想把线条改一改，他把没画好的擦掉，又重新去画，但是这只让情况越来越糟，暗笑声就越来越大。于是他将全部的注意力都放在了画画上，好像下决心不能被大家的嘲笑给打倒了。他觉得这会儿所有的人都在盯着他看，他想着自己越画越好了，但是嗤笑声还是不断传来。甚至到最后是在明显地越来越大。不过这些是情理之中的，因为楼顶上有个阁楼，而校长的头正对着一个天窗，从天窗里吊下来了一只腰上拴着线的猫，它的头和嘴都被捆了起来，以防它乱叫。当它缓缓下降时，它拼命地翘着身子，拿爪子去抓吊着自己的绳子，然后又在空中乱舞一番，晃晃悠悠地往下降，惹得人们笑声越来越大——现在猫距离心无旁骛的校长的头顶只有六英尺远了——往下，往下，一点点地往下，结果它就绝望地挥舞着爪子一下抓起了校长头上的假发，还紧紧抓住不放，然后眨眼之间，它就被拉进天窗里了，连同它爪子里的战利品也被拉了上来！最令人喷饭的是，此刻校长的光头在灯光的照射下闪闪发亮——因为画广告牌家的儿子早已在校长头上刷了一层金漆！

就此考试结束了，孩子们也报了仇，暑假就来啦。

注：本章的几篇作文都是一字未改地出自《一个西部女人的散文和诗集》，但是这些文章的的确确是按照女学生的风格来写的，因此它们比纯粹的模仿要有趣些。

第二十二章

　　汤姆参加了一个新的组织——少年节制会，因为他被该组织人员佩戴的徽章所吸引。他保证只要当会员一天，就要克制自己，不去抽烟，不嚼烟，不渎神。结果他发现了一种现象，那就是你越发誓不去做某事，就会越想做那件事。汤姆很快就发现他自己想抽烟、想骂人，想得难受，这种欲望变得那么的强烈，现在也只有想到能戴上徽章显摆显摆，才能让他克制住自己，不去退会。七月四日就要来了，但是他不久就放弃这一想法——在受困于节制这一牢笼中还没到四十八个小时，他就放弃了利用这一机会——他又把希望寄托在老法官弗兰茨身上，老弗兰茨显然就快要死了，而且因为他官位很高，必然会举行个盛大的葬礼。在接下来的三天，汤姆密切地关注起大法官的状况，急切地想听到报丧。有时他的愿望看上去很有可能实现，以至于他都想要把徽章弄到手，然后在镜子前先练习一遍。但是大法官的状况时好时坏，这可让汤姆大受打击，最后人们都说他的情况有所好转，已经在恢复了。汤姆对此十分生气，他感到自己被深深地伤害了，于是他立马上交了退社申请，但是就在他交了申请书的那一晚上，大法官就咽气儿了。汤姆决定再也不那么相信别人了。

　　葬礼隆重地举行了，节制会的孩子们带着徽章得意扬扬地列队游行，那神气的样子好像专门是要嫉妒死这个退会的会员。但不管怎样，汤姆现在是个自由人了，他又可以抽烟骂人了，但是他却惊奇地发现自己现在并不是很想抽烟，也不想骂人。他现在能这样做了，反倒让他失了兴趣，没了渴望。

汤姆不久还感到这心心念念的暑假又长又无聊，让人都受不了了。

他尝试着记个日记，但是这三天什么也没有发生，于是他就放弃写日记了。

最出色的黑人歌手要到镇上来表演了，这引起了一时轰动。于是汤姆和乔·哈泼也组了个乐队，乐呵呵地过了两天。

接下来原本光辉的七月四日却在一定程度上成了个败笔。因为这一天下着大雨，结果没有人进行列队游行，而且这个世上最伟大的人（汤姆猜的）本顿先生——美国一名参议员，着实让人大跌眼镜，因为他的身高还没有二十五英尺，任何一个邻居都能比他高。

又来了一组马戏团，在这以后，孩子们在破地毯做的帐篷里自己演马戏，又玩了三天，入场费是，男孩三个别针，女孩两个，玩腻了之后，马戏也被放弃了。

接下来又来了一个颅相学家和催眠师，他们来了又走，这使得暑假的生活更加的枯燥、乏味了。

当然也有一些男孩、女孩的聚会，但是数量很少，而且那短暂的快乐只会让没有聚会的日子变得更加苦闷了。

贝琪·撒切尔跟父母一起到康士坦丁堡家中度假去了，这让汤姆的生活没有了一丁点阳光。

而关于那次谋杀案，隐藏在汤姆心中可怕的秘密长期地折磨着他的灵魂。已经像癌症一样，不停地带给他痛苦。

接下来，汤姆又得了麻疹。

他在床上躺了两个星期，像一个囚犯一样与世隔绝。汤姆这回病得很严重，他对什么都没了兴趣，当他能够坐起来，并撑着虚弱的身子在镇子上走动时，他发现周围的一切都发生了让他感到悲伤的变换。镇上已经举行过一场"复兴会"，现在每个人都在信上帝，不仅仅是大人们信，每一个小男孩、小女孩都在信上帝。汤姆到处都走了走，想要找到一张充满罪恶的脸，但是他都失败了。他看到乔·哈泼都在读《圣经》，于是赶忙从这个让人觉得压抑的地方离开了，他去找本·罗杰，发现他正提着一篮子布道用的小册子挨家挨户地访问穷人，于是他又找到了吉姆·霍丽斯，他却提醒他要从麻疹病中吸取教训，是上帝的祝福才让他得以康复。他找到的每一个男孩无疑都在他的沮丧上又加了一码。最后他飞奔到密友哈克贝利·费恩那里寻求安慰，但是哈克也引用一句《圣经》里的话鼓励他，于是他带着一颗破碎的心回了家，他爬到床上觉得全镇人中，只有自己永远地、永远地迷失了。

那天晚上下起了一场暴风雨，雨水瓢泼而下，电闪雷鸣，天空一片混沌。汤姆用被单捂着头，恐惧地等待着命运之神的到来，因为他觉得外面这一切的骚动都毫无疑问是上帝要惩罚他，他想着上帝已经无法容忍他了，于是派了雷神来谴责他，但是他又觉得上帝这样子兴师动众有些大材小用了，这无疑是在用高射炮打苍蝇。然而他转念又想要把他这样的害虫打个底朝天，就算动用这惊天动地的暴雨也无可厚非。

过了一会儿，上帝发完了脾气，还没有破坏自己的目标，就收兵回家了。这个男孩的第一反应就是感激上帝，然后想要重新做人。他的第二反应就是等待，没准还会有暴风雨再来惩罚他。

第二天，医生们又来了，因为汤姆的病又复发了。他又在床上躺了三个星期，这一回跟过了一个世纪一样。最后当他能站起来到处活动时，他一点没觉得自己能逃脱此劫有多高兴，要知道他之前是多么的孤单，多么的无助和绝望。汤姆无精打采地走到街上闲逛，他看见了吉姆·霍丽斯正在演一个少年法庭的法官，他正在审理一桩谋杀案，被告是一只猫，而它的受害者，一只鸟，也出席了现场。他还看见乔·哈泼和哈克贝利·费恩正在吃一个从巷子里偷来的甜瓜，可怜的孩子们！他们跟汤姆一样，老毛病又犯了。

第二十三章

最后这让人昏昏欲睡的气氛被打破了，人们一下就兴奋了起来：马上就要审理谋杀案了，村子里的人马上就开始乐此不疲地谈论起这件事，人们的话也传到了汤姆的耳朵里，每听到一句对谋杀犯的控诉，他的心头就痛苦地一颤，他那受困的良心和心中的恐惧让他觉得人们是故意说给他听的，想探探他的反应。他不明白怎么会被怀疑跟这桩谋杀案有关，但是他一听到这些传言心里就很难受，这些话让他总处于发抖的状态。于是他把哈克找到一处偏僻的地方，想要跟他说说，也好让自己的舌头稍微透会儿气，把他的压抑分给另一个受折磨的人。而且他也想搞清楚，哈克有没有恪守约定。

"哈克，你有没有跟谁说起——那个？"

"说起哪个？"

"你知道的那个。"

"噢——我当然没有说。"

"一个字都没有泄露？"

"一个字都没有，我倒是想，你问这干什么呢？"

"唉，我很害怕。"

"喂，汤姆·索亚，要是你说出去的话，我们活不到两天就得死，这你是知道的啊。"

汤姆听着觉得更难受了，他顿了一会儿说：

"哈克，要是他们逼你说怎么办，他们会这样吗？"

"逼我说？嘿，要是我想被那个杂种给活活淹死的话，那他们倒是能逼我说。要不我死都不会说。"

"嗯，这样就好，我觉得只要我们保持沉默，咱们就能平安无事，不过我们还是再发一遍誓，这样比较保险。"

"我也这么觉得。"

于是他们又极其严肃地发了一遍誓。

"哈克，你听到大家都说什么了没？我听得可是够多了。"

"说什么，好吧，到处都在说穆夫·波特，穆夫·波特，穆夫·波特。听得我总是怕得慌，真想找个地方藏起来。"

"他们也是这么对我说的，我觉得他这回是死定了，你不会偶尔觉得他很可怜吗？"

"大部分情况下——大部分情况下，我都觉得他可怜。他虽算不上个人物，但他从没做过伤害别人的事啊。不过是钓钓鱼，然后卖点钱去喝酒——他就是有些游手好闲，但是上帝啊，我们都这样啊——最起码我们大部分人都这样——连牧师那些人也不例外。但是在某些方面他人还是很好的——有一回，他给了我半条鱼，当时可没有足够的东西让两个人都吃饱，而且当我倒霉的时候，他很多次都站在我这边，替我说话。"

"嗯，他还给我修过风筝哩，哈克，还帮我把鱼钩挂到钓鱼线上，我真希望能把他救出来。"

"天啊！我们不能救他出来，汤姆，而且这一点也不好，因为他们会再把他抓进去的。"

"是啊——他们肯定会这样的。但是我讨厌人们那样骂他，他压根就没有做过——那个。"

"我也是，汤姆，上帝啊，我听到人们说他是这个国家里最冷血的人，而且他们还说为什么他没被早点绞死呢。"

"对，他们就是这么说的，一直在说。我还听到他们说，要是他被放出来，他们就要私下弄死他。"

"没错，我也这么听到了。"

两个孩子就这样谈了很久，但是这并没给他们带来什么安慰。等到暮色降临的时候，他们跑到了那所孤零零的小监狱房外面转悠，希望能发生点什么事可以将他们心头的烦恼一扫而光。但是什么也没发生，看起来没有一个天使或者仙女对这个不幸的囚犯感兴趣。

两个孩子又像之前一样——走到监狱窗口那儿，给波特递进一些烟草和火柴。他被关在一个地下室里，周围没有警卫把守。

他十分感激他们送给他礼物，这让他俩的良心大受谴责——这次看望，他的话语像把刀一样深深地扎进了孩子们心头上。他俩觉得自己就是个懦夫，是个叛徒，波特说：

"你们对我真好，孩子们——比镇子里任何的男孩对我都好，我不会忘记你们的，不会。我经常对自己说，我过去总给所有的孩子们修风筝和其他东西，跟他们说哪儿能钓到最肥的鱼，我尽我所能地对孩子们好，但当老穆夫有难时，他们就都忘了他，只有汤姆没忘，哈克也没忘——他们没有把他忘了，我还跟我自己说，我也不会忘了他们的。唉，孩子们，我做了一件十分可怕的事情——那时我真是喝疯了——我只能这么想——现在我要因此而被吊死了，但我应该被吊死，我想，是应该的，而且也是最好的方式——我倒也想被吊死，唉，不说这个了吧，我不想让你们感到难过，你们对我这么好，但是我想告诫你们永远不要喝醉了，这样的话你永远就不会被关在这里。往西边去一点——对——就是这样。对于一个受苦受难的人而言，看一看几个友善的面孔是再安慰不过了。除了你们就再也没人来看过我，好孩子们——好孩子们。你们俩一个爬到另一个的背上，让我摸摸你们吧，对，我们握握手吧——你们的手可以从窗户伸进来，但是我的却太大了，多么脆弱的小手啊——但是它们给了穆夫·波特力量啊，要是它们能帮更多的忙，它们一定会帮的。"

汤姆痛苦地回到了家中，夜里他做了一晚上的噩梦。第二天，以及第三天，他都跑到法院附近晃悠，内心有着一股几乎不可阻挡的冲动想要进去，但是他还是强迫自己站在外面。哈克也跟他一样受折磨，他们故意不接触对方，每个人过了一会儿就走了，但是那股让他们坐立不安的吸引力又让他们马上折了回来。当看热闹的人从法庭里出来的时候，汤姆就使劲儿地竖着耳朵，想听听都什么消息，但是每次都令他更加沮丧——罗网正在一步一步，毫不留情地逼近可怜的波特。在第二天晚上的时候，人们都在说印江·乔提供的证据已经十分充分了，陪审团的裁决也是毫无疑问的。

汤姆那天晚上回家很晚，他从窗户爬到床上，由于异常的兴奋，他翻腾了好几个小时才睡着。第二天，村民们都涌到了法庭里，因为这可是个重要的一天。法院里挤满了观众，男的、女的都来了。观众们等了很久之后，陪审团的人才一个个进场入座，不一会儿，面容枯槁的波特被带了进来，他胆怯害怕，心里十分绝望，进来的时候，还戴着手铐脚铐。他坐在一个很显眼的位置，所有充满好奇的眼睛都能把他看得一清二楚。印江·乔的位置也同样显眼，他一如既往的淡漠冰冷。接下来是一阵沉默，然后法官到场，执法官宣布开庭。紧接着律师们像就往常一样交头接耳起来，只听见他们手中的纸张哗哗地飞舞。这些细节和开庭的推迟营造出一种让人敬慕的气氛，令人印象深刻。

现在一位证人被传出庭，他声称在发现谋杀案之后的一个大清早，他看见穆夫·波特在小溪里洗澡，接着穆夫就偷偷溜走了。在经过了进一步提问之后，原告方辩护律师说道：

"向证人提问。"

囚犯无力地提起了眼皮向证人瞅了一会儿，但当他的辩护律师开口时，他又垂下了眼睑，律师说道：

"我没有问题需要求证。"

第二位出庭的证人证实了他在尸体旁找到了穆夫的刀。于是原告方辩护律师说：

"向证人提问。"

"我没有要问的。"波特的律师答道。

第三个证人发誓说他经常看到波特带着那把刀。

"向证人提问。"

波特的辩护律师又拒绝提问，台下的听众们都开始觉得诧异，难道这个律师就想这么断送他当事人的命吗？

好几位证人都证实了，他们看到波特被带到犯罪现场时因为杀了人而感到愧疚的表现。被告的律师又什么也没问，他们就被允许退出法庭。

所有的证人都能清清楚楚地想起那天早上在坟地里发生的事情，他们能道出各种细枝末节，但是波特的律师对他们的描述一个也没有发出质疑。法庭上的人们不免感到困惑和愤慨，窃窃私语声四起，于是法官也对他进行了斥责。然而被告方辩护律师却说：

"所有的证人，证言均属实，毫无疑问，我们已经抓住了本案罪大恶极的凶手，就是席上这位不幸的犯人，我们就案情陈述完毕。"

可怜的波特呻吟了一声，用双手捂住了脸，他悲痛地身子不住前后摇摆起来，法庭也笼罩在一片痛苦之中。许多男人都觉得他可怜，很多女人则为他流下了悲痛的泪水。这时，被告律师站起来说：

"法官大人，在本案开庭初期，我们陈列出的事实似乎在暗示我们的目的，那就是要证实我的当事人有罪，酒精的作用使他神志不清，让他犯下了一件不负责任的滔天大罪。现在我们改变主意了，我们将重新抗辩。"（然后他转向书记员）"传汤姆·索亚！"

此刻，法庭上的每一个人都困惑不已，就连波特也不例外。当汤姆慢慢走进大厅站到自己的位置上时，人们都瞪大了双眼，惊讶不已地看着他。这个孩子看上去很胆怯，因为他被吓得不轻。他宣了宣誓。

"汤姆·索亚，六月十七日晚上，大概在半夜的时候，你在哪儿？"

汤姆瞥了一眼印江·乔那冰冷的脸，他的舌头就麻木了，讲不出话来。听众们屏住呼吸去听他要说什么，但是他还是一个字也说不出来，停了一小会儿之后，这个男孩找回了点勇气，于是他努力地提高了音量，但法庭内还是只有一部分人能听到他的声音，他说：

"在墓地！"

"请大一点声，别害怕，你在——"

"在墓地。"

印江·乔的脸上掠过一丝鄙视的笑。

"你是在霍斯·威廉姆的坟墓附近吗？"

"是的，先生。"

"大点声——再稍大一点，你离他的坟墓有多近？"

"就像我跟你现在这么近。"

"你是藏了起来吗？"

"我藏了起来。"

"藏在哪儿？"

"在坟旁的那棵榆树下。"

印江·乔的脸上闪过一丝几乎都察觉不出来的吃惊。

"你跟谁在一起吗？"

"是的，先生，我跟——"

"停——先停一下，不着急现在就说出你的同伴，适当的时候我们会传他出庭，你当时带了什么去吗？"

汤姆犹豫了一下，看起来很困惑。

"说出来吧，我的孩子——不要害怕，说实话的人总是会受到尊敬的，你当时带了什么？"

"就——就带了一只死猫。"

人们听到后一阵哄笑，法官立即要求大家安静。

"我们会出示那具猫的骸骨，但是现在，我的孩子，跟我们讲讲那天晚上发生的一切——你按自己的思路说就行——一个细节都不能跳过，别害怕。"

汤姆一开始讲得还犹犹豫豫的，但是后来他对这个话题熟悉了起来，于是他讲得越来越流利，越来越轻松。不久整个法庭都只能听见汤姆侃侃而谈的声音，每一双眼睛都注视着他看，人们张着惊愕的嘴巴，屏住呼吸听他讲每个字，每句话，忘记了时间的流逝，彻彻底底地被他讲述的恐怖故事吸引住了。最后压抑在汤姆心中的感情像火山一样喷涌而出，他说：

"——后来医生用那块板猛击了穆夫·波特的头，然后他就倒下了，此时印江·乔就拿着刀子跳了过来，接着——"

只听见"哗啦"一声，那个杂种就像一道闪电一样撞碎窗户，冲开所有阻拦的人，逃之夭夭了！

第二十四章

汤姆又成了闪闪发光的大英雄了，他是老人的骄傲，年轻人嫉妒的对象。他的名字甚至上了村上的报纸，永垂不朽。有些人还相信他有可能成为总统，要是他不被绞死的话。

这个变化无常、没有道理可言的世界又把穆夫·波特带回到了他原来的生活，跟以前虐待他一样宠爱他，关怀有加。但是世界就是这个样子，我们也不能苛责什么。

汤姆白天的时候，神气十足，得意扬扬，但一到晚上，就陷入恐慌。他的梦里全是像毒蛇般闪着眼睛的印江·乔。只要天一黑，这个男孩说什么也不出去玩了。可怜的哈克也是同样的诚惶诚恐，因为在开庭之前，汤姆已经把整个事情都告诉了律师，虽然印江·乔逃跑了，他就用不着出庭，但哈克还是十分害怕他也参与了这件事的消息会泄露出去，这个可怜的家伙虽然得到了律师的保证，不会把他说出去，但是这又有什么用呢？因为汤姆都会在良心的谴责下逼迫自己大半夜跑到律师家去，用曾经发过毒誓的嘴，讲出这一可怕的事情来。从此哈克对人类的信任就荡然无存了。

白天的时候，穆夫·波特会来跟汤姆道谢，这让他觉得把事实说出来真好，但是一到晚上，他就希望自己能把嘴封严了。

有时候，汤姆害怕会永远抓不到印江·乔，有时候，他又担心，真的会抓到他。他觉得只有印江·乔死了，而且还要看到他的尸体之后，他才能松口气，不再为安全担心。

政府发出了悬赏令，人们把整个镇子都搜了个遍，但是连印江·乔的人影都没找到。在这些无所不知、头脑灵活的追捕人当中，其中一位就是一个侦探，他从圣路易斯来到这里，他来了之后到处都转了转，不住地摇头晃脑，看上去身手不凡。最后他也像他那些同行一样，取得了惊人的成果，那就是，他"找到了一个线索"，但是你又没法儿将"一个线索"绞死，然后这个侦探结束了工作，回去了，但是汤姆觉得还是跟以前一样，没有安全感。

日子一天一天地过去了，每过一天，汤姆心里的恐惧感就会稍稍减轻一点。

第二十五章

在每一个健康成长的男孩子的生命里，都有一个时刻，在这个时刻他非常地渴望去某个地方挖埋在地下的财宝。这种渴望在某一天突然袭上汤姆心头，他出发去寻找乔·哈泼入伍，但失败了，于是他又去找本·罗杰，但是他出去钓鱼去了，最后，他突然想到可以去找阴辣杀手哈克贝利·费恩，哈克肯定会同意的。汤姆把哈克带到了一个没人的地方，然后满怀自信地跟他说了这个事情，哈克同意了，他总是会同意加入任何事情，只要足够好玩，而且不收一分钱。因为他可是有一堆不知道怎么打发的时间。"我们去哪儿挖呀？"哈克问道。

"噢，哪儿都能挖。"

"咦，那是说到处都有宝藏啦？"

"不，实际上不是的，必须在某个特定的地方才有，哈克——有时候是在岛上，有时候财宝装在朽木箱子里，然后埋在枯树的枝干下，正好在午夜时分树影洒落的地方，但是大部分的财宝埋在闹鬼的屋子里。"

"谁埋的啊？"

"嘿，当然是强盗们啦，你觉得还能有谁呢？主日学校的校长？"

"我不知道哇，要是我有这么多宝藏，我就不会埋了它，我会自己花，然后好好享受享受。"

"我也是，但是强盗们不那么干，他们总是把它埋了，然后一直放在那。"

"他们再也不会回来取了吗？"

"不，他们都想回来取，但总是忘记当初做的标记在哪儿，或者他们还没来挖，就死了。不管怎么说，反正财宝总是会在那儿埋很久，箱子也会烂掉，然后等过了些时候，有人就会找到一张泛黄的纸，上面写着怎样找到当初做的标记，这张图纸总是要花上一个星期才能弄明白，因为上面都是符号和象形文字。"

"什么文字？"

"象形文字，就是一些图形这样的东西，乍一眼看上去猜不出意思。"

"你有这种纸吗，汤姆？"

"没有。"

"好吧，那你怎么找到那些标记呢？"

"我不需要去找标记，他们总是把它埋在闹鬼的屋子里，或者是小岛上，又或者是埋在有一个大树枝伸出来的枯树底下。嗯，我们在杰弗逊岛上试过一回，过些时候我们还可以再去试一回，而且在酒厂岔道那边就有一个鬼屋，更何况到处都有那种枯树，太多了。"

"你说的这些，下面都藏有吗？"

"你说什么呢啊，不可能！"

"那你怎么知道去哪个下面挖呀？"

"我们把所有的地方都挖个遍。"

"不是吧，汤姆，这样一整个暑假就耗没了。"

"是这么说，但这又怎么样啊？说不定你就能找到一个小铜壶，里面有一百个生了锈、暗灰暗灰的硬币呢，又说不定里面塞满了生了锈的钻石呢，这还不好啊？"

哈克的眼珠子滴溜滴溜地转了几圈。

"这真是棒，对我而言棒极了。你把那一百块钱给我就行了，我一块钻石都不要。"

"可以呀，但是我不会把那些钻石都扔掉的。有的钻石一块都值二十块钱呢，基本上所有的钻石都能值个六毛或一块。"

"不是吧！真的啊？"

"当然是真的啊，每个人都可以告诉你，你没有见过钻石吗，哈克？"

"我记得我应该没见过。"

"噢，国王们有一堆钻石呢。"

"唉，我一个国王都不认识，汤姆。"

"我知道你不认识，但是要是你去欧洲的话，你就会看见一大群国王跳来跳去。"

"他们也会跳来跳去？"

"跳来跳去？我的天啊，他们当然不会啊。"

"好吧，那你刚说他们跳来跳去干什么啊？"

"哎呀，我就是说你会看到他们的，当然不是指他们真的跳来跳去，他们跳来跳去干什么呀？我是指你会看到他们到处走着，你知道，到处都能看到他们，就像老驼背查理。"

"查理？他姓什么呀？"

"他没有姓的，国王是没有姓只有名的。"

"真的没有？"

"真的没有。"

"好吧，汤姆，要是他们喜欢这样的话，也没关系。但我不想当个国王，只有个名，就像个黑鬼一样，但是话又说回来，你准备先到哪去挖呀？"

"呃，我也不知道，要不我们到酒厂岔道对面山上的那棵枯树下挖？"

"我同意。"

于是他们两个拿上一把残破的十字镐和一把铁锹，开始了他们三英里路的旅途。到那儿的时候，他们已经又热又累了，呼呼地直喘气，于是他们躺到了旁边一棵榆树底下，在阴凉地里抽了会儿烟。

"我喜欢干这个。"汤姆说。

"我也是。"

"嘿，哈克，要是我们在这找到了宝藏，你准备怎么花呀？"

"嗯，我每天都要吃一个派，还要喝苏打水。我还要去看马戏，一个都不能错过，我准会活得特别开心。"

"嗯，你不打算省一点下来吗？"

"省一点？省钱干吗呀？"

"哎呀，这样的话以后才有钱过日子啊。"

"好吧，这对我可没用，我爸过些时候就会回到镇上，要是我不花快点的话，他一定会对这些钱下毒手，而且我告诉你他会很快把钱花光花净。你会怎么花你的钱呀，汤姆？"

"我准备买一个新鼓，买把真剑，再买个红领带，还要买个小斗犬，然后我还要结——结——婚。"

"结婚！"

"对。"

"汤姆，你，嘿，你脑子没问题吧？"

"等着吧，你会懂的。"

"汤姆，这事儿是再蠢不过的了。你看看我爸和我妈，打架！哼，他们天天都在打架，我记的可是清清楚楚的。"

"跟你爸妈可没关系啊，我要娶的女孩不会跟我打架的。"

"汤姆，我可以肯定她们都是一号人物，她们都会跟你闹，你最好还是好好想想这事儿吧，我劝你还是好好想想，那个妞叫什么名字？"

"不能说她是个妞，她是个女孩。"

"我觉得都一样嘛，有些人说是妞，有些人又说女孩，都对啦，都差不多，管他怎么叫，她的名字是什么呀，汤姆？"

"我以后再告诉你，现在不能说。"

"好吧，那也行，要是你结婚了，我就比以前更孤单了。"

"不会的，你可以搬来跟我一起住，哎呀，先不说这个了，赶紧起来，我们快点去挖吧。"

于是他们大汗淋漓地挖了半个小时，结果什么也没挖到。接着他们又累死累活地挖了半个小时，又是什么也没有。然后哈克说：

"强盗们总是把财宝埋得这么深？"

"有时候是这样，但不全是。大部分情况下都没有这么深，我觉得我们可能没找对地方。"

于是他们又选了一个新的地方，开始了工作。他们这回挖得没那么快了，但是仍然坚持不懈，默默地挖了一阵子。最后，哈克倚着铁锨，用袖子把头上豆大的汗珠抹了下去，他说：

"这个搞完之后，你准备下一个往哪儿挖呀？"

"我觉得我们可以到卡迪夫山那边寡妇家后面的那棵老树下挖挖看看。"

"我觉得那儿是挺不错的，但是寡妇会不会从我们这儿把宝藏抢走啊，汤姆？那可是在她地盘上。"

"她会抢走！叫她试试看呀，谁第一个发现宝藏，宝藏就该归谁，这可不分在谁家地里。"

这个说法很令哈克满意，于是他们继续挖，过了一会儿哈克说：

"真见鬼，我们肯定又挖错地方了，你觉得呢？"

"这可真是奇怪，哈克。我就想不明白了，有时候巫婆会来捣乱，我想也许现在她们就在捣鬼。"

"乱讲！巫婆白天的时候根本没有法力。"

"好吧，这倒是，我没有想到这一点啊，噢，我知道问题出在哪了！我们真是一群大傻瓜！你必须要搞清楚午夜的时候，树枝的阴影落在哪儿才行，你要在那儿挖才对！"

"真是该死啊，我们傻乎乎地干了这么多，都是白干了。现在咱们收工吧，晚上的时候咱们再来，路程可不近啊，你能跑出来吗？"

"我想我能，而且我们必须今天晚上就干，因为要是有人看到这些洞的话，他们马上就能明白这儿有什么，就会来挖走。"

"嗯，那我晚上过去找你，在外面学猫叫。"

"没问题，我们把工具都藏到灌木丛里吧。"

于是两个孩子按约定的时间又来到了这里，他们先是坐在阴影里等着，这个地儿有些偏僻，而且又是在大半夜，这个时间可是各种传说中鬼怪都出来活动的时候，搞得这会儿阴森森的。叶子沙沙的声音是鬼在私语，无数的大鬼、小鬼正埋伏在角落里，从远处传来了低沉的狗吠声，一个猫头鹰用它那阴沉的叫声回应着。孩子们被这种阴森的气氛搞得很紧张，他们不敢说什么话。过了好一会儿，他们觉得已经到十二点了，于是便在地上的阴影处做了个记号，然后就开挖了。现在他们越挖报的希望越大，就越来越有兴致，挖起来就越起劲，也就越挖越深。但是每当他们听到镐碰到什么东西发出响声时，他们就心跳加速激动起来，但每次的结局都是希望落空。因为十字镐只不过是碰到了一块石头或者一段木头。最后汤姆说：

"这样是没用的，哈克，我们这回又挖错地方了。"

"好吧，但是我们怎么会又挖错了呢，我们确实是在阴影下挖的呀。"

"我知道，但是肯定是别的方面出了问题。"

"那是什么出问题了？"

"这个，我们只是猜测的可能是十二点，但有可能会早了点或者晚了点。"

哈克听完放下了铁锹。

"有道理，"他说，"问题肯定就在这，我们别挖了吧，我们也拿不准什么时候正好十二点，而且这种办法也太恐怖了，周围竟是巫婆和鬼怪，我觉得身后老有东西跟着我，搞得我都不敢回头，因为也许前面也有鬼在等着机会下手呢，自从来这以后，我就一直害怕得直打哆嗦。"

"嗯，我也跟你差不多呀，哈克，强盗们总是会在埋宝藏的树下埋个死人来看宝藏。"

"我的天啊！"

"我可不骗你，他们经常这样做，我总听人家这么说。"

"汤姆，我可不想在死人堆里瞎转悠，要不一定会遭遇不幸的，肯定的。"

"我也不想惊动他们。要是这个地方的死人把骷髅头伸出来，开口说话怎么办呀。"

"别说了汤姆，这太吓人了。"

"嗯，真是很吓人，哈克，我心里也堵得慌。"

"喂，汤姆，我们放弃这儿吧，到别处挖挖试试。"

"行，我也觉得我们最好这样。"

"那我们到哪儿呢？"

汤姆想了一会儿，说道：

"鬼屋，就去那吧！"

"我的个天啊，我可不喜欢闹鬼的房子，汤姆，那里比死人还可怕，死人也许会开口说个话什么的，但是他们不会趁你不注意悄悄地溜过来，突然扒到你肩膀上，露出獠牙，但是鬼总会这样做，我根本就受不了那种地方，汤姆，没人会受得了的。"

"是这样，但是，哈克，鬼们只会在晚上出来吓人呀，我们白天的时候去挖，他们就不能伤害我们了。"

"好吧，话是这样说，但是你也知道，不管是白天还是夜里，人们都不会去那间鬼屋。"

"哎，这大概是因为他们不想去一个发生过谋杀案的地方——但除了晚上，那房子周围什么都没被看见过——晚上的时候，也只能透过窗户看到些蓝火——没有你说的那种鬼。"

"好吧，但是汤姆啊，当你看见有蓝火飘飘悠悠的时候，你就能推断出附近有鬼埋伏着。这么说是有道理的，因为除了鬼谁还会点这种火呢。"

"嗯，这倒是，但不管怎么说，他们不会大白天出来的，我们怕什么呀？"

"唉，好吧，既然你这么说，那我们就去瞧瞧吧，但是我觉得我们只是在碰运气。"

这时候，他们已经开始下山了。那间闹鬼的屋子就伫立在他们身下那月光照耀的山谷中间。那是一间孤零零的房子，周围的栅栏早都不知道哪儿去了，房门口的台阶上杂草丛生，烟囱倾塌，窗户已经没有了玻璃，房顶的一角也塌陷下去了。孩子们定睛看了一会儿，带着半期待的心情想看看蓝火飘过窗户，在这种场合、这种气氛下，他们不由得压低了声音说话，接着他们就从右边远远地绕过鬼屋，穿过卡迪夫山后的树林，然后回到了家中。

第二十六章

第二天大概是中午的时候，孩子们来到了昨晚的枯树旁，拿回他们的工具。汤姆迫不及待地想要去鬼屋寻宝，显然哈克也很想去，但是他突然说道："嗨，汤姆，你知道今天星期几吗？"

汤姆在脑子里快速地算了算日子，然后他突然抬起了眼睛，十分惊讶地说：

"我的天啊！我可真没料到，哈克！"

"唉，我也是，但突然我就想到了今天是星期五。"

"真见鬼，一个人再怎么认真也不为过，哈克，我们在星期五干这种事，可能会出事的。"

"可能！还不如直接说一定会呢！这世上可能有那么几天是比较幸运的日子，但绝对不会是星期五。"

"傻子都知道啊，你肯定不是第一个发现这个道理的啊，哈克。"

"好吧，我也没说过我是第一个发现的，我说过吗？我们今天还不仅仅是碰上了星期五呢，昨天晚上我做了一个很糟糕的梦——梦到了一群老鼠。"

"不是吧！这可是凶兆啊，它们有打架吗？"

"没有。"

"哎，这倒能好点，哈克。它们没打架就只是在说你可能会倒霉，我们必须要做的就是要高度警惕，防患于未然。我们今天不干这个了吧，咱们玩一天，你知道罗宾汉吗，哈克？"

"不知道，谁是罗宾汉？"

"嘿，他可是英国历史上最伟大的人之一，而且是最能干的。他是一个强盗。"

"太棒了，我真想我也是个强盗，他都抢谁呀？"

"他只抢王室的人、一些大主教还有有钱人和国王，就是抢这种人。但是他从不找穷人麻烦，他很疼爱穷人，总是会把抢来的财宝平分给他们。"

"哇，那他肯定是个大好人。"

"我能保证他肯定是，哈克，噢，他是有史以来最高尚的人，我可以跟你讲，现在这种人可不多了。他能单手打败英国任何一个人，一旦拉开他那紫杉大弓，然后你在一英里半外搁一枚一角钱硬币，他都能射穿。"

"紫杉大弓是什么？"

"我也不知道，当然它就是一种弓箭。要是他就打到硬币的一个边，他都会坐下来大哭一场，还要骂上一顿。我们来演罗宾汉吧，非常好玩，我教你。"

"我同意。"

于是他们玩了一整个下午的罗宾汉，时不时地还瞟一眼那座闹鬼的房子，说着明天去那儿可能会发生什么情况。当太阳慢慢西落时，他们横穿过长长的树影，开始往家里走，不一会儿就消失在了卡迪夫山的树林中。

周六中午刚过，孩子们就前往枯树了，他们在树荫下抽了会儿烟，又聊了一阵，然后就着他们最后挖的洞，又挖了几下，这倒不是因为他们觉得很有希望挖到，而是汤姆说很多情况下人们挖到离财宝只有不到六英尺的地方，就停了下来，结果其他的人来，轻轻一挖就挖出来了。然而这回他们又挖了几下也没有挖到。所以孩子们就扛起铁锹走开了，心里觉得自己没有浪费这次挖财宝的机会，觉得自己该做的都做了。

当他们到达鬼屋时，就立刻感觉到一种怪异的气氛。烈日当空，这里却死一般的寂静，荒凉破败，让人不由觉得很压抑。他们害怕了好一会儿，不敢冒险进去。最后还是慢慢挪到门口，然后畏畏缩缩地向里面偷看。里面野草丛生，没有地板，墙上也没有刷漆，他们看见了一个老式的壁炉，屋里的窗户都没有了玻璃，楼梯已经破破烂烂的了，到处都破烂不堪，结满了蜘蛛网。于是他们悄悄地走了进去，大气不敢出一下，小声交谈着，耳朵竖得直直的，一点细微的声音都不放过，全身肌肉都紧绷着，预备着随时都有可能撤退。

过了一小会儿，他们对周围的环境熟悉了之后，就不再那么紧张了。两个孩子开始带着好奇心，仔仔细细地审视这个地方，对自己勇敢的行为既惊奇又佩服。接着他们想到楼上看一看，这一举动就意味着切断了自己的退路，但他们还是互相壮了壮胆，于是就产生了这个结果——他们把工具放到了墙脚，上了楼。楼上也是同样的衰败，他们在一个角落里发现了一个壁橱，颇有藏宝的希望，但不过是空欢喜一场——里面什么也没有。现在他们的胆子大了起来，准备下楼开工，突然——

"嘘！"汤姆说。

"怎么了？"哈克轻声地问，脸色吓得发白。

"嘘！……那边！……听到了吗？"

"听到了！……噢，我的天啊，我们快跑吧！"

"别动！你可不能动！他们就要到门口了。"

"孩子们赶紧趴在地上，眼睛对着木板的节孔盯着门口看，他们无比恐惧地等着。

"他们停住了……不——又来了……他们就在这儿了。别再说一个字了，哈克，我的老天啊，我真希望我今天没来。"

有两个人进来了，每个男孩都暗自想道："有一个是那个又聋又哑的西班牙老头，他最近来过镇上一两回——另一个没见过。"

另一个人衣衫褴褛，邋邋遢遢，整个脸都给人一种不舒服的感觉。西班牙人身披一件华丽的披肩，蓄着白色浓密的络腮胡，长长的白头发从宽檐帽里飘了出来，鼻子上还架着一副绿色的护目镜。当他们进来的时候，这个人正低声说了几句话，然后他们坐在地上，面朝着门，背对着墙，他又接着说了起来，说了一会儿之后，便放松了警惕，话也听得清楚了：

"不行，"他说，"我想了很多遍了，但是我不同意这样做，这样太危险了。"

"危险！"那个"又聋又哑"的西班牙老头咕哝着——这着实让孩子们吃了一惊，"胆小鬼！"

一听到这个声音，孩子们就倒抽一口气，他们害怕得颤栗起来。这个人就是印江·乔！沉默了一会儿后，乔说：

"我们在那边干的事比这危险多了，这以后还会有什么危险事呢。"

"这可不一样，那时候是在河上，而且附近也没有人住，我们干多久都没人会知道，尽管我们最后没有成功。"

"好吧，这样的话，那还有比大白天到这里来危险的事吗？——任何看见我们的人都会起疑心。"

"我知道这个，但是干了那傻事之后，就只有这里最安全了。我不想在这破房子里待了，昨天都想走了，要不是那两个可恶的小子在山里玩，会把我们的行为看得一清二楚，我早都想离开这了。"

"这两个可恶的小子"听了这话，立马就明白了他在说谁，此刻他们觉得昨天能想起来是星期五，从而等了一天，该有多么的幸运啊。他们在心里想着要是能等上一年才更好。

这两个人拿出了一些食物，做了顿午饭吃。在一阵深思熟虑之后，印江·乔说：

"喂，老兄，你回到河上住的地方，在那儿等我消息。我会找机会再次潜入镇上，探探风。我们到附近侦查一遍，等我觉得时机成熟了，我们再干那件'危险'的事，接着我们就去得克萨斯！我们一起去！"

"这听起来倒不错。"两个人不一会儿就打起了哈欠，然后印江·乔说：

"我睡一会儿！该你望风了。"

于是他蜷缩在草堆里，不一会儿就起了呼噜。他的同伴推了他一两次，他就不再打了，过了一会儿，看守的人也开始打鼾了，他的头越点越低。此刻，两个人都睡着了。

两个孩子深深地喘了口气，他们不由得谢天谢地，接着汤姆小声说：

"机会来了——走吧！"

哈克："我走不了——要是他们醒了的话，我就死定了。"

于是汤姆使劲催——哈克就是不起来。最后，汤姆缓缓站了起来，准备自己走。但是他刚迈出了一步，脚下那破烂的地板就突然发出了"咯吱"一声，于是他吓得赶忙趴在了地上，死都不敢再动一下。孩子们就这样躺在那里，一分一秒地数着，直到他们觉得时间已经全都流走，永恒之神已满头白发。最后他们激动地看见夕阳正在落山。

正在这时，一个人的鼾声突然停止了，印江·乔坐了起来，向四周望了望——朝着他的同伴冷笑了一番，那个人的头已经点到膝盖上了——他用脚踢了他几下，把他弄醒，然后乔说：

"哼！你真是会把哨，不是吗？好吧，好在没发生什么事。"

"我的天啊！我睡着了吗？"

"噢，差不多，差不多，伙计，现在该要出发了，剩下的那点钱怎么处理呢？"

"我不知道——我觉得就放在这儿吧，跟以前一样。在我们南下之前都没必要把它弄出来。背着五百六十个银元可不好走。"

"好吧——那就这样吧——反正再来一次也没什么大不了。"

"是啊——但是我觉得还跟以前一样晚上来——这样比较好。"

"嗯，但是看看这儿，我还要好一阵子才能找到机会下手，而这里随时都能发生意外，所以我们这回把它埋起来吧，埋得深深的。"

"好主意，"他的同伴说道，这个人走到了屋对面，跪下来，拿开了炉子后面的一块石头，然后掏出一个叮当作响的钱袋，他从里面拿出了二三十块来给自己，然后又给了印江·乔这么多，最后他把袋子给了乔，此刻乔正跪在一个角落里用猎刀挖坑。

两个孩子这会儿已经忘记了害怕，把所有的不幸都一股脑抛到九霄云外了。他们暗自狂喜地看着下面的一举一动，真是走运！运气好得简直无法想象。六百块钱足够让六个男孩一下子变成阔少！这次寻宝真是交了狗屎运了——他们再也不用为在哪儿挖坑而烦恼了。于是他们不时地互相碰碰，意思简单易懂，就是在说："噢，你现在真该高兴我们今天来了！"

乔的刀碰到了什么东西。

"嗨！"他喊道。

"这有一个半破的木板——不，我觉得这是一个箱子，到这来——

帮我一把，我们来看看这里面会是什么，不要紧，我已经把它弄了个洞。”

接着他把手伸到洞里，又抽了出来——

"伙计，是钱!”

这两个人抓起一把硬币检验了一番，结果发现都是金的，于是他们高兴极了，楼上的孩子此时跟他一样兴奋，一样高兴。

于是乔的同伴说：

"我们得加快了。壁炉另一边的杂草丛里有一把破旧的十字镐——我刚才看到的。”

说完他跑去拿来了孩子们的十字镐和铁锹。印江·乔接下了十字镐，仔仔细细地打量了一番，他看过后摇了摇头，自言自语地说了些什么，就开始挖了。箱子很快就被挖了上来，箱子并不大，外面包着一层铁皮，岁月侵蚀之后就没有那么结实了。这两个人沉默地看着宝箱，心里喜不自胜。

"伙计，这里面能有一千块呢。”印江·乔说。

"人们一直都说，有年夏天莫里尔那帮人经常在这一片出没。”那个陌生人说道。

"我知道，”印江·乔说，“这迹象看起来是他们。”

"现在你不用干你那活计了。”

那个杂种皱着眉头说：

"你不了解我，最起码你不了解所有的事情，我根本就不是为了抢劫——是为了报仇!”说着，他的眼中闪过一丝凶意，“我需要你帮我，干完这之后，我们就去得克萨斯，你回家找你的南希和孩子，然后听我的信儿。”

"好吧，如果你需要这么做的话，我们怎么处理这——埋了它?”

"行。（楼上暗自欢喜）不行！好家伙，不行！（楼上有一阵失落）我差点都忘了，这把镐头上还沾有新鲜泥土呢！（楼上的孩子一时间恐惧无比）这里怎么会有十字镐和铁锹呢？而且上面怎么会有鲜土呢？谁把这些拿来的？他们走了吗？你听到有人在附近吗？看见谁了吗？好家伙！怎么能重新埋起来让他们看到被挖过的迹象呢？不能这样——这样不好。我们要把钱搬到我那去。"

"嗯，当然得这么办！我早该想到这一点，你是说一号地点？"

"不是——二号——十字架下面。别的地方不好——都太普通了，不好认。"

"那就这样吧，外面天也足够黑了，我们也该行动了。"

于是印江·乔站了起来，在窗户那里来回走动，小心翼翼地窥测着外面，过了一会儿他说：

"到底是谁把这些工具拿过来的呢？你觉得他们会不会在楼上？"

两个孩子一听，吓得气儿都不敢出，印江·乔把刀子掏了出来，他犹犹豫豫地又停了一会儿，最后还是朝着楼梯走了过来。孩子们想钻到壁橱里，但是他们现在吓得一点力气都没有了。下面不断传来乔踩在楼梯上的声音——情况已经刻不容缓，这一下就激发了孩子们的决心——他们正要跑到壁橱里去，下面就发出了一阵朽木断裂的声音，印江·乔，连带着满是灰尘的木头"扑棱"一下摔了下去。他骂骂咧咧地站了起来，然后他的同伴说：

"现在好了，去上面看有什么用啊？要是那里有人，就让他们待在那儿好了，谁管他们呀？要是他们现在想跳下来，自找麻烦，谁也不会反对啊。不到十五分钟天就会完全黑下来，要是他们想跟踪我们，就让他们跟呗，我是没意见。依我看，把这些东西带过来的人肯定是看见了我们，然后把我们当成鬼或者是恶魔之类的东西了，我打赌他们现在正在逃跑呢。"

乔咕哝了几句，他同意了同伴的看法，天已经快黑了，要赶紧在天黑之前收拾好东西，准备离开。片刻之后，他们就在沉沉的暮色中溜了出去，抬着他们那个宝贝箱子往河边跑去了。

这时，汤姆和哈克撑着虚弱的身体站了起来，他们这会儿大松了一口气。他们俩从房子的木缝中盯着这两个人，跟踪他们？他们可做不了。现在能不扭断脖子安全着地，再翻过山走到回镇子的路上，就已经不错了。此刻他们并没有再说什么，因为他们正沉浸在对自己的悔恨当中——恨自己运气真不好，竟然把十字镐和铁锹放在了外面。要不是因为这，印江·乔就不可能起疑心，他就会把财宝箱埋在地下，直到报完了仇，等他回来的时候，就会不幸地发现钱已经不翼而飞了。真是倒霉，怎么能把工具带到这里来呢，太倒霉了！

他们下定决心，等那个西班牙人进城找机会复仇时，他们一定会紧盯着他，追踪着他找到"二号"的位置，突然一个可怕的念头袭上汤姆的心头。

"报仇？他不会是想找我们报仇吧，哈克！"

"天啊，不要啊！"哈克叫道，他差点就吓晕过去了。

他们这一路上都在讨论这件事，当走上镇子之后，他们一致认为他很可能是要找其他的某个人报仇——最起码他只会找汤姆报仇，因为只有汤姆出庭作证了。

汤姆孤身一人陷入危险，这让他心里很不安，他觉得要是有个伴就好受多了。

第二十七章

那天晚上，汤姆在梦里还深受白天这事的折磨。在梦中，他四次抓住了财宝箱，结果只是四次从梦中醒来回归不幸的现实，财宝箱从他手中溜走，手里空空如也。一大早他就醒了，躺在那里回想那段惊心动魄的冒险经历，觉得它们是那样的模糊，那样的遥远，不知怎的，就像发生在另一个世界里一样，也像是很久很久之前发生过的事。于是他觉得这次冒险之旅肯定是个梦！有一点很有说服力，那就是他看到的钱数额太大了，根本不会发生。他以前从来都没有一下子见过五十块钱，而他也像他这个阶段、这个年龄的孩子们一样，认为根本就没有"几百啦""几千啦"这样的数额存在，这不过是一种夸张的说话方式罢了。他从来都没想过，一个现实中的人能有几百块这么大数额的财宝。如果你分析一下他脑中对于钱的概念，你就会发现，它只不过是一把当一角的银币，再加上一堆金光闪闪的金币，而且这些金币的具体样子在他头脑中是模糊不清的，因为他根本想象不出来。

但是在反复思索之后，那冒险之旅就变得越来越清楚，简直是历历在目。所以他又觉得这些事情可能不是一场梦。他觉得一定要弄个明白才行，于是在匆匆忙忙地塞了几口早饭后，汤姆就跑去找哈克了。哈克正坐在一只平顶船的船舷上，百无聊赖地把脚垂在水中拨弄着，他看起来有些悲伤。汤姆决定让哈克主动提到这个问题，要是他不提的话，那么这趟冒险之旅就纯粹是个梦。

"好啊，哈克！"

"你好啊。"

接下来是一阵沉默。

"汤姆，要是我们把工具就放在枯树那里，我们现在就有钱了啊，天啊，真是太难受了！"

"这么说这不是一场梦啦，是真的啊！不知道怎么回事，我倒希望是场梦，骗你我是小狗，哈克。"

"什么一场梦呀？"

"噢，就是昨天发生的事，我都分不清是不是场梦了。"

"一场梦！要是昨天那楼梯没有塌，你才会知道一场梦是个什么样子了！我昨天晚上做了一整夜的梦——那个眼睛上带有罩子的西班牙魔鬼一直都在追我——去死吧他！"

"不能死，不能叫他去死，要找到他！拿回钱！"

"汤姆，我们找不到他的，机不可失，失不再来，我们已经失去机会了，而且我要是见到他，我肯定会吓得直发抖。"

"唉，我也是这样的，但是不管怎么样我一定要找到他，一定要把他挖出来——到他说的二号去。"

"二号——对，就是这，我也在想这事。但是我一点头绪都没有。你觉得那会是哪里？"

"我也不知道，这太难想了，我说哈克，也许是个房子的门牌号。"

"对呀！……不对，汤姆，不是个门牌号。要是的话，也不是镇上的房子，镇上的房子都没有编号。"

"唉，还真是。让我想一会儿，嘿，是个房间号，你知道的，就是旅馆的房间号。"

"噢，就是这样！这里只有两个旅馆。我们很快就能搞明白了。"

"哈克，你先待在这，等我回来。"

汤姆说完就走了。他不喜欢在公共场所跟哈克在一起，汤姆去了有半个小时，发现在那家好一点的旅馆里，二号房住的是一个年轻的律师，而且现在仍然是他在住。那家条件差些的旅馆里，二号房却有点不对劲。旅馆老板的小儿子说那个房间一直都在锁着，除了晚上的时候，他从来没见过人从那里面进出。他也不知道为什么会这样，他对这事只是有那么一点好奇，并没把它当回事。他暗自想着那里是在"闹鬼"，所以才显得不对劲。他昨天晚上还看见屋里有亮呢。

"我就发现了这些，哈克。我觉得这个二号房就是我们要找的。"

"我也这么觉得，汤姆，现在你要怎么办？"

"让我想一想。"

汤姆思索了良久，然后他说：

"你听我说，二号房后门通往一条小巷，它夹在旅馆和那个又旧又破的砖厂中间。现在你去把所有能找到的钥匙弄来。我去把姨妈所有的钥匙都偷来，然后天一黑我们就去用钥匙一个一个地试试。还有你要小心警惕着印江·乔的出现，因为他说他会在镇子里到处侦查一遍，寻找报仇的机会，要是你看见他的话，你就尾随着他，要是他没有进二号房，那么钱就不在那个地方。"

"我的个天啊，我可不想一个人跟踪他！"

"没事儿，他肯定是晚上出现的，到时候他也看不见你，就算是看见了，他也不会有什么怀疑的啊。"

"好吧，要是真是晚上的话，那我就会跟着他，肯定会的，我会试着跟踪的。"

"那你发誓要是晚上，你就跟着他，哈克。因为他很有可能发现没有办法复仇，然后就拿着钱跑了。"

"我发誓，汤姆，我发誓，我会跟踪他的，真的，老天作证！"

"现在你可发誓了啊！千万别动摇了，哈克，我也不会动摇。"

第二十八章

　　那天晚上汤姆和哈克已经准备好去冒次险，他们在旅馆旁一直转悠到晚上九点钟。然后便一个在远处守着巷子，一个试着开旅馆的门。在这期间，巷子里没有一个人进出，连那个西班牙人的影儿都没见着。这一晚月色正好，于是汤姆就回家了，他想着天一旦够黑，哈克就会在外面学猫叫，那时他就又会溜出来，试钥匙。但是那一夜月光都很亮，哈克也放弃了盯梢，大概十二点的时候，就钻进一个空糖桶里睡觉去了。

　　星期二孩子们的运气也不好，星期三也同样如此。但是星期四晚上就好多了。汤姆趁机偷偷溜出来了，顺带把他姨妈的旧锡皮提灯也拎了出来，还拿了一个大毛巾来遮光。他把提灯藏到了哈克的空糖桶里，然后就开始盯梢。十一点的时候，旅馆打烊了，里头的灯灭了（这里附近唯一的光亮）。但是他们没有看见西班牙人，巷子里没有一个人进出，所有的一切都顺利进行着。终于，黑暗完全笼罩着大地，只有远处偶尔传来的雷声将这一绝妙的寂静打破。

　　汤姆在糖桶里点亮了提灯，然后用毛巾紧紧包住。然后这两个冒险鬼在黑暗中蹑手蹑脚地走到旅馆后面。哈克站在那儿当哨兵，而汤姆则摸索着走进小巷。接着哈克焦急地等待着，紧张的他像肩头压了一座大山一样，他站在那里盼着巷子里出现一道光——这会让他吓一跳，但至少能说明汤姆还活着。他等啊等，感觉汤姆都走了好几个小时。也许汤姆已经吓昏了，也许他已经死了，或许他在极度恐慌、极度兴奋之下，心脏受不了炸裂了。不安之中，哈克发现自己越来越逼近巷道，他脑子里不停地想着各种可怕的事情，内心惶恐极了，时时刻刻都在警惕着会发生什么灾难，他吓得都快要断气了，而实际上他也没什么气儿了，因为他现在虚弱得只能一点点吸气，他的心脏扑通扑通地跳着，再这样下去心脏很快就会炸裂的，突然，一阵光飞了过来，汤姆从他身边狂奔过去：

"快跑！"汤姆说，"快点，逃命吧！"

他根本就用不着再重复一遍，只说一遍效果就足够了。哈克已经以每小时三四十英里的速度在狂奔了，没等汤姆重复第二遍，他就跑出去很远了。孩子们一口气就跑到了村子地势较低的那一头空旷的屠宰场的木棚下。他们刚一到达，雨水就瓢泼而下，汤姆缓过气来就说：

"哈克，真是太可怕了！我试了两把钥匙，每次都是尽我所能地轻手轻脚，但钥匙就是响个不停，我太害怕了，简直都无法呼吸。没有一把能把门打开，后来我都不知道我干了什么，一把抓住门柄，门就自己开了！压根就没锁，于是我跳了进去，扯下毛巾，结果，真是比见鬼还可怕！"

"怎么了！——你到底看见什么了，汤姆？"

"哈克，我差点都踩到印江·乔的手了！"

"天啊！"

"真吓死人了，他就躺在地板上，睡得很死，他的眼罩还戴着呢，胳膊伸得长长的。"

"我的天啊，你进去干什么了？他醒了吗？"

"当然没有，他一动也没动，我觉得他是喝醉了，于是我赶忙抓起毛巾，就飞奔了出来！"

"要是我，我肯定想不到拿毛巾的！"

"嘿，我可是一定要拿，要是我弄丢了的话，姨妈肯定会饶不了我。"

"喂，汤姆，你看见藏宝箱了吗？"

"哈克，我根本就没能站在那好好看看，我没有看见财宝箱，也没有看见十字架，除了地上的一个酒瓶还有一个锡制杯子以外，我什么都没有看见。我在屋子里还看见了两个大桶和很多个酒瓶。现在，你看明白了吗，知道那个房子为什么闹鬼了吗？"

"为什么？"

"嘿，那里是在闹酒鬼呀！也许所有的禁酒旅店都会闹酒鬼，是吧，哈克？"

"好吧，我觉得可能是这样，谁会想到这种事呀？但是话说回来，汤姆，要是印江·乔喝醉了的话，现在是个绝好的机会拿走箱子。"

"说得好听！你试试！"

哈克吓得直哆嗦。

"唉，不行，我可干不了。"

"我也干不了，哈克。印江·乔旁边就放了一个酒瓶，这个不够，要是他喝了三瓶酒，倒会醉得稀里糊涂，那我就能干。"

他们没说话想了好一会儿，然后汤姆接着说：

"听着，哈克，只要没看见印江·乔从屋里出来，就不准行动，要不太吓人了，现在要是我们每天晚上都盯梢，我们就逮着他出去的时候，早晚都会有机会，然后我们就以闪电般的速度冲进去抱走箱子。"

"嗯，我同意，我会彻夜盯梢的，每天晚上都盯，你就负责去抱箱子。"

"没问题，我干，你要做的一切就是从琥珀街跑过来，然后在街头学猫叫，要是我睡着了，你就往窗户上扔个小石头，这样我就醒了。"

"我同意，真是个好主意！"

"现在，哈克，暴风雨也停了，我要回家了，再过两个小时天就大亮了，这几个小时你再回去看守着，行吗？"

"我说过我会做，汤姆，我就一定会做的，我每天晚上都守着那个旅馆，守一年都行。"

"那就这么办了，你准备睡哪儿呢？"

"我就睡在本·罗杰家的干草棚里，他让我睡那儿，他爸爸的黑鬼杰克大叔也让我睡那儿，他随时有需要，我都会帮他提水。每回我问他要吃的，他都会给我分点。他真的是个很好的黑鬼，汤姆。他喜欢我，因为我在他面前并不表现得高人一等。有时候我会跟他坐在一起吃东西，但是你可别跟别人说这个，一个人饿极了的时候，什么都能干。"

"好吧，要是白天我不需要你帮忙，我就让你好好睡觉，我不会来打扰你，晚上的时候，只要你看见有动静，你就赶快溜来，学声猫叫。"

第二十九章

　　星期五早上，汤姆听见的第一件事就是桩好消息——撒切尔法官一家昨天晚上回到镇上了。印江·乔和宝藏都退居第二了，贝琪立马在这个孩子心头占据了主要地位。他见到了她，他们俩和同伴们一起玩了"捉间谍"和"地道防守"的游戏。这一天玩得特别高兴，而且还有一件喜上加喜的事情：贝琪缠着妈妈，让她答应第二天就举行大家期待已久却迟迟不来的野餐活动，妈妈同意了。孩子们一听到这个消息，高兴得都能蹦上天了，汤姆也乐得不行了。各个邀请在太阳下山之前就送出了，所有的年轻人都热火朝天地忙碌起来，准备着第二天的野餐，村子里一派欢乐。晚上睡觉的时候，汤姆兴奋不已，他激动得迟迟无法入睡，他还期待能听见哈克的"猫叫"，这样第二天的时候，他就能带着他的财宝让贝琪和其他的孩子们大吃一惊，但是他的希望落空了，那天晚上他一声"猫叫"也没听见。

　　第二天早晨终于到来了，在十点、十一点左右，一群叽叽喳喳、无比兴奋的孩子在法官撒切尔家集合完毕，就等着出发了。大人们照例不参加这样的野餐，以免孩子们玩得不痛快。因为有几个十八岁的姑娘和几个二十三岁左右的小伙儿参加，所以大人们也不必担心孩子们的安全问题。这回大人们给他们租了那艘旧蒸汽渡船，不一会儿，他们就兴高采烈地拎着饭篮子走在了大街上，一时大街上人头攒动。西德尼生病了，不得不错过这次精彩的野餐，玛丽也只能留在家照顾他。走的时候，撒切尔夫人跟贝琪说：

"要是玩得晚的话，你就不用回来了，就跟家在码头附近的女孩们住在一起吧。"

"那我就住在苏珊·哈泼家，妈妈。"

"很好呀，注意自己的言行，不要给别人添麻烦哦。"不一会儿，他们就上路了，路上汤姆对贝琪说：

"喂，跟你说，别去乔·哈泼家住，我们到时候爬过山头，然后去道格拉斯寡妇家住，她家有冰淇淋！几乎每天都有，多得不得了，要是我们去的话，她肯定会很高兴的。"

"噢，那真是太开心了！"

接着贝琪想了一会儿说：

"但是妈妈会说什么呢？"

"她怎么会知道呀？"

小女孩在脑袋里不停地想着这个主意，最后她不情愿地说：

"我知道不能这样——但是——"

"什么但是呀！你妈妈不会知道的，而且这又没什么不好，她就是想让你安安全全的，我敢打赌要是她知道的话肯定会让你去，我知道她会的！"

道格拉斯寡妇的热情好客让她实在无法抵抗这一诱惑，再加上汤姆的怂恿，她终于决定跟汤姆一起去寡妇家，于是他们没有跟任何人说起晚上安排的计划。不久，汤姆又想到了也许哈克这天晚上会来叫他，一想到这，他就兴致减半。但仍然抵抗不了去道格拉斯寡妇家玩的诱惑，而且他为什么不去呢？他估摸着——哈克昨天晚上都没来报信，那怎么可能今天就恰好来了呢？野餐的乐趣就摆在眼前，而宝藏还说不好什么时候有消息，汤姆终究是个孩子，于是他决定今天好好地玩一场，不再去想宝藏的事。

渡船停在了村子下游三英里的地方，停船的位置正对着灌木丛生的山谷入口。孩子们一窝蜂地涌上了河岸，不一会儿茂密的树林里和峭壁间就回荡起了欢声笑语，所有让人筋疲力尽、大汗淋漓的东西都被玩了个遍，过了一会儿，森林里的探险者就陆陆续续回到了营地，胃口大开，接着就是一番狼吞虎咽。饱餐之后，孩子们坐在橡树的阴凉地里，休息谈天，过了一阵子，有人喊道：

"谁想去山洞里看看？"

每个人都想去，于是大家拿来了成捆的蜡烛，蹦蹦跳跳地往山上出发了。山洞在半山腰上，开口像一个字母A。洞口巨大的橡木大门没有上闩。进去了之后，是一个很小的空间，跟冰窖一样的冷，墙壁上的天然石灰岩溢满了冰凉的水滴。在这伸手不见五指的黑暗中驻足，看那绿色的山谷在阳光下闪着金光，颇有一番神秘感和情调。但是孩子们很快就把注意力转移到别的地方了，他们又吵闹嬉笑起来，蜡烛一被点亮，大家就扑上去抢，点蜡烛的孩子也积极地防御，结果蜡烛要么被推掉在地上要么就被弄灭了，于是大家又互相追逐，嬉笑起来。但是所有的事情都有个头，不一会儿长长的队伍就干起了正事，他们从主道上沿着台阶一个一个地走了下去，这一排的烛光忽隐忽现的，几乎都能照见他们头顶上大概六十英尺高的两壁相接处。这条主道不过八到十英尺宽，每走上几步，两手边都会遇到又窄又高的岔道——因为麦克杜格尔山洞其实就是个七扭八拐的大迷宫，里面有着各种岔道，相互交错，不知通往何处。有人说你在这错综复杂的岔道中走上好几天，都无法找到出口，你可能会越走越深，越走越深，走到地球里面去，而那里也是一样的情况——是迷宫中套着的迷宫，这些迷宫没有一个有尽头。没有人对这个山洞真正了如指掌，也不可能做到。大多数的年轻人都对山洞的某一部分比较熟悉，而且大家在进行冒险活动时都不会跑出这一区域。汤姆·索亚也和别人一样，都是只熟悉一小部分。

队伍在主道上走了四分之三英里，然后孩子们三人一群、两人一组，走进不同的岔道中，在黑暗的通道里摸索前进，当他们在岔道交接点遇见时，又把彼此都吓一跳。在这半个小时的时间里，大家可以在岔道中随心所欲地探险，既可以避免和同伴相撞，又不会走出熟悉的区域。

渐渐地，三三两两的孩子们都筋疲力尽地回到了洞口，他们累得直喘气，到处都是欢声笑语，大家身上从头到脚，全是蜡烛油，还抹上了泥土，可是尽管如此，孩子们都在为这一天尽兴的玩耍开心地嬉闹。他们惊奇地发现，时间在不知不觉中飞驰而过，暮色已经降临了。船上的铃声已经催了半个小时，不过就这样结束了一天的冒险还是比较浪漫，令人满意的。当渡船发动引擎激荡着水花前进时，没有人觉得这样的一天是在浪费时间，除了船长以外。

渡船上的灯光忽闪忽闪地飘过码头时，哈克已经开始蹲守了。他没有听见甲板上有什么声音，因为船上的年轻人都累得半死，动弹不得了。哈克还纳闷儿着这到底是个什么船，为什么它会不靠港停呢？他又马上把思绪拉了回来，专注在他要干的正事上。夜色渐浓，不一会儿就到十点了，街上已经没有车辆来来往往，零零散散的灯光也开始熄灭，路上的行人都回家去了，整个村子都开始昏昏欲睡，独留下这个可怜的蹲守人和这漫天的寂静与鬼怪。十一点到了，旅馆的灯亮了起来，现在到处都是一片死寂。哈克等了仿佛有一个世纪，但是什么都没有看见，现在他心里的希望之火正在渐渐熄灭，在这里等有用吗？真的有用吗？还不如回去睡大觉呢。

突然，一个声音落入耳中，他的神经一下子绷紧了。巷子的门慢慢关上了，于是他赶紧跑到砖厂拐弯的地方，接着就有两个人闯进他的视线，其中一个看上去还在胳膊底下夹了什么东西。那肯定是财宝箱！他们肯定是要转移宝藏，现在可怎么去叫汤姆呀？那样就太蠢了——他们会带着箱子跑得无影无踪。不行，他一定要盯紧着，跟在他们后面，反正这漆黑的夜色也不会将自己暴露出来。于是他在心里嘀咕了一番，然后就悄悄地跟在了这两个人身后，他光着脚走，声音轻的就像一只猫一样。哈克跟得不远不近，保持着一个始终能够看清他们行踪的距离。

他们往上游走了三个街区后，就左拐转到了一个十字路口，然后径直往前走，来到了通往卡迪夫山的小道。接着就走过了半山腰上威尔士老头的住处，然后他们丝毫没有停留，又一个劲向上爬。真是太好了，哈克想道，这样看来他们会把宝藏埋在老采矿石场里。但是他们在矿石场也没有停，还是径直地往上爬，一直爬到了山顶，接着突然转向了漆树丛中的小径，立马就消失在这漆黑之中。于是哈克紧跟了上来，缩短了距离，因为这么黑的话，他们也不可能看到他。他呼呼地跑了一阵，但又害怕自己跟得太紧了，然后就放慢了步伐，之后他停了下来，竖起耳朵听了一阵，什么声音都没听到，只听到了自己砰砰的心跳声。远处飞来一只猫头鹰，这可是不祥的预兆！但他就是没听到脚步声，老天啊，难道我跟丢了？他刚想飞奔着追下去，一个人在离他不到四英尺的地方清了清嗓子！哈克的心一下子提到嗓子眼了，但是他又把它咽了下去，于是他站在那里吓得直打哆嗦，就像打疟疾一样，一个劲儿地发抖。此刻他浑身无力，觉得自己马上就要晕倒了，他现在知道自己在哪个位置了，就在离道格拉斯寡妇家院子不到五步远的地方。好极了，他心里想，就让他们把宝藏埋在这里吧，这样的话就不难找回来了。

一个声音开始说话了，很低沉的声音，那是印江·乔：

"真是见鬼，她屋里可能还有别人，尽管现在很晚了，她屋里还亮着。"

"我谁都没看见啊。"

这是那个陌生人的声音——鬼屋里的陌生人。哈克的心一阵抽搐，这该不会就是要进行"复仇"吧！他这时第一反应就是扭头就跑，但是他记得道格拉斯寡妇对他很好，帮过他都不止一次了，也许这些人是想杀了她。他这会真希望自己有胆量跑去跟她报告，但是他知道自己不敢——他们会马上来抓住他的。这些想法在他的脑袋里打着架，与此同时，印江·乔又跟陌生人说话了：

"因为灌木挡住了你的视线，你往这边站站，现在看得见了吗？"

"嗯，看见了，我觉得确实还有别人，你最好放弃这一打算吧。"

"放弃，怎么可能！我就要永远离开这个国家了，放弃了也许就再也没机会了。我再告诉你一遍，之前也跟你说过，我根本就不在乎她那点破钱——也许你会在乎，但是她丈夫曾经那样虐待我——他那样对我很多次了——就因为他是镇上的法官，就说我是个无赖，而且这根本都不算什么，这只是他对我种种不公的万分之一！他用鞭子抽我！——在监狱前用鞭子打我，就像对一个黑鬼一样！——镇上所有的人都看见了！抽打我！——你明白吗？他利用了我之后就死了，我必须报复在她身上。"

"噢，不要杀她啊！不要这么做！"

"杀了她？谁说要杀她了？要是她丈夫在这我就会杀了他，但是不会杀她。你要找一个女人报仇你根本就不用杀掉她——那样太蠢了！你要毁掉她的容貌，你把她的鼻子挖掉，再把她的耳朵割了，就像一只母猪一样！"

"我的天啊，这真是——"

"有意见你还是自己留着吧！别给自己找麻烦。我会把她绑在床上，要是她失血过多而死了，那会是我的错？要是她真这样死了，我一滴眼泪也不会掉。我的朋友，你要帮我才行——看在我的分上——把你叫来就是因为这个——我一个人干不了。要是你逃跑的话，我就杀了你，听懂了吗？要是我不得杀了你，那我也会杀了她，这样就不会有人知道是谁杀的了。"

"好吧，要是必须要做的话，那我们就赶紧做，越快越好——我现在都在发抖。"

"现在做？有别人在场也做？看样子，我真有些怀疑你了，不行，我们必须要等到灯都灭了，不用这么着急。"

哈克觉得接下来肯定是一番寂静——这可是比任何可怕的谈话都要令人恐怖。于是他屏住呼吸，小心翼翼地往后退，战战兢兢地稳住每一个步伐，他先是一条腿向后，晃晃悠悠地险些摔倒，等稳住之后，他又迈开了另一只脚，这次又花了同样的精力，冒了同样的危险，接下来是上只脚，再下只——突然他踩到了一枝小树枝，脚底下嘎嘣一响！于是他屏住了呼吸，听了一番，结果没听到任何动静——还是一片死寂，于是他庆幸极了。现在他才在漆树丛中转过身来——小心翼翼地转着身子，就像他这会儿是一只船一样，接着就沿着树丛谨慎而敏捷地走着，当他走到采石场时，觉得已经脱离危险了，于是他开始大跑起来，脚底下跟生了风一样。他直朝山下奔，一直跑到威尔士老头家，敲了敲门，然后老人和他两个强壮的儿子从窗户那里探出了头。

"谁站在那里？谁在敲门？你想要干什么？"

"让我进去——快点！我会告诉你们所有事情的。"

"什么事，你是谁？"

"我是哈克贝利·费恩——快点，让我进去吧！"

"哈克贝利·费恩，确实是你！我打赌，这个名字可是叫不开许多门的！不过，孩子们，让他进来，我们来看看到底怎么了。"

"请别跟别人说是我说的，"哈克一进门就说了这句话，"求你们别说，要不我会被杀的——但是寡妇时常对我很好，我想要告诉你们——你保证不会说是我说的，我就告诉你。"

"嗬，他肯定是有事情要讲，否则他就不会这样说话！"老人大声说道，"快说吧，这里没有人会讲出去的，孩子。"

三分钟之后，老人和他的儿子都带好武器上山去了，他们手里拿着枪，蹑手蹑脚地走上了那条漆树小道。哈克躲在一个大圆石头后面，专注地听着动静。在一阵子寂静之后，突然就听到一片枪响和一声惊叫。

哈克没等弄明白是怎么回事，便拔腿就跑，他以最快的速度一溜烟冲下了山。

第三十章

星期天早晨天刚蒙蒙亮，哈克就爬上了山，轻轻地敲响了威尔士老人家的房门。他们还在睡觉呢，但是由于发生了昨天晚上的事，大家现在处于警惕状态。很快窗户边就传来了一个声音：

"谁在那！"

哈克用吓得发抖的声音低声说道：

"让我进去吧！不是别人，是我呀，哈克贝利·费恩！"

"凭着这个名字，无论白天还是黑夜，这里都欢迎你，孩子！——欢迎你来！"

这个流浪小孩从来都没有听到过这样的话，他心里温暖极了，他想不起来以前还有谁跟他说过"欢迎"。门很快就关上了，哈克进到了屋里，坐了起来，老人和他那两个又高又壮的儿子迅速地穿好了衣服。

"嘿，我的孩子，你现在肯定又饿又渴了吧，太阳一出来，早饭就会做好，咱们就能热气腾腾地吃一顿了，你放心吧！我们昨天晚上还期望着你能回来，在这里过上一夜呢。"

"我害怕极了，"哈克说，"然后一听到枪声我就跑了，一直跑了三英里远，我现在回来是因为我想知道到底发生了什么，而赶在天亮前来是因为我怕碰上那两个恶鬼，就算他们已经死了，我也不想碰上他们的鬼魂。"

"哎，可怜的孩子，你看起来昨天晚上真够难受的，吃完饭了之后，就在这里的床上休息吧，孩子，真是太对不起了，我们没有把他们打死，我们就照你说的跑到了能放倒他们的地方，然后我们轻手轻脚地跟了上去，离他们只有不到十五码的距离——那条小路黑得伸手不见五指，就在这时我忍不住想打喷嚏，可真是倒霉透了！我很努力地想要忍着，但是没有用，该来的总是要来！我端着枪走在前面，结果打了个喷嚏惊动了那些坏蛋，他们挣扎着逃跑，于是我喊道：'孩子们，快开枪！'然后我就朝着有动静的地方开了几枪，孩子们也放了几枪。但是这些混蛋还是逃走了，我们穷追不舍，穿过森林一路追下去，我想我们就没打中他们，他们也朝我们开枪了，但也没中。最后我们听不到他们的脚步声了，于是就放弃了追赶，下山去叫警察了。他们派了一队人马，到河岸盯守，天亮后，州长还会带着部下到树林里搜索，我的孩子们也会马上过去，我希望你能给我们提供一些这两个混蛋的外貌特征，这会很有帮助的，但是我觉得在黑暗中，你也看不太清楚他们长什么样子吧？"

"我知道他们的样子，我在镇上就见到他们了，然后一直跟过来的。"

"这真是太棒了！描述一下——描述一下吧，孩子！"

"其中一个是曾经来过镇上一两次的那个又聋又哑的西班牙老头，另一个长得很难看，穿得破破烂烂的——"

"说这么多就足够了，孩子，我知道他们是谁了！我们曾经在寡妇家树林的后面遇到过他们，当时他们溜走了，快去吧，孩子们，快告诉州长去——今天就不吃早饭了，明天再吃吧！"

于是威尔士老人的孩子们立刻就出发了。他们刚一转身，哈克就跳起来说：

"噢，请不要告诉任何人是我看见他们的！求你了！"

"要是你这么说的话，当然可以了，哈克，但你做了这些总该得到应有的奖赏呀。"

"噢，不用，真的不用了！求你别说啊！"

当两个年轻人离开后，威尔士老人说：

"他们不会讲出去的——我也不会。但是你为什么不想让别人知道呢？"

哈克没说别的理由，只说他很了解其中一个人，不想让他知道自己一直以来都在和他作对，要不他肯定会送命的。

老人又向他保证了不会说出去，接着他说：

"你是怎么跟上他们的，孩子？他们看起来很可疑吗？"

哈克没回答，心里在谨慎地想着要怎么回答才好，想了一会儿他说：

"呃，你也知道，大家都说我是个坏孩子，而且我也觉得大家没说错，有时候我都睡不着，因为我一直都在想着这个问题，想要想法子重新做人。昨天晚上就是这样子的，我睡不着，于是就到街上走走，大概是夜里十二点多，当我走到旅馆旁边的老砖厂时，我靠在墙上又想了一会儿这个问题，就在这时，这两个家伙从我身边溜了过去，胳膊底下还夹着什么东西，我觉得他们肯定是偷了别人什么。然后他们其中的一个人吸起烟，另一个就问他借火，他们就站在我面前，然后雪茄火照亮了他们的脸，我看到其中一个就是那个又聋又哑的西班牙人，他长着白色的长胡子，眼神凶狠，另一个穿得很破烂。"

"你就着雪茄的光就能看出他衣着破烂？"

这一问可让哈克一下子说不出话来，然后过了一会儿他解释道：

"我倒没有看清楚，但不知怎的，我就是觉得他穿得很烂。"

"然后他们又接着走，你——"

"对，我就跟着他们了，就是这样的，我想看看到底是怎么回事，他们走起路来这么鬼鬼祟祟。我跟着他们到了寡妇家的楼梯口，然后就站在暗处，听到那个穿得破烂的人在为寡妇求情，而西班牙人发誓要让寡妇毁容，就像我跟你和你的两个儿子说的那样——"

"什么！一个又聋又哑的人说了这些！"

哈克又犯了一个致命的错误！他已经在很努力地不让老人知道这个西班牙人是谁了，一丁点的暗示都没有给他，尽管他万分小心，但是他的舌头似乎已经下定决心要给他带来麻烦，他好几次都想从自己挖的坑里爬出来，但老人的眼睛一直盯着他，于是他越说越乱，过了一会儿威尔士老人说道：

"孩子，不要害怕我，我不会伤害你一根头发的，绝不会——我会保护你的——保护你。这个西班牙人不是聋的也不是哑的，你知道他的真实情况，现在你需要相信我——告诉我真相吧，相信我——我不会出卖你的。"

哈克盯着老人真诚的眼睛看了一会儿，然后低下头，在他耳边轻轻说道：

"他不是个西班牙人——是印江·乔！"

威尔士老人听到这差点从椅子上跳了起来，片刻之后，他说：

"这下一切就清楚了，当你说到要割耳挖鼻的时候，我还以为那是你自己添油加醋的说法呢，因为白人们不会用这种方式来报仇，但他竟然是印江·乔！那就没什么奇怪的了。"

早饭期间，他们继续谈论着，老人说他们昨天晚上上床睡觉之前做的最后一件事，就是拎着提灯检查一下小路上有没有留下血迹，但他们什么都没有看见，就找到了一捆——

"一捆什么？"

哈克突然就从嘴里闪电般地蹦出这几个字，他的眼睛睁得大大的，此刻他屏住了呼吸，等待着老人的回答。威尔士老人被哈克这一举动惊住了，他吃惊地看着哈克——三秒——五秒——十秒，然后他回答说：

"一捆工具，怎么啦，你怎么了啊？"

哈克一下子松了下来，轻轻地喘了口气，但却仿佛如释重负一般。威尔士老人严肃地看着他，摸不着头脑，过了一会儿他说：

"对，是偷东西用的工具，这好像让你松了一大口气啊，你为什么会这样呢？你期待我们找到什么呀？"

哈克这下被问得很窘迫——一双审问的眼睛盯着他看——他愿意用一切来换一个合理的答案——但是什么也想不出来——审问的眼神越逼越紧——一个很荒唐的理由突然在脑中冒出——没有时间来掂量了，于是他决定冒险一试，结结巴巴地说：

"主日学校的书，也许是这个。"

可怜的哈克此刻太紧张了，脸上没有一丝笑容，但是老人听到这个回答马上就大笑了起来，笑得从上到下的每一块肌肉都在抖个不停，他还说能这样开怀一笑就跟得了钱一样美好，因为它能让你在医院里少花点钱，老人还接着说：

"可怜的孩子，你脸色这么苍白，看上去筋疲力尽了——你的状态一点也不好——怪不得你有一点语无伦次，找不到方向，但是你会好起来的，我相信多休息休息你就会好起来的。"

哈克想到自己刚才表现得就像只笨鹅，激动得差点露馅，就十分懊恼，因为他一听到他们说要向寡妇报仇，就知道他们从旅馆里拿出来的并不是财宝。他只觉得那不是财宝，并不知道其实里面确实不是财宝，所以当听到那是一捆东西时，他就觉得那会是很大的宝贝。但现在他很庆幸发生了刚才的事，因为这至少让他确信这捆东西并不是宝藏，所以他这会儿能把心放在肚子里，好好地休息一下了。事实上所有的事情都在向着正确的方向发展，宝藏一定还藏在二号房间里，那两个坏蛋当天会被抓住送进监狱，而他和汤姆那天晚上就会抓住这个黄金机会毫不费力地取到宝藏，根本不用害怕有谁会发现。

刚吃完早饭，就有人来敲门。于是哈克赶忙躲到一个隐蔽的地方，因为他不想被过多的和昨天晚上的事牵扯到一起。威尔士老人让几个女士和先生进了门，其中就有道格拉斯寡妇，老人还注意到有一群人在往山上爬——要看清楚事情发生时的石阶，显然消息已经很快就传开了，威尔士老人不得不把昨天晚上的事情向来访者一五一十地说清楚，寡妇幸免于难，不停地表示着感激之情。

"夫人，不用再谢啦，除了我和我的孩子们，还有一个人更加值得你感谢，但是他不许我说出他的名字，要不是他，我们是不会出去的。"

这一下子就激起了大家的好奇心，以至于都忘记了最要紧的事，但是老人依然信守承诺，因为他们若是知道了的话，就会传遍整个镇子，当大家弄明白了所有的事情后，寡妇说：

"我那天躺在床上看书，外面十分吵闹，我都睡不着，你们怎么不来找我呢？"

"我们觉得没必要这样做，那些家伙不太可能再来第二回，他们把工具丢在这里了，不可能再有什么动静，所以，把你叫醒然后吓个半死有什么用呢？我的三个黑人伙计那天晚上一直站在你门口守卫着，所以他们也不可能再回来。"

不一会儿，又有更多的人来询问情况，于是老人不得不再把事情解释一遍，一直说了两个多小时才结束。

在放假的时候人们是不用上主日学校的，但是大家都提早到了教堂。那天晚上的可怕事件已经传得沸沸扬扬的了，有消息说，还是没有发现那两个坏蛋的行踪。当做完祷告时，法官撒切尔的妻子和哈泼太太一起随人群走下过道，她说：

"我家贝琪是要睡一整天吗？我就知道她会累得要死。"

"你家贝琪？"

"对呀，"她惊讶地看着哈泼太太，"昨天晚上她没在你家住吗？"

"什么，没有啊。"

撒切尔太太的脸色一下子就变得很苍白了，她一屁股坐到了椅子上。就在这时，波丽姨妈正跟一个朋友轻快地说着话，然后波丽姨妈对她们说：

"早上好，撒切尔太太，早上好，哈泼太太，我家有个男孩找不到了，我想汤姆昨天晚上是在你家吧——你们其中的一家，现在他竟然不敢来教堂了，我真要好好跟他算算账。"

撒切尔太太虚弱地摇了摇头，这会儿她的脸色更加苍白了。

"他没有在我们家住啊，"哈泼太太说，脸上露出不安，波丽姨妈的脸上也立即露出了明显的焦虑。

"乔·哈泼，你今天早上看见我家汤姆了吗？"

"没有啊。"

"你最后见到他是什么时候？"

乔尽力地去回忆，但是想不出来确切是什么时候。人们停止了往教堂外走，处处都在窃窃私语，每一张面孔上都显露出不安，大人们都在不停地询问孩子，年轻的教师们也在不住地回答各种询问。但是他们都不确定当渡船开回港时汤姆和贝琪到底有没有上船，当时天很黑，没有人想到要清点一下人数，以防有人迷失。一个年轻小伙最后突然害怕地叫道，他们还在洞穴里！撒切尔夫人一下子就晕了过去，波丽姨妈也开始号啕大哭，着急得不停地搓着手。

这个恐怖的消息一传十，十传百，大街小巷的人都知道了，不到五分钟街上的钟就开始疯狂地敲打着，整个镇子的人都开始着手寻找他们！卡迪夫山事件一时间就被抛在一边，显现不出任何意义，那些坏蛋也暂时被抛在了脑后。人们迅速装好马鞍，小艇上配备好人手，渡船也按令出发，不到半个小时，两百号人马就已如潮水般沿着公路和顺着河流朝向洞穴奔去了。

那天漫长的下午，村子似乎已经空了，到处都是一片死寂。女人们都来陪伴波丽姨妈和撒切尔太太，努力安抚她们的心。她们跟她俩一起哭，这可比说话有用得多了。这一夜是那么的寂寥，整个镇子的人都在等候消息，但是当黎明再次来到时，所有能听到的话语只是"再多送些蜡烛来——送些食物"。撒切尔夫人几乎都快疯了，波丽姨妈也是如此。撒切尔法官派人传些令人鼓舞、重塑希望的消息，但是这也没有让大家提起兴致。

天快亮时，威尔士老人回到了家，身上滴满了蜡烛油，蹭上了泥灰，累得几乎动不了了。他发现哈克仍然在先前的床上躺着，发着烧，神志不清。所有的医生都到山洞里去了，所以道格拉斯寡妇就来照顾这个小病人，她说她一定会尽全力来照顾他，因为不管哈克是好是坏还是不好也不坏，他都是上帝的孩子，只要是上帝的东西，都不应该被忽视。然后威尔士老人说哈克骨子里还是有很多优秀的地方，于是寡妇说：

"确实是这样的，那是上帝留下的记号，上帝不会不管任何人，从来都不会。经过他的手，每个生灵上都留下了一些好的记号。"

刚到下午，一些累得筋疲力尽的人开始拖着沉重的步子返回村子，而身强体壮的人则继续进行着搜寻工作。大家能够得到的消息就是人们正在以前从来没有到过的地方搜查，准备将每一个角落，每一条小岔道都彻底搜查一遍，在这错综复杂的迷宫里，老远就能看见到处都是闪烁的灯光，叫喊声、枪声在这昏暗的洞穴中回荡。在一个人迹罕至的地方，人们发现贝琪和汤姆的名字用蜡烛烧出黑烟熏在了墙上，而且在这附近还找到了一段油乎乎的缎子。撒切尔夫人认出了这是贝琪的东西，抱着它哭个不停，她说这是她那可怜孩子留下的最后的东西，再也没有比这个遗物更珍贵的了，因为在死亡来临之前，这东西最后离开她鲜活的生命。时不时地有人叫道，洞里远处好像有灯光在闪烁，然后人群终究会爆发出一阵欣喜的叫喊，一二十个男人就会沿着回声萦绕的小道下去寻找，结果就是又一次的希望落空，孩子们并不在那里，只不过是搜寻者的灯光罢了。

三个可怕的白天、黑夜就这样一点一滴地熬过去了，村子沉浸在一种绝望的气氛中，没有人有心情做任何事，就连碰巧发现了旅馆老板偷偷地藏了烈酒这种本该令人震惊的事，都没有在人们心中荡起一丝波浪。哈克醒了之后，小心翼翼地将话题引到小旅馆上面，最后他问道——心里暗自想着最坏的可能——从他生病以来，有没有在旅馆里找到什么东西。

"找到了啊。"寡妇回答说。

哈克躺在被窝里，一下子坐了起来，瞪大了眼睛，说：

"什么？找到什么了？"

"烈酒呀！——现在旅馆被关了，快躺下，孩子——你真是把我吓了一跳！"

"就再跟我说一件事吧——就一件——求你了！是汤姆·索亚发现的吗？"

寡妇立即哭了出来，"别说话，别说话，孩子，安静下来！我告诉过你多少次啦，你现在不能讲话，你病得非常、非常严重！"

就只发现了烈酒，要是发现了金子的话，村子里肯定会议论纷纷的，所以那财宝肯定是再也找不到了——再也找不到！但是还能有什么事能让她这么哭呢？她居然哭了，真是奇了怪。

这些想法在哈克的脑子里捣鼓了一阵，最后想得有些累了，他就睡着了。这时寡妇自言自语道：

"唉，他终于睡了，可怜的小家伙，还说是汤姆·索亚发现的呢！可惜还没有人能发现汤姆·索亚在哪呢！唉，现在能依然抱着希望，能有体力去继续寻找的人已经没几个了呀。"

第三十一章

　　现在让我们回到汤姆和贝琪的野餐吧。他们跟伙伴们一起在昏暗的小道中穿行，在那些熟悉的洞中奇观里游玩——各种奇观的名字都很夸大，比方说"客厅""大教堂""阿拉丁的宫殿"，等等。不一会儿孩子们就玩起了捉迷藏的游戏，汤姆和贝琪也饶有兴致地加入了大家的队伍，直到有点玩腻了。接着他们举着蜡烛，沿着一条蜿蜒的小道往下漫步，边走边念叨着墙上用蜡烛烟熏出来的人名啦，时间啦，地址啦，还有格言之类的东西。他们一边走着一边聊天，压根就没注意到已经到了一片新地方，这里的墙壁上什么熏字都没有。他们又在一块突出的石壁上熏上自己的名字，然后接着往前走去，不一会儿，就来到了一个地方，这里有一股细流从突出的岩石上涓涓流下，水里还掺杂着石灰沉渣，日积月累，已经形成了一个起伏不平、闪闪发光、经久不消的石幕，它周围好似镶了一层边，活像一挂瀑布。为了逗贝琪开心，汤姆将自己小小的身体挤到石幕后面，然而他发现在两个狭窄的墙壁之间有一些天然形成的石阶，于是汤姆的心头一下子涌起一阵好奇，使他想要下去看个究竟。贝琪也积极地响应他这一想法，于是他们在墙上熏了些记号以便以后不至迷路，然后就开始了探险之旅。他们在洞里一会儿这边走，一会儿那边拐，在这个神秘的洞穴里越走越深，接着又做了些记号，就拐进了一个岔道里寻找些更刺激的场面，好讲给人们听。在一处，他们发现了一个宽敞的石洞，在洞顶有大量闪闪发光的钟乳石，每一个都有人的大腿那样粗、那样长，他们在洞里转来转去，惊叹不已。过了一会儿，就沿着众多的出口中的一个出去了。这一拐又把他们带到了一个泉水面前，泉底结着很多晶莹剔透的晶状物，泉水位于石洞的中央，这个石洞由很多精美柱子支撑着，柱子上面交织着钟乳石和石笋，印证着几千个世纪的水滴不息。在洞顶有着大片的蝙蝠栖息在上，成群结队，数以千计。烛光惊动了这些生灵，它们成百上千地飞腾下来，尖叫着扑向蜡烛，汤姆知道它们的习性以及它们呼啸而下带来的危险，于是便一把抓住贝琪的手，将她拉进了一个夹道里，这一拉可正是时候，因为当贝琪从洞里出来的时候，一只蝙蝠就扑过来打翻了贝琪手中的蜡烛。蝙蝠追着这两个孩子跑了好久，逼得两个逃亡者一见到岔道就钻进去，最终得以摆脱这些危险的东西。汤姆不一会儿又发现了一个地下湖，它往四周延伸着，直到轮廓消失在黑暗中。他想下去探个究竟，但最后决定还是坐下来稍作休息比较好。此刻，这个洞穴的死寂第一次用它冰凉的爪子抚摸着这两个孩子的灵魂，贝琪说：

"呀，我都没有发现，好像很久都没有听到其他人的声音了。"

"仔细想想吧，贝琪。我们现在离他们可是很远的，在洞底下，而且我也不知道我们到底是向南、向北、向西还是什么方向跑了有多远，我们在这里可听不见他们。"

贝琪开始有些不安了。

"我在想我们到这里有多久了呀，汤姆？我们该回去了。"

"我想也是，我们应该回去了。"

"你能找到回去的路吗，汤姆？在我看来这就是个大迷宫啊。"

"我觉得我应该能，但是又会遇到那些蝙蝠，要是它们再把蜡烛弄灭了，那就糟糕了，我们试试走别的路吧，避开那里。"

"行，但希望我们不会迷路，那就太可怕了！"这个姑娘一想到迷路的可怕就禁不住打了个寒战。

于是他们走进了一条小道，不声不响地在里头走了很久，每到一个新岔道时，就四下看看有没有熟悉的道路，但是他们看见的都是陌生的出口。每当汤姆去检查是否有熟悉的出口时，贝琪就仔仔细细地盯着他的脸看，想要看看是否有希望的表情，于是汤姆就会打起精神说：

"噢，没关系，不是这个出口，不过我们会找到的。"

但是经过了一次又一次的失败之后，他也变得越来越绝望，最后他干脆见到岔道就胡乱地钻进去，拼命地想要找到正确的路口。他嘴里仍然说着"没关系"但是心里早已如一团乱麻，说出的话都失去了光泽，听上去就像在说"没救了"。贝琪十分恐惧地跟在他的身边，努力地抑制住泪水，但还是没忍住，最后她说：

"噢，汤姆，不要再管那些蝙蝠了，我们原路返回吧！现在看起来越来越找不到路了。"

"停！"他说。

听到的只是无尽的沉寂，静得连他们的呼吸都听得一清二楚，于是汤姆大叫了一声，叫声在空旷的洞穴里回旋，逐渐远去，听上去就像是一阵的嘲笑。

"噢，别这样了，汤姆，这听起来太可怕了。"贝琪说。

"这是可怕，但是这样做有好处的，贝琪，他们有可能听见我们的声音。"接着汤姆又叫了一次。

汤姆口中的"可能"却比这鬼怪般可怕的回声更叫人害怕，它表明了希望正在慢慢消失，孩子们站在那里，竖着耳朵听，但是什么回应也没听见。于是汤姆立刻按原路往回走，走得很快，但他只走了一会儿就开始犹豫不决了，这让贝琪觉得很害怕——汤姆找不到回去的路了！

"噢，汤姆，你没有做一个记号！"

"贝琪，我真是个傻子！大傻子！我压根就没想到我们会回来！不——我找不到路了，我们迷路了。"

"汤姆，汤姆，我们迷路了，我们迷路了！我们再也不能从这个可怕的地方出去了！天啊，我们干吗要远离其他的人！"

贝琪一屁股坐到了地上，号啕大哭起来，这可把汤姆吓了一大跳，他以为她会死掉，或者会发疯。于是他坐到了贝琪身边搂着她，然后贝琪将头埋在了他的怀里紧紧抱着汤姆，将自己的害怕以及无用的后悔一股脑地说了出来，这声音传到远处就变成了嘲笑声回荡在洞穴里。汤姆祈求她鼓起希望，但是她说她做不到，于是汤姆开始自责，埋怨自己让她陷入了这样悲惨的境况里，这样一来反倒产生了好效果，贝琪说她会尝试着鼓起勇气，勇敢地站起来，不管他走到哪里她都会跟随，只要汤姆不再像刚才那样说话，而且她还说要是论错的话，她也一样应该感到愧疚。

于是他们又继续往前走——漫无目的——就是随意地走走——他们所能做的也就是向前走，不停地走，过了一小会儿，希望就开始复苏了——并没有什么原因，仅仅是因为时间还不长、失败还不多，希望的灯火还没有就此熄灭，它自然而然地就会再次升起。

过了一会儿，汤姆拿起贝琪的蜡烛，然后熄灭了它，这种节约太有必要了！根本就不用说话，贝琪就明白这意味着什么，她心中的希望再次破灭了，她知道汤姆的口袋里还剩下一整支蜡烛和三四节短蜡烛——但他必须要省着用。

又过了一会儿，疲惫开始爬上肩头，孩子们努力不去管它，因为现在时间非常的宝贵，在这个地方休息真是太可怕了，只要往前走，不管向着哪个方向，就会有那么一点收获，而在这里坐着就是在等死，而且毫无结果。

最后，贝琪疲惫的双腿再也走不了一步了，她坐了下来，汤姆也坐到了她身边，他们谈起了家，聊起了外面的伙伴以及舒服的大床，最重要的还有外面的灯光！说着说着贝琪就哭了，汤姆努力地想要安慰她，但是所有的法子都用尽了，说来说去还是那一套，听起来更像是在嘲笑她，贝琪越来越累，终于开始打盹了，汤姆这时心里也轻松了下来，他看着她的疲惫的脸庞开始舒展开来，浅浅地展露出睡梦中的甜蜜，过了一会儿，她的脸上浮现出了笑意，这张安详的脸闪现出平和，安抚着汤姆的灵魂，他的思维开始游走，忘却了时间，沉浸在美妙的回忆中。就在他默默沉思的时候，贝琪笑着醒来了——但是害怕马上就又袭上了她的嘴边，变成了一声呻吟。

　　"哦，我怎么能睡着了呢！真希望我永远、永远都不曾醒来！不要！不要醒来，汤姆！不要这样子看我！我再也不这样说了。"

　　"很高兴你睡了一会儿，贝琪，现在你会觉得好些的，我们再去找路出去。"

　　"我们可以试试，汤姆，但是我在梦里看到了一个美丽的国家，我觉得我们会去那里。"

　　"也许不会，也许不会，振作起来吧，贝琪，我们再去试试。"

　　于是他们站了起来，手拉着手走着，心里绝望极了。他们试着计算在洞里到底待了多长时间，但是他们只知道过了有几天、几个星期那么久，但是这也不可能，因为他们的蜡烛都还没有烧完。又过了很久之后——他们也不知道到底是多久——汤姆说他们必须轻轻地走，听听哪里有滴水声——他们必须找到泉水。不久他们真的发现了泉水，然后汤姆说是时候该休息休息了，两个孩子都累得不轻，但贝琪说她还可以再走上一阵子，汤姆没同意，这让她感到很惊奇，完全理解不了。于是他们就坐了下来，汤姆用一些灰浆将蜡烛固定在面前的岩石上，两个人就很快陷入沉思，好一段时间，彼此都没有说一句话，然后贝琪打破了沉寂，她说：

"汤姆，我好饿啊！"

于是汤姆从口袋里拿了些东西出来。

"你记得这个吗？"他问道。

贝琪几乎笑了起来。

"这是我们的结婚蛋糕，汤姆。"

"是呀，我真希望它能有桶那么大，因为我们就只剩这点东西了。"

"我在野餐的时候省下的，想以后玩的，汤姆，大人们也都是这样做的——但是这将是我们俩的——"

她只说了一半，然后汤姆分了蛋糕，贝琪开始大口吃了起来，汤姆则一点一点地咬着自己的那部分，最后他们喝了一通凉水，结束了这顿饭。片刻之后，贝琪建议说他们接着走，汤姆先是沉默了一会儿，然后他说：

"贝琪，要是我告诉你一些事的话，你能承受得了吗？"

贝琪的脸一下子就变白了，但是她觉得她能承受。

"是这样的，贝琪，我们必须待在这里，因为这里有水喝，我们所剩的蜡烛也只有这最后的一截了。"

贝琪开始号啕大哭，汤姆尽全力去安慰她，但是没有用，最后贝琪说道：

"汤姆！"

"怎么啦，贝琪？"

"大家肯定会想我们的，他们会来找我们！"

"嗯，他们肯定会的！当然会的！"

"也许他们现在就在找我们，汤姆。"

"嗯，也许是的，我希望他们在找我们。"

"他们什么时候会想起我们，汤姆？"

"我觉得等回到船上就会。"

"汤姆，那时候天肯定很黑了——他们会察觉到我们没有回来吗？"

"我也不知道，但是不管怎么说，他们一到家你妈妈就会问起你呀。"

这时贝琪脸上划过一道恐怖的神情，让汤姆意识到自己犯了一个大错，贝琪那天晚上不会回家！这两个孩子变得沉默起来，各自思索着，又过了一会儿，贝琪脸上的一阵悲伤显示出汤姆脑中想着的事跟她的一样——当撒切尔夫人发现贝琪不在哈泼太太家时，周日上午都过了一大半了。

孩子们紧盯着他们那一小截蜡烛，看着它一点一点、无情地燃烧，最后只剩下半英尺长的灯芯还在燃烧，烛光忽高忽低，晃晃悠悠，顺着细长的烟往上飘，飘到最高处时停了一会儿，接着恐怖的黑暗就统治了整个洞穴！

过了一会儿，贝琪才慢慢意识到她在汤姆的怀里痛哭，谁也不知道到底过了多久，只知道好像过了很久，两人从昏睡中醒过来，再次面对着悲惨的人生。汤姆说现在可能是星期日了——也可能是星期一。他努力让贝琪说点话，但是贝琪太伤心了，她已经彻底地绝望了。汤姆说他们肯定迷路了很久，而且毫无疑问大家现在都在找他们，他要叫喊几声，也许会有人听见，然后汤姆试着叫了几声，但是黑暗中，那远处的回声听起来十分可怕，于是他再也没有试了。

时间一分一秒地过去了，他们现在饥肠辘辘。汤姆刚才吃的蛋糕还剩下一半，于是他们分了蛋糕，然后吃掉了，但这样他们比之前更饿了，这点食物只能勾起他们的食欲。

过了一会儿，汤姆说：

"嘘！你听到了吗？"

两个孩子都屏住呼吸，仔细聆听，远远地好像有人在叫喊，汤姆马上答应了起来，牵着贝琪的手，摸索着顺着声音往通道里走，不一会儿，他又听了听，这次声音已经听得到了，而且明显近了一点。

"是他们！"汤姆说，"他们来救我们了！快过来，贝琪——我们有救了！"

两个被困在监狱中的人立刻欣喜若狂，然而他们却走得很慢，因为地上坑坑洼洼的，必须要小心才行。不久他们就碰到一个大坑，也许有三英尺深，也许有一百英尺——不管怎么弄都不可能过去。于是汤姆趴在地上，尽可能地伸手去摸，但是摸不到底。他们必须待在这里等待救援的到来，他们又听了听，那些叫喊声变得越来越远了！一会儿工夫之后，声音已经完全听不到了，孩子们的心又沉了下来！汤姆拼命地叫着，直到嗓子都变哑了，但没有一点作用。他满怀希望地和贝琪说话，可是在一阵焦虑的等待之后再也没有听到一丝声音。

孩子们又摸索着回到了泉水旁，时间拖着脚步往前挪动，他们又昏睡了一阵，醒来之后，又饿又累，汤姆说这回肯定到星期二了。

突然汤姆又想出一个主意，附近有很多岔道，与其坐在这里忍受时间的拷打，还不如去冒冒险，于是他从口袋里掏出一个风筝线，把线一头拴到一个突出的石头上，然后他和贝琪开始探路，汤姆走在前头，边摸索前行边放线，在走了二十个台阶后，走到了小道的尽头，转弯处又是另一条路，于是汤姆跪了下来，用手往下摸，他尽可能地想要在转弯处摸得远一点，他努力地往右边使劲地够着，就在这时，不到二十码远的地方，石头后面伸出了一只拿着灯笼的人手！于是汤姆高兴地叫了起来，手的主人马上就显露了出来——印江·乔！汤姆立刻就被吓瘫了，他坐在那里动弹不得。当看到"西班牙人"拔腿就跑，离开了汤姆的视线之后，他激动得感谢天感谢地。汤姆想着，乔肯定是没有认出他的声音，要不他肯定会过来杀掉他，谁叫他在法庭上出来作证呢，山洞里的回声肯定让他的声音变得难以辨别，没错，肯定是因为这，他想着，此刻他全身已经毫无力气了。汤姆对自己说，要是有力气回去的话，他一定会待在泉水旁不乱动，什么都不能再诱导他冒着遇上印江·乔的危险跑出来，他小心翼翼地不让贝琪知道他看见了什么，只是告诉她大叫一声是为了寻个好运。

　　但是时间一长，饥饿和苦难就战胜了恐惧，他们先是在泉水边等了一会儿，接着又昏睡了很久，然后事情就发生了变化，孩子们饥肠辘辘地醒了过来，汤姆相信现在已经是周三或者周四了，也说不定是周五或者周六了，现在也许人们都已经放弃寻找了，因此他说应该接着找出路，这回他觉得就算是冒着遇到印江·乔的危险，或者是其他的危险，也不能退缩。但是贝琪现在很虚弱，她有些神志不清，怎么都鼓不起力气，她说自己想在这里等着，然后死去，这不会太久，她告诉汤姆如果他想的话，他可以用风筝线找出路，但是她想让他时不时地回来跟她说会话，还让他答应当那个可怕的时刻来临时，能待在她身边，握紧她的手直到生命的尽头。

　　汤姆吻了吻她，嗓子里哽咽着，表面上还表现出一定会找到搜寻者或者出口的信心，然后拿出风筝线，从一个通道爬着往前不断摸索，饥饿让他万分沮丧，一想到将要来临的命运，他就难受极了。

第三十二章

星期二下午来了，一直到黄昏的时候，圣彼得堡村子仍然沉浸在哀痛之中。迷路的孩子们还没有找回来，人们为他们举行了公开的祷告，很多人还在私下里为他们做祷告，大家都真心真意地希望他们能够平安无事，但是洞里仍然没有好消息传出。大部分的搜救者都放弃了救援，回到了自己的日常工作，因为他们觉得现在能找到孩子简直都不可能了。撒切尔太太病得很重，大部分的时间都处于昏迷状态，大家说听着她迷迷糊糊地喊着孩子的名字真是太让人伤心了，有时候她抬起头听上整整一分钟，然后又无力地躺下去呻吟起来。波丽姨妈也非常悲伤，她那灰白的头发已经全白了，晚上的时候，村子仍笼罩在一片悲伤、绝望之中。

大概到了半夜的时候，村子的大钟发出一阵隆隆的响声，不一会儿，街上已经涌出大群欣喜若狂的人，大家连衣服都没有穿好就跑出来了，人们叫道："出来啦！出来啦！找到他们啦！找到他们啦！"随后还能听见锡盆和号角的喧闹声，人们自动汇聚起来，朝着河岸走去，看见孩子们正坐在敞开的篷车上，拉着马车的人大声嚷嚷着，人们也涌过来将他们团团挤住，加入到孩子们回家的道路，大部队浩浩荡荡地走上街头，欢声高呼！

村子里灯火通明，没有人想要睡觉，这是小镇上最欢腾的一夜，前半个小时，村子里的人们接连不断地跑到撒切尔法官家里，抱住两个被救的小家伙，亲吻他们，还使劲地握住撒切尔太太的手，想要说些什么，但又表达不出来——如雨般的泪花洒得到处都是。

波丽姨妈也完全沉浸在喜悦之中，撒切尔太太也差不多是这样，等到送信的人将这个好消息告诉了她还在山洞中的丈夫时，她就会更加开心了。汤姆躺在沙发上，周围一群竖着耳朵的观众渴求地听着他讲着洞里的冒险之旅，他边讲还不忘边添油加醋，最后描述到他是怎么样离开贝琪然后一个人踏上冒险的旅途，怎样沿着两条小道走到风筝线到达不了的地方，以及他怎样走上第三条小道，直到风筝线全部扯了出来，当他看到远处一个小亮点，好似白天的亮光时，他压低了头，缩起了肩膀，从一个小洞里挤了出去，结果看见了滚滚流动的密西西比河！要是碰巧外面是黑夜的话，他就不可能从那个小洞里爬出去了！他还讲了他是怎样回去叫醒贝琪，把好消息告诉她，而贝琪则叫他不要用这种事情烦扰她，因为她现在很累，知道自己马上就要死了，所以想安静地死去。他描述了如何费尽口舌让她相信自己，最后帮着她逃了出去，他们是如何坐在外面，高兴得又叫又跳，然后讲到人们如何划着小艇经过，以及他是如何跟他们打招呼，告诉人们他俩的境遇以及现在饿极了的状态，他还描述了人们一开始是怎样不相信他们所说的冒险故事，"因为，"他们说，"你们在山洞所在的山谷下游五英里处。"——接着人们把他俩带到船上，划到一所住处，让他们吃了晚饭，天黑了之后还让他们休息了两三个小时才送他们回家。

天亮之前，送信的人在山洞里，根据撒切尔法官以及他身边的几个搜救者留下的线索找到了他们，并把这个好消息告诉了他们。

很快汤姆和贝琪发现，在洞中三天三夜的劳累和饥饿让他们不可能一下子就好起来，周三、周四两整天，他们都躺在床上，而且看起来越来越疲惫，越来越没有活力，周四的时候，汤姆出去稍稍活动了一会儿，周五的时候就能到镇上去了，周六几乎就完全恢复了，但是贝琪直到周日才能下床出门，她看上去就像是生了一场大病。

汤姆听说了哈克的病情，于是在周五的时候去看了看哈克，但是寡妇不准他进卧室，周六和周日的时候也不能去。在这以后，他被允许可以天天都来，但却被警告不能讲他的冒险经历，也不能提起任何令哈克激动的话题，道格拉斯寡妇还会坐在旁边监督他是否遵守了规定。汤姆在家里听说了卡迪夫山事件，也知道了那个"衣衫褴褛"的人最终在渡船码头旁边的河中被发现了，他大概是在逃跑的时候被淹死的。

汤姆在从洞中获救大概两个星期之后就开始去找哈克玩，现在他被养得结实了许多，可以听一些让人激动的话语了，汤姆想，自己倒是有一些话能让哈克感兴趣。汤姆在去的路上路过了撒切尔法官家，然后他就顺便进去看了看贝琪。法官和几个朋友跟汤姆畅聊了起来，其中有人讽刺地问他，是否愿意再去洞里冒一次险，汤姆说他倒是不介意再去一次，然后法官就说：

"嗯，我一点都不怀疑，有些人会跟你想的一样，汤姆。但是我们已经处理过了，没有人能再进洞里了。"

"为什么呀？"

"因为两个星期之前我已经将洞口用锅炉铁板封上了，还上了三道锁——只有我有钥匙。"

汤姆的脸唰的一下就变得像纸一样白。

"怎么了，孩子！喂，谁快去倒杯水来！"

水马上就拿来了，扑到了汤姆脸上。

"啊，你可算好了，刚刚是怎么啦，汤姆？"

"噢，法官，印江·乔还在洞里呢！"

第三十三章

不到几分钟的时间，消息就传开了，十二支小艇装满了人就上路去麦克杜格尔山洞了，小艇后面跟着载满了乘客的渡船，汤姆·索亚和撒切尔法官同乘一条船。

当人们打开洞口上的锁时，昏暗的灯光下，一切呈现出一片凄惨的景象。印江·乔直直地躺在地上，显然已经是死了，他的脸紧贴着门缝，看上去好像在生命的最后一刻，仍将双眼死死地盯住门外，渴求着外面世界的光亮和欢乐。汤姆被这一景象震惊了，因为在经过了山洞这一劫之后，他清清楚楚地知道印江·乔所经历的痛苦，不免觉得印江·乔很可怜，但不管怎么说，他现在能大松一口气，感到前所未有的安全了。自打他在法庭上昂首挺胸地发出自己的声音对抗这个冷血的恶棍，他的肩上就压了多么大的一个石头啊。

印江·乔的那把猎刀躺在他的身边，刀刃已经裂成两半了。支撑大门的柱子被凿通了，显然是费了很大的工夫才办到的，然而这也是无用功，因为外面的石头形成了一个天然的门框，用一把钝刀在这坚硬的石头上费工夫简直是螳臂当车，这样做唯一的损失就是刀被磨断了。但就算外面没有这样坚硬的石头他也不可能从洞里出来，因为就算柱子被砍断了，印江·乔也不可能从门缝下挤出来，他也是知道这一点的，所以他砍石头是为了找点事做，为了消磨无聊的时间，让他有所慰藉。平常的时候，你可以在大门的缝隙中找到六七截蜡烛，都是来游玩的人们留下的，但是现在一个也找不到，因为这个囚犯在死之前已经把它们全都抠出来吃掉了，他还成功捕捉到了几只蝙蝠，并把它们吃得一干二净，只留下了一些爪子，这个可怜的倒霉鬼显然是饿死的。在他附近有一个石笋已经随着时间慢慢流逝，长了好些年了，它是洞顶上的钟乳石滴下水来形成的。这个囚犯把石笋弄断了，在断面上放了一块石头，他在石头上凿了一个小凹槽，用来接水，每三分钟才会从上面的钟乳石上滴下一滴宝贵的水，那声音就像一个摆钟机械地摆着双臂，一整天才会滴满一勺水。金字塔刚建成时，这水就在滴，当耶稣被绞死，建立罗马大帝国时，这水也在滴，直到征服者威廉创建不列颠帝国，直到哥伦布出发航海，直到列克星敦屠杀还是新消息的时候，这水还在滴，现在它仍不停地坠落，等到现在所有的事也随历史化为乌有，被人们遗忘，被浓重的夜色吞噬，它仍然会一直地滴淌下去。所有的事都要有目的和使命吗？这水滴静静地流淌了五千年是不是在为这个可怜的家伙作准备呢？不管是不是，在这个倒霉的杂种凿开石头来盛接这无价之水之前，已经过了很多很多年，但到了今日，游客们来欣赏麦克杜格尔山洞时，总会长久地注视这奇异的石头和那缓缓滴下的水，在这洞中奇观中，印江·乔的杯子是首屈一指的，就算是"阿拉丁的宫殿"也不能与之媲美。

印江·乔被埋在洞口，各个镇子农场上的人们，乘着小船或者坐着马车，从七英里外的地方赶来，他们还带着孩子和各种食物，都表示能参加印江·乔的葬礼跟亲眼看到他被绞死一样满足。

这场葬礼阻止了一件事，那就是人们不再向州长请求赦免印江·乔了。很多人都在请愿书上签了字，各种讨论会上大家都涕泪横流，一群多愁善感的女人组成了请愿团，身穿葬服，跑到州长身边请求他大发慈悲，睁一只眼闭一只眼，不要管这件事了。据说印江·乔牵连着五桩命案，但是这又怎么样呢？就算他自己就是撒旦恶魔，也会有大量乱发慈悲的人联名上书，为他请愿，并从他们那永远修不好的漏水眼睛里洒出泪水来。

葬礼的第二天早上，汤姆把哈克拉到一个隐蔽的地方谈了谈。此时哈克已经从威尔士老人和道格拉斯寡妇那里得知了汤姆的冒险经历，但是汤姆发誓说还有一件事哈克不知道，他现在就想跟他谈谈这件事，哈克听完脸一下就沉下去了，他说：

"我知道是什么，你去过了二号房间，而且除了威士忌酒之外什么也没有发现，没有人告诉我这是你揭发的，但是我知道那个人肯定是你，我一听到是威士忌酒的事，我就知道是你干的，而且你没有找到钱，要不虽然你对别人闭口不言，但肯定会对我说的，汤姆，我总觉得我们永远也捞不到那笔宝藏了。"

"哈克啊，我从来没有告发过旅馆老板，你知道当我周六去野餐时他的旅店还是好好的啊，你不记得了吗，那天晚上你还在那里盯梢？"

"是呀！嘿，这听起来好像一年前的事了，就是那天晚上我跟着印江·乔去寡妇家的。"

"是你跟踪的他？"

"对——但是你别告诉别人，我觉得印江·乔还有同伙，我可不想让他们来整我，折磨我，因为要不是我，他现在都已经在得克萨斯了呢。"

然后哈克将他那天晚上的历险一五一十地告诉了汤姆，在这之前，汤姆只从威尔士老人那里听过故事的一部分。

"唉，"过了一会儿，哈克回到正事上说道，"现在谁在二号房间里发现了威士忌酒，谁就肯定会弄到那笔钱的，不管怎么说，我们都和它无缘了，汤姆。"

"哈克，那笔钱不在二号房间里！"

"你说什么！"哈克激动地认真看着同伴的脸，"汤姆，你又查到那笔钱的线索了吗？"

"哈克，钱在洞里呀！"

"再说一遍，汤姆。"

"钱在洞里！"

"汤姆，你是认真的还是在开玩笑呀？"

"认真的，哈克，我的一生都是这么认真，你愿意跟我一起去洞里把钱拿出来吗？"

"当然愿意啦！只要我们能边做记号边走，并且不迷路的话，我就愿意。"

"哈克，我们可以不费吹灰之力就拿到钱的。"

"真是太棒了！你怎么知道钱在洞里——"

"哈克，你先别急，等到我们进了洞里你就知道了，要是我们没有找到钱，我愿意把我的小鼓和我在这个世界上所有的家当都给你，老天作证，我会信守诺言。"

"好极了，一言为定，你说什么时候去呢？"

"现在就去，要是你愿意的话，你现在恢复得还行吗？"

"要进到很深的地方吗？已经过了三四天了，我也恢复了一些，但是我走不了太远，只能走一英里，汤姆，至少我觉得我只能走那么远。"

"别人走的话要走上五英里，但是哈克，我知道一条别人都不知道的近路，哈克，我会划着一条小艇把你带过去，我会让艇漂在那，然后回来的时候我自己划，你根本不必费一点力气。"

"那我们现在就出发吧，汤姆。"

"行，但是我们需要一些面包和肉，还要带上我们的烟斗，一两个小口袋，还有两三条风筝线，还要带上一些人们所说的'摩擦火柴'

这样的洋玩意，跟你说，之前我在那里时，好几次我都希望能有这玩意。"

刚过了中午，这两个孩子就趁没人"借"了一条小艇，然后马上就出发了，当他们划到离"空心洞"七英里的时候，汤姆说：

"现在你瞧，从空心洞到这里的这片悬崖峭壁看起来都是一个样——没有一处房子，没有一片森林，全都是灌木丛。但是你看见山坡塌陷的地方那块白色的地方了吗？嘿，那就是我们的一个记号，现在我们该上岸了。"

于是他们就上岸了。

"现在，哈克，就在我们站着的这块地方，你用一个钓鱼竿就能找到我钻出来的那个洞，来看看你能不能找到。"

哈克在所有的地方都搜寻了一遍，但是什么也没有发现，于是汤姆信心满满地踏着大步走进了一片浓密的漆树丛中，然后说道：

"你看！看看这，哈克，这可是最最隐秘的洞口了，你可别对别人说，一直以来，我都想当一个强盗，但我知道我需要有一个隐蔽的洞穴，但是上哪里找呢？现在我们可算有了一个啦，必须把紧嘴关，我们只能让乔·哈泼和本·罗杰进来，因为我们必须要有个帮派，要不就成不了大器，汤姆·索亚帮，这听起来很不错吧，哈克？"

"嗯，是不错，汤姆，那我们抢谁呀？"

"噢，差不多谁都能抢，拦路抢劫——通常都是这样做的。"

"抢完了然后杀了他们？"

"噢，不总是这样的，把他们关进洞里，直到拿出赎金。"

"什么是赎金？"

"就是钱，你让他们把钱全都拿出来，朋友的钱也要拿出来，然后把他们关上一年，要是一年之内都拿不出赎金来，你就把他们都杀了，强盗们通常是这样子干的。但是女人是不能杀的，你把她们关起来，但是不能杀了她们，女人们总是又漂亮又有钱，还总是害怕得要死，你就把她们的表还有其他值钱东西拿走，但是你做什么事都要脱帽行礼，注意礼貌，这世上再也没有比强盗更有礼貌的人啦——任何书里都是这样写的。然后，女人们都会爱上你的，她们在洞里待了一两个星期之后就不会再哭闹了，在这之后，你就能放她们走了，这时，你把她们赶出洞，她们转身就会回来，所有的书里都是这么说的。"

"嘿，那可真是棒极了，汤姆，我觉得这比当个海盗还好。"

"是呀，在某些方面是好些，比方说，离家和马戏团都会近些。"

说着话，一切都已准备就绪，孩子们钻进了洞里，汤姆打头，他们费了很大劲才走到通道的尽头，接着他们将接在一起的风筝线拴好，然后继续往前走，走了几步就到了泉水边，汤姆一到这里，就浑身打颤，他给哈克展示了靠在墙边的那一些小蜡烛，还跟他讲了当时他和贝琪望着烛火缥缈，直到熄灭，是什么样的心情。

此刻，山洞里一片死寂，这阴郁的气氛压迫着孩子们的神经，他们安静了下来，开始小声地说话，接下来就继续往里走，不一会儿就进到了另一个通道，一直来到了之前碰见印江·乔的那个转弯处，借着烛光，他们看见了这个地方不是个悬崖，只不过是个二三十英尺高的陡坡，汤姆悄悄地对哈克说：

"现在我要带你看个东西，哈克。"

说罢汤姆高高地举起蜡烛，然后说：

"尽量往远处看看，你能看到吗？那边，一个大石头上——用烟熏出来的。"

"汤姆，是个十字架呀！"

"那么你的二号在哪里呢？十字架下面吗？我就是在那里看见印

江·乔拿出了蜡烛，哈克！"

哈克盯着那神秘的记号看了一会儿，然后用发抖的声音说道：

"汤姆，我们从这里出去吧！"

"什么！丢下财宝就走？"

"对——不管了，印江·乔的鬼魂肯定还在这里呢。"

"不会的，哈克，他不会在这里，他的鬼魂会在他死去的地方——就在洞口处——离这里有五英里远呢。"

"不，汤姆，不是这样的，他会在财宝旁边游荡，我知道鬼魂总是这样干，你也是知道的。"

汤姆开始担心哈克说的有道理，他的脑子里充满了疑虑，但是马上就有一个主意蹦了出来，他说：

"快看这里，哈克，我们真是太蠢了啊！印江·乔的魂是不可能到一个有十字架的地方的。"

这句话说的在理，很快就产生了功效。

"汤姆，我倒没想到这个，但事实就是这样的，我们真是太幸运了，这里有个十字架，我觉得我们应该爬下去，找一找那个宝箱。"

于是汤姆先下去了，边下边砍出一些简单的凹陷当作脚踏的台阶，哈克紧随其后。在那块大石头后边，又岔开了四条小路，孩子们检查了其中的三个都没发现什么可疑之处，然后他们又看了看离石头最近的那条路，结果发现了一个小凹洞，里面铺了一个垫子，有个旧吊篮，还有一块熏肉的皮以及几根啃得干干净净的鸡骨头。但是没有发现财宝箱，于是孩子们又仔仔细细地检查了一遍，但还是一无所获，汤姆说：

"他说是在十字下面，这里可是离十字最近的地方呀，而且肯定不可能是就在大石头下面，因为石头下面结结实实的呀。"

于是他们又四下里找了一遍，结果只能是灰心丧气地坐在了那里。

哈克也搞不清个所以然，过了一会儿，汤姆说道：

"快到这来看看，哈克，这个石头的一面有些脚印还有蜡烛油，另一面却没有，嘿，你觉得这意味着什么？我打赌钱就埋在石头下面，我去挖一挖。"

"这倒不是个坏主意，汤姆！"哈克激动地说。

于是汤姆立刻掏出了他的那把正宗的巴洛牌刀，还没挖到四英尺深他的刀就碰到了木头。

"嘿，哈克！你听到了吗？"

哈克也过来又挖又刨，不一会儿的工夫，他们就把盖在上面的几块木板掀开移走了，结果在大石头下面发现了一个天然的裂口，于是汤姆钻了进去，高高地举起蜡烛，想要看个究竟，但他说看不到洞的尽头。然后他决定向前打探打探，于是他弯着腰往里面走，这条小路越走越窄，他在蜿蜒的洞中一会儿向右转，一会儿向左转，哈克也紧跟着他的步伐，过了一会儿，汤姆就走到了一个弧形的通道，接着他突然叫起来：

"我的天啊，哈克，快来看看！"

听着汤姆激动的叫喊，无疑下面就是财宝箱，它被藏在一个小石洞里，那里还放有一个空弹药桶，两支装在皮套里的枪，两三双旧鞋，一个皮腰带还有一些湿漉漉的破烂儿。

"我们终于找到啦！"哈克双手插在一堆失去了光泽的钱币中叫道，"天啊，我们有钱啦，汤姆！"

"哈克，我就觉得我们一定能找到的，这可真是太棒了，都有些难以置信了，但我们终究是找到了！伙计，咱们不要呆站在这里啦，把它搬出去吧，让我看看能不能抬得起来它。"

这箱子大概有五十五磅重，汤姆费了好大力气才把它拎起来，但却不能行动自如。

"我就知道会是这样，"他说道，"那天在闹鬼的屋里时，我就觉得他们有些吃力，看来带上这些小袋子来是正确的。"

于是孩子们很快就把钱装进了袋子里，搬到了刻有十字的岩石旁。

"现在我们来把枪和其他的东西都抬出来吧。"哈克说。

"不，哈克，就把它们放在那里，我们当强盗的时候就需要这些东西，现在就放在那里，到时候就在那里纵酒狂欢，这可是纵酒的绝佳地方呀。"

"什么叫纵酒狂欢呀？"

"我也不知道，但是强盗们总是这样做的，我们当然也会这样呀，走吧，哈克，我们在这里已经待很久了，天肯定都快黑了，而且我也饿了。等我们到小艇上时就能吃点东西，抽抽烟。"

片刻之后，他们就从漆树丛中钻了出来，警惕地向四周望了望，发现没有什么可疑的迹象，就跑到船上吃饭、抽烟了。当太阳朝着地平线渐渐西落时，他们已经撑船离开了，黄昏之中汤姆划着船掠过河岸，跟哈克欢快地谈了会儿天，在天完全黑了之后就立马上岸了。

"眼下，哈克，"汤姆说，"我们把钱藏在寡妇家柴火棚的阁楼上，然后早上我会过去，把钱查清楚后就分一分，然后我们要在森林里找个安全的地方藏起来，你就静静地待在这里看着钱，我去把本尼·泰勒的小推车偷来，要不到一分钟我就会回来的。"

说完他就跑了，不一会儿就推着车子回来了，接着他们将两小袋子钱放在车上，并在上面盖了些破布，然后拉着货物就出发了。当孩子们走到威尔士老人家门口时，他们停下来休息一会儿，就在他们准备前行时，威尔士老人从屋里出来了，看见他们就说：

"好啊，那是谁呀？"

"哈克和汤姆·索亚。"

"好极了，跟我一起来吧，孩子们，你们让大家等了好久呢，你们先去吧，赶紧呀，我来替你们推车，咦，这没有看起来的那么轻呀，里头是砖还是废铁？"

"废铁。"汤姆答道。

"我猜也是，村里的孩子们都喜欢费尽心思地找一些废铁卖到铸造厂去，不过就能挣六七毛钱，要是好好地干个活，就能挣到两倍多的钱。但人就是这样喜欢折腾，快点走吧，孩子们，快点！"

孩子们想知道到底是什么事那么着急。

"没事的，当我们到了道格拉斯寡妇家，你们就知道了。"

于是哈克内心不安地问道——因为他经常被人诬陷：

"琼斯先生，我们可什么坏事都没干呀。"

听到这话，威尔士老人笑了起来。

"嘿，我不知道，哈克，我的好孩子，我不知道是什么事呀，你跟寡妇不是好朋友吗？"

"嗯，这倒没错，不管怎么说她对我总是不错的。"

"那就好嘛，那你干吗要害怕呢？"

在哈克那反应慢半拍的脑袋里，这样的说法算不上个回答，还没想个明白呢，他就和汤姆一起，被推进了道格拉斯太太的客厅里，琼斯先生把推车靠在了门口，也进去了。

屋里灯火通明，村里有头有脸的人都被请来了，撒切尔一家在场，哈泼一家、罗杰一家、波丽姨妈、西德尼、玛丽、牧师还有报社编辑都在那里，除此之外还有很多权威的人物都来了，他们全都穿着平时最拿得出手的衣服。寡妇热情地迎进了这两个孩子，叫谁谁都会热情地对待这两个小家伙的。他们满身都是灰泥和蜡烛油。波丽姨妈看到汤姆的样子，羞愧得满脸通红，朝着汤姆又是皱眉又是摇头。然而没人能有这两个孩子一半的不自在，琼斯先生说：

"汤姆本来不在家，我刚开始不打算再找他了，但我刚好在家门口碰到了他还有哈克，所以我就急忙把他们带回来了。"

"你做得很好呀，"寡妇说道，"跟我一起来吧，孩子们。"

接着她把他们领到了一间卧室，然后说道：

"现在你们好好地洗一洗，打扮打扮，这里有两套新衣服——衬衫、袜子，样样都有。这些是哈克的——不，不用谢，哈克——琼斯先生给你买了这一套，另一套是我买的，但是你们不管穿哪一套都很合适呀，快穿上吧，我们在外面等着，穿好了就下来。"

说完她就出去了。

第三十四章

哈克说："汤姆，要是我们能找个绳子的话，我们就能溜走，窗户离地不是很高呀。"

"真见鬼！你为什么要溜走？"

"呃，我不习惯在一大堆人面前，我简直无法忍受，汤姆，我不想下去。"

"噢，好哥们儿！这没什么的呀。我一点都不介意，我会照顾好你的。"

这时西德尼上来了。

"汤姆，"他说，"姨妈整个下午都在等你，玛丽为你准备好了做礼拜的衣服，大家都在为你担心，喂，你这衣服上不是蜡烛油和灰泥吗？"

"现在，西德尼先生，你管好你自己吧，跟我说说人们这都是来做什么的？"

"寡妇在举行宴会呀，她总是这样，这会是为了威尔士老人和他的儿子们而办的，因为那天晚上他们帮她脱离了险境。喂，要是你想知道的话，我还可以告诉你点事情。"

"呵，什么事？"

"就是老琼斯先生今晚要跟大家宣布一件事，但是我早就听到他跟姨妈谈论这个秘密了，不过现在也算不上什么秘密了，每个人都知道了，寡妇当然也知道，因为她竭力地想掩饰这个事实，琼斯先生说，非要哈克出席不可，他那天大的秘密离了哈克可不行，你也是知道的！"

"什么秘密，西德尼？"

"就是哈克跟踪强盗跑到寡妇家这件事啊，我觉得琼斯先生想要制造个大惊喜，但是我跟你打赌，效果不会很好的。"

说完西德尼咯咯地笑了，他笑得很开心。

"西德尼，是你告的密吗？"

"噢，别介意是谁告的状，反正有人告状了就行了。"

"西德尼，村子里可只有一个人会如此卑鄙能做出这样的事，那个人就是你。要是你处在哈克的位置，你就会从山上溜下来，绝对不会跟别人说那里有强盗。你就只会干卑鄙无耻的事情，你眼里见不得任何人被表扬做了好事，赏你这个——用寡妇的话来说，不用谢。"汤姆一边扇西德尼耳光一边踢着把他弄到门外，"要是你敢去告诉姨妈，明天就要你好看！"

几分钟之后寡妇的客人都就座了，十几个小孩也在客厅里规规矩矩地坐在旁边的小桌子上，这可是那个国家当时的习俗。等到大家都坐定了，琼斯先生开始了他简短的演讲，主要是感谢寡妇为他和他儿子举办这一场宴会，但他还说有一个人十分谦虚——

他说了一堆话之后，突然戏剧性地说出哈克在此次历险之中所占的分量，这可是他擅长的表演方式。但是人们表现出来的惊讶很大程度上都是装出来的，要是真正的大惊喜，气氛会更加喧闹，更加活跃。然而寡妇却表现出非常吃惊的样子，而且对哈克大夸特夸了一番，以至于哈克都差点忘记了穿着新衣服还要忍受众人注视的浑身不自在的感受。

寡妇说她想收养哈克，还要供他上学，当她说到等自己攒够钱，就会让他做个小买卖，汤姆觉得时机到了，于是他说：

"哈克不需要钱，哈克自己有钱。"

听到这个有趣的"笑话"，人们本想开怀一笑，但是要保持良好的举止这一观念压在人们肩头，让他们竭力忍着，但这沉默气氛让人感到有些尴尬，于是汤姆又说：

"哈克有钱，也许你们不相信，但是他现在有很多钱，噢，你们不用嘲笑，我发誓我能证明给你们看，请稍等一分钟。"

汤姆说完立刻跑出房间，客人们你看我，我看你，心里又困惑又好奇，他们用审问的目光看着哈克，但是哈克一句话都说不出来。

"西德尼，汤姆葫芦里卖的什么药？"波丽姨妈问道，"这孩子，唉，从来都猜不透他要干什么，我从来都是——"

还没等波丽姨妈说完，汤姆就吃力地拎着他的两个口袋进了屋，然后汤姆将黄灿灿的金子哗的一下倒在了桌子上，说道：

"瞧，我说什么来着？这些钱一半是哈克的，一半是我的！"

这一下，人们都惊得目瞪口呆，所有人都瞪大了眼睛，惊得一句话都说不出来，接着大家一直要求汤姆讲讲事情的来龙去脉。汤姆说，他会讲的，而且他确实一五一十地讲了出来。故事虽长，但却相当有趣。汤姆滔滔不绝地讲着，几乎没人打断他的讲述。当他讲完时，琼斯先生说：

"我原以为我为这次宴会制造了一些小惊喜，但是现在看来什么都算不上啦，说句真心话，跟这个惊喜相比，我的那个简直是小巫见大巫。"

钱被数了一遍，加起来总共有一万两千多块，在场的人之前谁都没有一下子看到这么多钱，尽管在他们当中，有些人的家产远远超过这个数目。

第三十五章

汤姆和哈克的意外之财在这小小的圣彼得堡村子里引起了一场轰动，读者们也可以心满意足、松一口气了。如此巨大的数额，而且全都是现金，这看起来几乎让人难以置信。到处都能听到人们谈论这事，看到大家无比羡慕的眼神，称赞的神情，直到后来很多人被这种异常的激动弄得神志不清。圣彼得堡村以及它周围的村子里的每一座闹鬼的房子都被掘地三尺，根基都被挖开，人们在屋子里大搜特搜一番，都是为了找到埋藏着的宝藏，——不是孩子们在挖，而是大人们——其中一些人干得相当热火朝天。不管汤姆和哈克走到哪里，他们都被人羡慕地注视着，两个孩子记不清楚他们说的话在这之前是否很有分量，但是现在他们说的每个字都被人们宝贝着，不断重复着，他们所做的一切都被看作是意义重大的。显然，他们已经失去了平民般的生活，而且人们将他们过去的一切都作为资料搜集起来，发现他们从小就富有极大的创造力，村子里的报纸还刊登了他们的传记。

道格拉斯寡妇将哈克的钱拿出去按六分利息放债，在波丽姨妈的要求下，撒切尔法官也把汤姆的钱做了同样的处理。现在每个孩子都有收入了，而且异常巨大，一年当中的每个工作日以及半数的星期日都会有一块钱的收入。这相当于一个牧师的收入——不，实际上这只是政府许诺给牧师的收入———一般情况下，他是得不到这么多的。那个时候，一块二毛五就是养大一个孩子并供他上学所需的所有费用，而且还包括孩子的穿衣、洗澡所需的花费。

撒切尔法官十分重视汤姆，他认为若是一个普普通通的小孩是不可能有本事将他的女儿从洞中救出的。当贝琪悄悄地告诉她父亲，在学校时汤姆是怎样大义凛然地替她挨打时，法官被深深地感动了，当她说出汤姆为了替她挨打撒了谎并乞求父亲原谅时，法官称赞道，那是多么美丽的一个谎言啊，既高大又无私，真是一个有雅量的谎言——这个谎言完全有资格昂首挺胸、阔步前行，和乔治·华盛顿的那句关于斧头的受人称赞的大实话肩并着肩，永垂青史。当父亲在屋里跺着脚走来走去，说出此话时，贝琪从来都没有见过父亲如此高大如此激动。于是她立马跑去把这情况告诉了汤姆。

撒切尔法官希望汤姆将来做个大律师或者一名出色的军人。他说他打算将汤姆送到国家军事学院，之后再送到最好的法律学校学习，这样的话他既能当个大律师，又能成为一名军人。

哈克贝利·费恩现在有钱了，而且要接受道格拉斯寡妇的管教。这将他引入了上流社会——不，他是硬被拉进去的，被扔进去的——所以他现在忍受了极大的痛苦，都快承受不住了。寡妇的仆人把他收拾得干干净净的，又是给他梳头，又是让他洗澡，而且夜夜给他铺上无情的床单，干净的床单上没有一个污点、一个脏东西可以让他抱在心口窝上，当作好朋友。他吃饭的时候还必须要用餐巾、杯子和盘子，他还要读书、进教堂，还要有礼貌地讲话，说出的话就变得相当乏味。无论他走到哪里，文明的枷锁和链条都将他捆住，束缚住他的手脚。

他鼓起了勇气，忍受了三个星期的痛苦，但是一天，他终于忍不了了，人们发现他不见了。寡妇心急如焚，到处找他，找了两天两夜。人们都非常焦急，大家这里寻，那里找，还去河里打捞他的尸体，第三天早上汤姆·索亚脑子一转，跑到废弃的屠宰场后面，在几只空桶中乱扒一气，于是在其中的一只桶中，他找到了逃亡已久的哈克。他晚上就睡在那里，眼下刚刚吃完偷来的残羹剩饭，正舒舒服服地躺在桶里叼着烟管抽着烟，他蓬头垢面，身上正穿着之前让他自在快活的破烂衣服。汤姆把他叫了出来，告诉他给大家带来了多大的麻烦，然后就催促他赶紧回家，于是哈克的脸上神采奕奕的样子一下子就消失了，立刻显露出悲伤忧郁来，他说：

"不要再跟我说这个了汤姆，我已经努力了，但是没有用，没有用汤姆，我不适合那样生活，我根本习惯不了，寡妇对我很好，挺够意思，但是我就是受不了这种生活方式，她每天早上都要在同样的时间把我叫醒，还要我洗澡，给我的头发梳得油光油光的，她不准我在木棚里睡觉，我还要穿那该死的衣服，我简直都要窒息了，汤姆，不知道怎么回事，那些衣服好像一点也不透气，它们这么干净，我既不能坐在地上，也不能躺下，更不能到处打滚，我已经很久没有偷偷进过别人家的地窖了，唔，都有好几年没有了。我还必须要去教堂，真是太让人讨厌了——我恨那些狗屁不通的布道！我不能在那里抓苍蝇，也不能嚼东西，所有的周日我都要穿上鞋子，寡妇吃饭要摇铃铛，睡觉要摇铃铛，起床也要摇铃铛——所有的一切都太无聊了，叫人真是受不了。"

"嘿，每个人都要忍受这些的，哈克。"

"汤姆，这跟我有什么关系呢，我又不是别人，我一点也受不了了，这真是太可怕了，要吃东西也丝毫不费功夫，我不喜欢这种活法，我要去钓鱼，也要经过寡妇的同意，我要去游泳还要经过寡妇同意，真是见鬼，什么事都要她同意才行，哼，我还要说漂亮话，真叫人别扭死了——我非得每天到阁楼上大骂一通，嘴巴才能好受点，要不我就熬不过去了，汤姆。寡妇不让我抽烟，也不让我打哈欠，不让我大声讲话，不能伸懒腰，不能在别人面前挠痒痒——"（接着哈克讲起话来仿佛特别仇恨与委屈）——"还有啊，她整天祷告个没完！我从来没见过这样的女人！我必须要逃跑，汤姆——我必须要这样做。而且，学校就要开学了，我要不跑就非得上学不可，唉，我真是受不了这些，汤姆，瞧瞧吧，汤姆，有钱可不是这么好受的，每天就只是让人焦躁难忍，咒骂不停，你总是希望能快点死了才好。现在这里的衣服我穿上舒服，这个大桶睡着也舒服，我再也不要回去受苦了，汤姆，要不是因为那些钱，我就不会被搅进那么多的麻烦事里，现在你把我的那份钱也拿去吧，时常给我几毛钱就行了——不用太多，因为我觉得很容易到手的东西太没意思了——你现在去到寡妇那里给我求情吧，让我走吧。"

"噢，哈克，你知道我不能干这么缺德的事呀，这不公平，而且你再试着忍几天，或许你就会喜欢这种生活。"

"喜欢！嘿，这种生活就像让我长时间地待在烫屁股的炉子上一样，我不干，汤姆，我不想当个有钱人，我不想住那种憋得要死的房子，我喜欢树林，喜欢河流还有我的大木桶，我离不开它们，真是见鬼！我们本来就得到了几支枪，还有一个洞穴，这当强盗再好不过了，现在生出了这种蠢事，全部都砸了！"

汤姆此刻找到了机会——

"嘿，哈克，有钱也不妨碍我当强盗呀！"

"是吗？噢，这太好了，你是说真的吗，汤姆？"

"那当然，就像我此刻站在这里一样真，但是哈克，如果你不体面，我们就不能让你入伙，这你是知道的。"

哈克欢乐的情绪立刻被这一大火扑灭了。

"不能让我入伙，汤姆？你不是都让我当过海盗了吗？"

"是的，但是这不一样呀，一个强盗可比一个海盗气派多了——通常就是这样。在大多数的国家里，强盗总是大家显贵才能当的——就像公爵啊这样的。"

"汤姆，你一直对我都不错是吗？你不会把我踢出去的对吗，汤姆？你不会那样做的，是吗，汤姆？"

"哈克，我不想那样做，但是人们会怎么说？喏，人们会说：'哼！还汤姆·索亚帮呢！里面还有只坏老鼠！'他们指的就是你，哈克，你不想被人们那样说，我也不想让你变成那样。"

"哈克沉默了一会儿，脑袋里的两个小人不停地做着斗争，最终他说：

"唉，好吧，我就回到寡妇那里，再忍受一个月，看看我能不能受得了，要是受得了，到时候你就让我加入你们，汤姆。"

"那当然啦，哈克，就这么说定了！快走吧，老朋友，我会跟寡妇说让他对你松一点的，哈克。"

"是吗，汤姆？你会说吗？这可真是太好了，要是她能除去那几条最严格的规矩，我就偷偷地抽上几口，骂几句，拼命地熬过去。你准备什么时候成立强盗帮呀？"

"噢，快了，我们把孩子们集合到一起，然后举行入伙仪式。"

"举行什么？"

"举行入伙仪式呀。"

"入伙仪式是什么？"

"就是发誓互相帮助，就算被剁成肉酱，也绝不泄露帮派秘密。要是有兄弟被害，就把凶手全家都杀光。"

"这真好玩——太好了，汤姆。"

"嘿，我也觉得肯定很好玩，所有的入伙仪式都是在午夜举行的，而且要在你能找到的最安静，最吓人的地方——一个闹鬼的房子是再好不过的了，但是现在它们都被拆掉了。"

"嗯，但不管怎么说，半夜来举行还是不错的，汤姆。"

"是呀，还要对着棺材发誓，歃血为盟。"

"这可真不赖！嘿，这可比当海盗要好上一千倍一万倍呀。我到死都会跟着寡妇的，汤姆，到时候我成了一个名震千里的海盗，人人都会谈论我的伟大，我想她也会为把我从水沟里救出来而骄傲。"

尾声

　　故事讲到这里就该停止了，因为这是本严格的儿童书，所以必须要停在这里，要是讲一个成人的故事，还要再多讲一点，写一本成年人的小说，作者清清楚楚地知道该在何处停笔，也就是说，要写到结婚为止。但是写青少年的小说，他必须在最佳的收笔处停止。

　　本书大部分的人物都还活着，而且过得很富裕、很快乐。将来也许有一天，这些年轻人长大后的故事也值得一看，到那时我们再来看看他们长成什么样子了，因此，眼下还是不去揭露他们所过的生活比较明智。

L
I
F
T
E
D

A CULTURAL HISTORY

OF THE ELEVATOR

ANDREAS BERNARD

TRANSLATED FROM GERMAN BY
DAVID DOLLENMAYER

NEW YORK UNIVERSITY PRESS
NEW YORK AND LONDON

NEW YORK UNIVERSITY PRESS
New York and London
www.nyupress.org

Translated from German by David Dollenmayer

Originally published as *Die Geschichte des Fahrstuhls:
Über einen beweglichen Ort der Moderne* © 2006 Fischer
Taschenbuch Verlag in der S. Fischer Verlag GmbH,
Frankfurt am Main. All rights reserved by S. Fischer Ver-
lag GmbH, Frankfurt am Main.

The translation of this work was funded by Geisteswis-
senschaften International—Translation Funding for
Humanities and Social Sciences from Germany, a joint
initiative of the Fritz Thyssen Foundation, the German
Federal Foreign Office, the collecting society VG WORT,
and the Börsenverein des Deutschen Buchhandels (German Publishers and Booksellers Association)

References to Internet websites (URLs) were accurate
at the time of writing. Neither the author nor New York
University Press is responsible for URLs that may have
expired or changed since the manuscript was prepared.

Library of Congress Cataloging-in-Publication Data
Bernard, Andreas, 1969–
[Geschichte des Fahrstuhls. English]
Lifted : a cultural history of the elevator / Andreas Bernard ;
translated from German by David Dollenmayer.
pages cm
"Originally published as Die Geschichte des Fahrstuhls :
über einen beweglichen Ort der Moderne, ©2006 Fischer
Taschenbuch Verlag in der S. Fischer Verlag GmbH,
Frankfurt am Main"—Title page verso.
Includes bibliographical references.
ISBN 978-0-8147-8716-8 (hardback: alkaline paper)
1. Elevators—History. 2. Elevators—Social aspects—
History. I. Title.
TJ1370.B4713 2014
621.8'77—dc23 2013035477

New York University Press books are printed on acid-
free paper, and their binding materials are chosen for
strength and durability. We strive to use environmen-
tally responsible suppliers and materials to the greatest
extent possible in publishing our books.

Manufactured in the United States of America

Book designed and typeset by Charles B. Hames

10 9 8 7 6 5 4 3 2 1

Also available as an ebook

CONTENTS

INTRODUCTION

THE HISTORY OF TECHNOLOGY: NEW YORK, 1854

The history of the elevator begins with a piece of theater.

From May to October 1854, the mechanic Elisha Graves Otis gave repeated performances at the Exhibition of the Industry of All Nations in New York City, designed to demonstrate the effectiveness of a safety device he had invented. On September 20 of the previous year, Otis founded the E. G. Otis Elevator Company in Yonkers, New York. But having received only one order in his first seven months of business, he was happy to accept an invitation to introduce his apparatus to the public. In the Crystal Palace on Forty-Second Street (an imitation of the Crystal Palace built for the London World's Fair in 1851), he installed a platform on guide rails on which he had himself hoisted into the air before the onlookers. When the platform had risen to its maximum height, to their horror, he severed its suspension cable. But instead of plunging fifty feet to the ground, the elevator stopped short after only a few inches of travel. "All safe, gentlemen, all safe," Otis reassured the shocked fairgoers, and then explained his newly developed safety catch: a flat-leaf cart spring attached to the roof of the platform remained flexed as long as the elevator's hoisting rope was taut, but flattened out as soon as the rope is severed, engaging notches cut into the guide rails and holding the platform in place. This experiment raised public awareness of the invention and in the following years resulted in numerous orders for freight elevators. Eventually, on March 23, 1857, the first passenger elevator was installed in the retail establishment of the New York porcelain and glass dealer Haughwout and Company.

Otis's 1854 performance is regarded as the primal scene in the history of the elevator. In every encyclopedia article and handbook of the history of technology, as well as in individual monographs and collections of essays on the topic, this event serves as a demarcation line, dividing the predecessors from the canonical figures, the mere curiosities from the fully developed, production-ready apparatuses. It was only "by executing this stunt, before a gasping crowd, [that] Otis had heralded the birth of the elevator industry," declared a publication about the development of the firm.[1] At first glance, the consensus that his experiment represents a historical caesura, "one of the authentic great moments in architectural history,"[2] stands in surprising contrast to the relatively modest scale of the innovation that Elisha Otis presented in 1854 and finally patented in January 1861, three months before his death. For the New York mechanic was by no means the inventor of the basic principle of the hoisting apparatus. His only addition to the machines already in existence was the safety device whose reliability he proved by using himself as a guinea pig.

A glance at the literature on architectural history reveals just how old the practice of vertical transport of goods and people is. In classical antiquity, hoisting devices appeared in the writings of Archimedes and Vitruvius. Isolated examples of passenger elevators also cropped up between the late seventeenth century and the early nineteenth century and are regularly mentioned in histories of technology. The Jena mathematician Erhard Weigel, for example, had a house built around 1670 in which he installed an arrangement of pulleys to convey him from one of its seven stories to another. In her final years, the ailing Austrian empress Maria

Ground floor-elevator, E. V. Haughwout and Company, 488–492 Broadway, New York City, August 1970. Photograph by Cervin Robinson. From Historic American Buildings Survey, Library of Congress.

Theresa would be lowered into the Crypt of the Capuchins by means of an elevator to pray at the graves of her parents. In 1804, a freight and passenger elevator was built for a six-story cotton mill in Derbyshire, and in 1830, the English diplomat Charles Greville described in his memoirs an apparatus in the palace of the Sardinian royal couple in Genoa: "For the comfort of their bodies he has a machine made like a car, which is drawn up by a chain from the bottom to the top of the house; it holds about six people, who can be at pleasure elevated to any storey, and at each landing-place there is a contrivance to let them in and out."[3]

Thus one wonders why the history of the elevator should rest on a single, canonical incident despite the multifarious data, a heterogeneity that only increased in the decades preceding Otis's experiment. From the 1830s on, there was a multiplicity of well-documented elevator installations, both planned and completed, in Europe and the United States. By about 1830, freight elevators had been installed in numerous British textile factories, as one can read in the seventh edition of the *Encyclopedia Britannica*. In European mines, moreover, the transition from hemp ropes and chains to the much greater load-bearing capacity of the iron-wire cable, invented in 1834, led to the rise of so-called rack-transport, a conveyance we can think of as the underground equivalent of a freight elevator. From then on, ore or coal was no longer hoisted to the surface in barrels dangling from a rope, but rather in multistory compartments running on guide rails and capable of carrying a large number of containers. (As we shall see, this development at first had no influence on the vertical transport of the miners themselves.) During the same period, however, there were increasing references to passenger elevators as well. The Bunker Hill Monument in Boston, a 221-foot granite obelisk erected in 1842, contains a steam-powered elevator that can carry six passengers to an observation platform. For the 1853 opening of the Exhibition of the Industry of all Nations (the very fair at which Elisha Otis would demonstrate his invention the following year), the architect James Bogardus planned a 325-foot tower whose top could be reached by a steam-powered elevator. That same year, the New York steel producer Peter Cooper had a nine-story elevator shaft added to the company's headquarters, although the mechanism was not installed until eleven years later. And finally, *Harper's New Monthly Magazine* reported in June 1853 the imminent "introduction of a steam elevator" into private homes in New York, by means of which "an indolent, or fatigued, or aristocratic person" could have himself conveyed to the upper floors.[4]

One thing becomes clear from all these projects and installations: the dispersed and untidy beginnings of the elevator's history cannot be easily consolidated into a unified foundational narrative. Elisha Otis's "All safe, gentlemen, all safe" is less the "incunabular maxim of the modern passenger elevator"[5] than a single voice in a mighty chorus of mid-nineteenth-century mechanics. So how did his 1854 experiment achieve its unparalleled status? What was so epoch-making about Elisha Otis's invention if even a recently published official company history states that his elevator in the New York Crystal Palace followed "already existing models": "a platform set between vertical guide rails and raised and lowered on a rope wound around an overhead drum, the drum turned by belting that looped across the factory floor to the central, continuously turning steam engine."[6] Thus by 1854, both the propelling force and the mechanism itself were already well-known elements of the apparatus. The decisive difference, the detail that transformed scattered instances of the use of hoisting devices primarily for freight into the passenger elevator—an all but obligatory installation in every multistory building—consisted solely of Otis's invention of the automatic safety catch. As one historian of the elevator put it, "Although people had been building hoists for at least two thousand years before that, their hoists had the serious fault of falling to the bottom should the lifting cable break. But Mr. Otis invented something that no one had ever seen before. He built a hoist equipped with an automatic safety device to prevent the car from falling."[7]

In light of the unanimous opinion that the real history of this means of conveyance begins only with Otis's emergency brake, it is worthwhile to direct our attention to contemporary reactions to the event. In hindsight, the elevator experiment in the Crystal Palace appears to be the celebrated centerpiece of the Exhibition of the Industry of All Nations. In a 1911 biographical sketch in honor of the hundredth anniversary of Elisha Otis's birth, his son Charles Otis re-marked that the demonstration had been "one of the most interesting and attractive in the Fair," a judgment that continued to hold sway in the following decades.[8] Even the most recent publication on the history of the Otis Company states that by the end of the fair, the demonstration had "long since eclipsed the bigger show it was part of."[9] Apparently, the public was already aware of the historical dimensions of the scene.

However, if one sets out to look for evidence of the demonstration in New York newspapers and magazines between May and October 1854, a different picture emerges. While the *New York Times* carried almost daily reports on the Exhibition of the Industry of All Nations following its ceremonious reopening on May 1 (it was closed during the winter of 1853–1854), including enthusiastic full-page articles about main attractions such as the hot air balloon ascent from the fairgrounds on June 9,[10] not a single line was devoted to the epoch-making event in the Crystal Palace. One must comb painstakingly through the archives to find any trace whatsoever of the experiment. In its issue of June 10, 1854, in a sidebar entitled "Crystal Palace Notes," *Scientific American* presented some novelties to be found in the fair's "machine arcade." Between appreciations of a cigar rolling machine and a whaling harpoon, mention is made of a "new and excellent platform elevator, by Mr. Otis, of Yonkers, N.Y. . . . It is worked by steam power, and operates like some of the elevators in cotton factories. It has a plain platform, which runs up and down on guides. . . . It is self-acting, safe, and convenient."[11] There was no mention of the safety device or its spectacular demonstration. In the major American daily newspapers and magazines, the 1854 event showed up only in two marginal locations. In addition to the *Scientific American* article, a brief report appeared on May 30, 1854, in the *New York Daily Tribune*, which mentioned the daring of the inventor "who, as he rides up and down the platform occasionally cuts the rope by which it is supported."[12] No further contemporary traces can be found (just as there were no obituaries of Elisha Otis in 1861). Thus it is no exaggeration to say that the demonstration in the Crystal Palace, that "authentic great moment in architectural history," went almost completely unnoticed by the public.

If one sets out to trace the contemporary perspective on the emergence of the elevator in the United States between 1850 and 1880, one is more likely to discover a different foundational narrative. Up to the beginning of the twentieth century, every account of the elevator's history credits another mechanic with a similar-sounding name, Otis Tufts, with its invention, although he is almost forgotten today. In 1859, Tufts patented an apparatus called a "Vertical Railway" or "Vertical Screw Elevator." It was the first to have a completely enclosed cab, propelled by a twenty-inch-wide steam-driven iron screw running through its center.[13] In the same year, the only examples ever produced of this slow and costly but extremely safe elevator were installed in the Fifth Avenue Hotel in New York City and the Continental Hotel in Philadelphia. While the proprietors of the Haughwout store had Elisha Otis's first passenger elevator of 1857 removed three years after its installation because the public refused to accept it,[14] the two elevators built by Tufts remained in service into the 1870s and for a while transformed the hotels into overrun tourist attractions.

It is instructive to realize how definitively the earliest texts on the history of the elevator ascribed the pioneering role to the Boston inventor, hailed after his death in November 1869 as "one of the most successful inventors of the last thirty years."[15] In 1880, the *American Architect and Building News* began its extensive article "Notes on Elevators" by remarking how recently these "now indispensable conveniences" were born. "Although steam freight-hoists have been known for forty years, it is about twenty since the first passenger-elevator or 'vertical railway,' as it was called, was constructed by the late Otis Tufts. . . . This cumbrous and costly apparatus kept the field to itself for some time."[16] Two years later, Sloane Kennedy, writing for *Harper's Monthly*, made the not quite accurate claim to be the first historian of the new means of conveyance: "The story of the invention of the passenger elevator has never up to this time been told, and the present paper is therefore a new chapter in the history of inventions."[17] He too regarded Tufts's role as beyond question: "It is to the brilliant genius and energy of the Boston inventor (now deceased) that the credit is due of inventing and constructing the first passenger elevator in the world driven by steam power."[18] The name Elisha Otis appears in Kennedy's essay only once, in a sentence about "other early inventors and patentees of portions of elevator machinery."[19] His emergency brake, *the* decisive watershed in the canonical history of the elevator, was in 1882 still considered an inessential addition. Otis Tufts was the definitive historical figure, an opinion still held in the following decades. Thus the *New York Times* included the "vertical railway" (not the "elevator") in an 1891 article on epoch-making inventions of the nineteenth century, and one of the largest elevator manufacturers in Chicago, when queried in 1903 about the early history of his product, answered, "The first elevators for use as passenger lifts, of which I have any knowledge, were the screw-elevators built by Otis Tufft [*sic*], of Boston, in 1859."[20]

We need to grope our way back to the turning point at which a figure like Otis Tufts slipped into the background and the currently accepted foundational narrative began to take hold. When and why did an experiment that for fifty years was perceived as a subsidiary anecdote at best metamorphose into an epoch-making moment? How is it that for decades, all research on the history of the elevator referred to an event for which, because of the absence of contemporary interest, there is hardly any evidence? (In fact, it was falsely dated time and time again: according to Jeannot Simmen and Uwe Drepper, Otis's experiment took place "in the New York Crystal Palace in 1853,"[21] and Jean Gavois also wrote that "Otis demonstrated his safety elevator

Otis Elevator Company plant, main building. Photograph by Wurts Brothers. Courtesy of the Milstein Division of United States History, Local History and Genealogy, New York Public Library, and the Astor, Lenox, and Tilden Foundations.

. . . in 1853."[22]) Without doubt, the ex post facto valorization of this primal scene has to do first and foremost with the business interests of the world's largest producer of elevators. From the 1870s onward, Otis Brothers and Company, the business founded by Elisha Otis's two enterprising sons, developed into the leading manufacturer of elevators. With the founding of the Otis Elevator Company in 1898, it absorbed its fourteen leading American competitors.[23] In addition to its monopoly of elevator production, the company was also intent on establishing historiographic hegemony over the apparatus. It is no accident that the historical account that first places the experiment in the Crystal Palace at the center of the elevator's history was written by Elisha's son Charles. In 1911, he declared his intention to replace the "kindly intentioned but somewhat inaccurate notices"[24] honoring the hundredth anniversary of the worldwide enterprise's founder with the true story. His account included a minute depiction of the demonstration that had excited so little notice in 1854 and declared it to be the birth of the passenger elevator. Otis Tufts, on the other hand, put in an appearance as a mere epigone who adopted the promising invention of Elisha Otis and wheedled the hotel owners of New York and Philadelphia into buying his shoddily constructed machines (Charles Otis mentioned a serious accident in the Continental Hotel, an incident for which no other evidence exists).

The influence of this text on the historiography of the elevator is obvious from the fact that after 1911, there was hardly a mention of the elevator's origins that did not begin by repeating the story of the event in the Crystal Palace.[25] At the same time Otis Tufts, whose contribution to elevator construction was by no means restricted to the exotic "Vertical Screw Elevator,"[26] was downgraded to a transient bit player of the early years. The most important producer of the conveyance was now regarded as its inventor as well, and one can trace how this narrative was cemented in place in the course of the twentieth century—especially, of course, by the Otis Company itself, whose publications in any case constitute a considerable part of the historical literature. On the 125th anniversary of the founding of the E. G. Otis Elevator Company, the firm even printed up a facsimile newspaper with imaginary historical articles, thereby creating out of whole cloth the contemporary interest in Otis's experiment that in truth did not exist. Under a masthead reading "New York, 1854" and in a layout reminiscent of the *New York Times*, one could read about a "young inventor" presenting his safety elevator "in a daring exhibition before thousands of viewers." "This reporter noted that as the platform went up, without question, everyone in the hall stopped to see what would happen next."[27] This "anniversary edition" also contained a striking iconographic embellishment of the event: next to the article was an illustration that was often reproduced in subsequent years. It purported to supply an impression of the excitement in the Crystal Palace.

According to the historian of the Otis Company, this illustration was based on a sketch made during the demonstration by an artist for the *New York Recorder*.[28] In all the older literature about the experiment, however (including that issued by the Otis Company itself), the event was sketched in a significantly more modest way. We are justified in assuming that the most famous and by now "official" illustration of the experiment was in fact drawn in 1978. The teeming, astonished onlookers as well as the assistant who has just severed the suspension cable are inventions of the recent past.

It is no surprise that the largest manufacturer of a technical apparatus has an interest in retroactively claiming credit for its invention. In the course of the last hundred years, however, the stage-managed event in the Crystal Palace was so consistently and unanimously depicted as the elevator's primal scene that there had to have been more at work in this consensus than just a public relations strategy of the company. It had to do, rather, with the question of how to construct a foundational narrative in the history of technology. If it is precisely this event among the dozens of possible candidates between 1840 and 1860 that establishes itself as the elevator's beginning, if after half a century of neglect it still retains the power to suppress competing dates, then one has to wonder what has made it so persistent. One answer lies perhaps in the way Otis's invention is presented. The theatricality of the demonstration (however unimpressed contemporary witnesses may have been) places this contribution to the elevator's development above the crowd of equally important but less dramatic turning points, such as the first installation of guide rails in a factory or the first construction of a completely enclosed cab. The concentrated format of a public demonstration satisfies the yearning for a clean, unambiguous beginning, a yearning endemic to the historiography of technology. The dramaturgy of the experiment in the Crystal Palace also contributes to this outcome: Otis focused his demonstration of the innovation on a radical moment—the assumed fatal severing of the

Illustration from Otis
Elevator Company,
*The Otis Bulletin: Special
125th Anniversary Edition*,
September 20, 1978.

Illustration from Otis
Elevator Company,
The First Hundred Years
(New York, 1953).

cable—and thus accommodated the interest of historians in locating the beginning in a single, visible moment. One must pay attention to the widely reproduced illustration of the experiment, drawn long after the event. It attempts to encompass precisely the historical moment: the cable has been severed, the witnesses freeze, yet the platform does not fall. Why then has the demonstration at the New York industrial exhibition established itself as the primal scene? Not because it is in fact clearly identifiable as the beginning, but rather for aesthetic reasons—because it makes the beginning tellable. Otis provides an appropriate narrative for the birth of the elevator, a classically Aristotelian narrative, in fact: the hero's rise into the air in the Crystal Palace moves toward a literal peripeteia, a tragic reversal[29]—until the safety catch interrupts his fall.

The epochal status of the event, at any rate, illustrates the discursive mechanisms by which the "origin of a technical fact" comes into being, to use the words of the historian of science Ludwik Fleck.[30] In his study of syphilis research around 1900, Fleck spells out how years of collective and anonymous work on serological experiments were retroactively attributed to a single investigator. A process of countless laboratory corrections and adjustments that in the end led to the reliability of the test was transformed into a datable act, an individual invention (the "Wassermann reaction" of 1906) in order to ensure a clear historical narrative. The "straight path to knowledge,"[31] which Fleck's discourse analysis exposes as a fiction, is preserved by all histories of the elevator that begin in the Crystal Palace in 1854; out of the "thinking collective" of mechanics in the middle of the nineteenth century, a single name and a single event are distilled. But the closer one examines this seemingly clear distillate, the cloudier it becomes.

INVENTING THE MULTISTORY BUILDING

In the second half of the nineteenth century, at the beginning of the restructuring process known as the era of urbanization, the architecture of residential and commercial buildings changed in fundamental ways. Up to that point, a building as a rule represented a self-contained, straightforward entity with at most one or two stories above the ground floor. As the autonomous sphere of an extended family and the domestic servants included in its collective, the "house" evoked, for instance, that sentimental image of the "integral house" that the cultural historian Wilhelm Heinrich Riehl attempted to breathe life into one last time in his well-known work *Die Naturgeschichte des Volkes* (*Natural History of the German People*) of 1854.[32] But what appeared there as the evocation of a lifestyle already in the process of dissolution—in view of the first "sad, bleak apartment blocks of our large cities"[33]—lost its significance entirely by the end of the century. Riehl's defense of an economic and social community under one roof became irrelevant to the extent that the house intended for a single family all but disappeared in the burgeoning cities, to be replaced by a new type of building.

In several respects, the new five- or six-story tenement houses that became a defining architectural feature of European cities between 1860 and 1900 began to extend and diversify the image of the house. For one thing, their vertical extension led naturally to the individual building being divided into a multiplicity of units housing a great variety of residents, a practice that dismembered the model of an "integral house" once and for all. For another, this extension pointed in a less visible direction: the simultaneous appearance of advances such as central heating, sewerage, intercoms, elevators, and, a little later, electricity ensured that from the 1870s on, the interior of the building was crisscrossed by a complex of pipes, cables, and shafts. Beneath the visible surface there arose an invisible network that organized the circulation of energy, data, and people. In the end, this process of mechanization and electrification made it necessary for the formerly independent unit of the house to become networked with its surroundings, for only the connection to external power sources and centrally regulated reservoirs and generators ensured the functionality of its technical installations. The demarcations between the individual buildings of a residential neighborhood became more and more porous.

The elevator played a major role in this profound reorganization of the building. Even the creators of the first multistory structures in New York and Chicago emphasized that above a certain number of floors, this means of conveyance was the basic prerequisite for further increases in building height. The installation of the elevator propelled the expansion and diversification of the building, and not just in the obvious sense that it is what made buildings of more than five or six stories possible in the first place. In the form of a cab closed to view from outside and moving through the middle of the building, it created a novel, hermetically sealed conduit. One of the most important characteristics of modern apartment and office buildings is that they consist to a large extent of previously unknown semi-public spaces such as stairwells and corridors. Suddenly, in the traditionally encapsulated family sphere of the residential building, it was possible to encounter strangers almost anywhere, and such encounters became even more focused in the elevator. Wilhelm Heinrich Riehl saw the incipient decline of the "integral house" in the contraction of the once generously proportioned communal spaces of urban middle-class houses "to a tiny corner."[34] The multistory apartment and office buildings that were standard by the end of the nineteenth century no longer had such spaces. The floor plan was divided into private residential or commercial parcels on the one hand and spaces devoted solely to traffic circulation on the other—a fragmentation vehemently criticized a century after Riehl by Gaston Bachelard in *The Poetics of Space*: "In Paris there are no houses, and the inhabitants of the big city live in superimposed boxes."[35] And precisely that fact raises a question that we will revisit in the following chapters: to what extent did the appearance of the new architectural element "elevator" (a shaft that in equal measure domesticates and obscures verticality, a conveyance in which for the first time one can reach the upper levels of a building without the slightest effort, a cab that irritates its occupants with its cramped interior but is invisible from the outside) determine the organization and perception of multistory buildings or, especially in European cities, massively reshape an already existing order?

Emerging in New York in the 1850s, the elevator became established at different rates of speed in Europe and the United States. In the United States it was already a standard feature of large East Coast hotels by the early 1860s,[36] and by 1870 was installed in New York's Equitable Life Building (its first use in a multistory office building[37]), but this means of conveyance remained almost unknown in Europe well into the late 1860s, at the most occurring as a purely hand-operated device for moving freight between floors in a factory. Only with the development of the extremely safe hydraulic elevator first exhibited at the 1867 Paris World's Fair (with its cab attached to a piston located below ground level, which pushed the elevator upwards when filled with water under pressure) did the apparatus begin to find widespread use in France and soon thereafter in Germany. For instance, the acceptance of the hydraulic technique led to the installation of passenger elevators in Berlin hotels and commercial buildings in the 1870s. The earliest articles on elevators in engineering and construction journals, however, revealed how unusual the device still was. An 1874 article titled "Hydraulic Elevators for Passengers and Light Freight" in Berlin, for example, listed every single building equipped with the new conveyance.[38] "Up to now," according to an 1887 monograph, "the number of passenger elevators installed in Berlin is small. The majority are in hotels, a smaller number in buildings with many offices, etc., and finally, a very small number in purely residential buildings."[39] In large American cities of the time, there were hardly any multistory residential or commercial buildings that could get by without an elevator. In Germany, by contrast, the vertical transportation of people remained an exception well into the 1890s, when elevators operated either directly or indirectly by hydraulics were replaced by installations with electric drives.[40]

Besides this difference in the speed with which elevators proliferated, there was also a difference in their location within buildings. In New York, Boston, and Chicago, the elevator soon functioned as the core of the building. From the 1870s on, every new multistory building was constructed around an elevator shaft. Open stairwells retrofitted with elevators, even today still frequently to be found in apartment buildings in Paris or Vienna, virtually disappeared in the United States by the end of the nineteenth century. Thus in large American cities, the verticality of the buildings was determined much sooner by the conduit of the elevator. In *Delirious New York*, Rem Koolhaas provides a particularly vivid image of this essential status of the elevator shaft when he describes the demolition of the old Waldorf-Astoria Hotel, beginning in 1929, and the start of construction on the Empire State Building on the same site. At a time when very few German buildings existed with a floor plan clearly determined by the elevator, it had long been utterly standard that the elevator shafts constituted the center of a building in the birthplace of this means of transport. "The destruction of the Waldorf is planned as part of the construction. Fragments that are useful remain, such as the elevator cores that now reach into the as yet immaterial floors of the Empire State." The supervising architect even mentioned the elevators in his autobiography, as quoted by Koolhaas: "We salvaged four passenger elevators from the old building and installed them in temporary positions in the new framework."[41]

The inseparable link between the rise of the elevator and the vertical extension of the building, especially in the United States, is well documented in the literature on the history of high-rise buildings. As early as 1891, a New York architectural historian noted, "The perfection of elevator work is the one fundamental condition for high buildings,"[42] and in the first monograph on the origin of the skyscraper, Francisco Mujica writes this lovely sentence: "The entire history of skyscrapers contains an homage to the inventors of the elevator."[43] This homage would need to point out that in the 1850s and 1860s, it would have been perfectly possible to construct hotels and commercial buildings with more than the prevailing six-story limit, but hotel guests or renters could not be expected to climb an even greater number of stairs. The author of an 1897 article addressed the increasing lack of space in the business districts of Manhattan: "Limited as to the ground, business sought in the air. It had to be done; but how? To pile up more stories on the sixth was useless, since no one would climb up to them. The problem became mechanical, and the financier and the architect were as helpless as the mason." The solution to the problem took the form of an automatic means of conveyance: "The passenger elevator was the solution. . . . It was to be to modern building what the steam-engine is to transportation, a revolutionary agent."[44]

In New York around 1875, the elevator enabled an increase in building height to about eleven stories. A series of insurance and newspaper buildings were constructed during those years and dubbed "elevator buildings," enshrining their *sine qua non* in their very name. Eleven or twelve stories, however, was their vertical limit, since for any additional stories the walls of the lower floors would have to be so massively expanded and stabilized that any gain in space and rent would be negligible. "There came a time," continued the same article on the commercial buildings of Manhattan, "when to go higher with the solid masonry method was to lose more income at the bottom than was won on the top."[45] This dilemma was famously solved at the beginning of the 1880s, in the wake of the great Chicago fire, by the development of steel frame construction, which greatly increased the potential number of floors by transferring the load-bearing function of masonry walls to a steel skeleton.[46] For a period of ten to fifteen years, the elevator machinery itself—the previously obligatory hydraulic apparatus—suddenly seemed to be the limiting factor. Thanks to steel frame construction, it would already be possible to construct a fifty-story building,[47] but the hydraulic technique imposed a limit of eighteen to twenty floors. "To build higher than that would be entirely uneconomic, due to the slowness of elevators and the excessive space occupied by them and their voluminous machinery."[48] In the end, it was electrically powered elevators with their more modest space requirements and improved speed (from 5 feet per second of hydraulic elevators to 9.8 to 16 feet per second within a decade[49]) that cleared the way for almost limitless increases in building height, a jump whose extent is suggested by the fact that in the 1890s, the highest building in the world was the twenty-story Masonic Temple in Chicago, but the Woolworth Building, completed in 1913, stood at fifty-five stories. In the twentieth-century literature on the history of architecture, there have been frequent debates about which element—the elevator or steel frame construction—was decisive for the rapid increase in vertical expansion. Even if one doesn't adopt the consistent position of the earliest historian of the skyscraper, who accords the elevator exclusive credit for this development ("It is the elevator that is the initial cause of the skyscraper. Steel skeleton is a *consequence* of the elevator"),[50] there is no question of the fundamental role played by this means of conveyance. No one has expressed this more succinctly than a German commentator on the opening of the Woolworth Building: "It must be admitted that the possibility of a fifty-five-story building is founded primarily on the perfect operation of passenger elevators. (Climbing to the top floor on steps with risers of 4.7 inches would take about ¾ of an hour!)"[51]

It is not the ambition of this book to be either solely a study of technical and architectural history or an intrinsically literary study that extracts the "motif of the elevator" from fictional texts. Rather, it will attempt to use a

A donkey, wearing a harness and reins held by a man, in front of an elevator inside a building, Chicago, 1903. Courtesy of the Chicago History Museum.

heterogeneous corpus of texts that includes novels and plays as well as legal regulations, articles from professional construction engineering journals, medical treatises, and handbooks of public hygiene to come to grips with what one might call the "imaginative organization" of the building within a particular time period. Among my questions are these: How was the collective image of multistory residential and commercial buildings changed by the element "elevator" in the decades before and after 1900? What effect did the technical apparatus have on the conceivability and expressability of what happens inside the buildings, about the distribution of spaces and people? With Michel Foucault, one could call this enterprise an "archeology" of utterances about the building with respect to the elevator. In discrete cross-sections through the strata of legal, scientific, and artistic utterances, primarily between 1870 and 1930, this work hopes to illustrate the multifarious ways the elevator disrupts familiar standards for the organization and perception of buildings and how its appearance puts its stamp on the principles of building codes as well as the concerns of the hygiene movement and the topography of the urban novel. Precisely because this book is concerned not just with the history of architectonic artifacts but also with the processes of historical imagination, it is essential that its textual material include both works of fiction and nonfictional documents. The structures and limitations of an epoch's topographic imagination leave traces in equal measure in building codes and the spatial conceptions of literary texts.

I am interested in the preconditions for the possibility of judgments or fantasies about the building, and a basic impulse for this book is the suspicion that the elevator fulfills the function of such a precondition, that one can understand it as a "technical apriority" for utterances about multistory buildings. This assumption, however, has consequences for how one treats the historical material and even how one understands historiography itself. The more we direct our attention to the preconditions for what is expressible, the more problematic becomes any reconstruction of "historical truth," any recounting of "what actually happened." On the contrary, in place of the most complete possible duplication of the past, we must attempt to extract those things about an epoch that it could not tell about or reflect upon itself—since for contemporaries they were far too self-evident, constituting as they did the unshakable foundation of their own words and deeds. Thus the following analyses will not necessarily be concerned to uncover the intentional core of scientific or literary texts, but will focus rather on what one might call their "unconscious" (to use a parlous term), those unspoken parameters of perception and imagination that can reveal themselves in the most marginal places—in the introduction to a monograph, for example, or in a dependent clause in a building description. In this context, it is important to always keep in mind the imaginative category of the multistory building before the advent of the elevator, a time that could not yet conceive of a vertical shaft running right down the center of a building. For this study stands exactly at the divide between the old and the new organization of a building, a divide that opened up around 1900.

One look at how the chapters of current histories of technology are organized or how informational material is presented in historical museums reveals that the way technical innovations become established continues to be portrayed as a chronicle of triumphant progress, an unbroken series of adjustments and improvements: an apparatus that is at first imperfect and exotic becomes progressively improved, right down to the present day. Half a century ago, Georges Canguilhem countered such a strictly teleological perspective by directing attention to a completely different kind of knowledge. Although he was addressing historians of science, his words apply equally to the history of technology:

> The history of science is not a retrospective history of progress nor the depiction of outmoded stages leading to today's truth. Its aim is rather to investigate and illuminate the extent to which concepts, attitudes, or methods that appear outmoded today represented progress in their own time and the extent to which, as a result, the outmoded past remains the past of an activity that must still be called scientific.[52]

For our study of the elevator, this involves repeatedly highlighting those historic turning points when what is today obsolete or taken for granted made its first appearance and began to unleash its disruptive power. This is precisely the reason the primary emphasis of this book, with the exception of its final chapters, will be on the early history of the new conveyance, the time before 1920 or 1930. In the early years, the recalibration of the building's system was clearly evident. What Sigfried Giedion once said about the chronicler of "anonymous history" in *Mechanization Takes Command* is particularly relevant for someone writing about an object that is so omnipresent and unspectacular today (at most, only capable of provoking irritation by its spatial constriction): "He has to see objects not as they appear to the daily user, but as the inventor saw them when they first took shape. He needs the unworn eyes of contemporaries, to whom they appeared marvelous or frightening."[53] The following pages will attempt to restore to the elevator, an object that has become dull and inconspicuous in the twenty-first century, the luster of strangeness.

ACCIDENTS

With respect to Otis's 1854 experiment in the Crystal Palace, there is another decisive circumstance besides the element of theatricality. The detail that the New York mechanic added to already existing elevator designs was an element of safety and the prevention of accidents. We must return to the sequence of events in the demonstration, about which Rem Koolhaas writes, "Otis introduces an invention in urban theatricality: the anticlimax as denouement, the non-event as triumph."[54] The sentence structure of a description of the experiment by an Otis Company historian illustrates this pattern: "Those who had morbidly anticipated a leg-breaking crash, however disappointed, were nevertheless impressed with the effectiveness of the Otis safety—when, as a matter of fact, nothing happened."[55] The caesura marked by the strategically placed dash is followed by the punch line: nothing happened. Thus at the beginning of elevator history stands the elaborately staged prevention of a catastrophe, and when one asks why this experiment is retrospectively anointed a historic moment, one has to consider the central role played by the potential for accidents in the early years.

It was not just that the very first Otis safety elevator was installed in New York in the wake of a fatal accident involving the preceding apparatus (two workers died because the platform was equipped only with a manually operated catch mechanism, whose activation at the moment the cable broke would have required extraordinary presence of mind).[56] In the articles on passenger elevators in German and American journals of construction and engineering between 1870 and 1900, it is repeatedly evident that the topic of accident prevention was at the forefront of concern. Paradigmatic for the approach to this new means of transport was Franz Reuleaux's assessment in his engineering report on the introduction of indirect-hydraulic Otis elevators in Germany: "The question of the safety of an elevator whose purpose is to transport passengers is without a doubt the most important of all."[57] The possibility of an accident served repeatedly as a catalyst for both technical improvements in the apparatus and the development of legal ordinances.[58] The problematics of accidents has been extensively studied in the last few years. The lack of forewarning stands in the way of portraying them, while their identity "gets lost between the poles of what precedes and what follows"[59]—that is, between statistical prognoses and traumatic consequences. This is particularly evident in the case of the elevator, in contrast to a train or airplane. Its enclosed shaft makes the moment of the accident impossible to witness, an invisible phenomenon. The result is the complete absence of graphic depictions of elevator accidents.

What is responsible for the development of such an acute sensitivity to potential accidents in the early years of the elevator? There are two answers to this question. First, it is a reflection of the quarter century dividing the establishment of the railroad from that of the elevator, the horizontal from the "vertical railways." People were completely unprepared for the shock of the first large-scale railroad disasters. An "accident" in this sense was a completely unknown type of occurrence and led to both a semantic adjustment in the meaning of the word itself and fundamental changes in medical diagnostics and the legal system. By contrast, the extraordinary precautions surrounding the introduction of elevators attest to the fact that in the decades after 1850, the destructive potential of modern means of transportation had completely permeated the collective imagination. Second, the fear of a cable breaking and the cab plunging to the ground is connected to another field

Elevated view of ambulances backed against a sidewalk to receive people injured in an elevator accident that took place in a building at South Wells Street and West Jackson Boulevard, Chicago. A crowd of people gathered on the sidewalk nearby. Negative DN-0005645. Courtesy of the Chicago History Museum.

in which the dangers of vertical transport had long been known, namely, mining.

Beginning in the late Middle Ages, when mineshafts in Europe first reached depths of more than just a few yards, mechanisms begin to be developed to bring the mined ore up to the surface. For centuries, cable winches powered by human, equine, or hydraulic power—and from the 1780s also by steam engines—managed the vertical transport of freight. As mentioned above, from the late 1830s, that transport took place using baskets attached to rails running up the mineshafts, a technical ensemble that one could call a freight elevator.[60] In the mid-nineteenth century, at the time of the first aboveground elevators in buildings, the depth of mineshafts in the upper Harz and Ruhr regions already reached more than two thousand feet, and one can best understand how high the risk was of an accident caused by a cable break by the fact that until 1859, German mining regulations prohibited the transport of people by cable. Miners were forbidden to ride into or out of the mine in the baskets meant for freight transport. In the slanting and more shallow shafts, miners used stairs and simple ladders. In the deeper, vertical shafts, so-called man engines were in widespread use from the early 1830s. These were steam-driven pairs of reciprocating ladders moving up and down past each other in such a way as to allow the miner quick access into the shaft.[61] The reason for this method was lack of confidence in the reliability of the cables. What the inventor of the iron-wire cable, the upper Harz mining engineer Wilhelm Albert, said in 1834 about the hemp cables and chains in use up to then—"Not a quarter year went by without hundreds of cable breaks . . . being recorded"[62]—did not improve much in the following decades, as shown by the annual accident statistics in the *Zeitschrift für das Berg-, Hütten- und Salinenwesen* (Journal of mining, smelting, and saltworks). According to a "Statistical Study of Mineshaft Cables" commissioned by the Royal Central Mining Office in Dortmund, as late as 1872 no less than 19.3 percent of all 114 transport cables under its jurisdiction had suffered a sudden break during that year.[63] As a consequence, when the Prussian *Bergpolizei* (mining constabulary) in 1859 became the first such authority in Germany to permit on principle the transportation of miners in ore baskets because the increasing depth of the shafts made the use of man engines difficult, the safety regulations were extensive. Paragraph 7 of the Dortmund police ordinances for mines, for instance, stated that, "before being used for human transport, the cable, its attachment to the receptacle, as well as the latter itself, must receive a thorough daily inspection of their durability by a responsible and capable person assigned to the task, before whose eyes the cable must be slowly wound and unwound down the shaft." And paragraph 11 required that "no worker may be forced to use the cable and a refusal to do so can never constitute grounds for dismissal."[64] In the 1860s and 1870s, most other German states followed Prussia's example, and one can trace in the pages of the *Zeitschrift für das Berg-, Hütten- und Salinenwesen* how extensive was the catalog of ordinances that every mine owner had to comply with if he wanted to obtain police permission to transport miners by cable.[65]

What this glance at the history of vertical transport in mines makes clear is that the remarkable focus on the possibility of a cab falling in the early years of the elevator was largely due to the precarious nature of the cables in mines and became more and more acute in the course of the nineteenth century. That the staged prevention of a fall, the presentation of an automatic braking device, retrospectively became the primal scene of elevator history is inseparable from this deeply ingrained mistrust of the cable, reinforced by numerous mining accidents. The suspension of containers for vertical transport represented a latent danger, and for an invention such as the passenger elevator to become accepted above ground, it first had to explicitly guarantee the safety of the unstable principle of suspension. It is important to note, however, that this "trauma of the cable" was more pronounced in Europe than in America. Since there was hardly any industrial mining to speak of in the United States before the first California gold rush in 1849,[66] the elevator cable was regarded with considerably less suspicion than in Germany, England, or France. How far-reaching the consequences of these differences in mining history were for the spread of the aboveground means of conveyance can be seen above all in the fact that the steam-powered elevators suspended from two to four cables that were standard in the United States until the rise of the Otis hydraulic elevator were used in Europe solely for carrying freight. Not until the direct-hydraulic technique dispensed entirely with the suspension principle of the cable did the passenger elevator begin to catch on. Here the cab is mounted directly on the drive piston. Ludwig Hintz gave a characteristic summary of this development in his *Handbuch der Aufzugstechnik* (Handbook of elevator technology): "The feeling of not hanging in the air on cables but standing on a column—of having a support directly beneath you that goes right down to the ground—had something very reassuring for apprehensive souls."[67]

When one tries to clarify the role played by mining in the early history of the elevator, one finds an interesting simultaneity under and above ground. The prevention of a cab fall by a reliable catch mechanism—according to an Otis Company history an accomplishment that "promised to make the hoist safe for the first time in 2,000 years"[68]—was also one of the central concerns of European mining engineers in the mid-nineteenth century. The voluminous *Leitfaden zur Bergbaukunde* (Guide to mining engineering) of 1873 stated in retrospect that between 1850 and 1870, "There is hardly anything in mining engineering that produced a greater number of experiments and inventions than the search for a catch mechanism to protect transport in mines from the danger of a broken cable."[69] Apparently the first ore baskets to be equipped with an automatic catch mechanism went into operation in an anthracite mine in Liège, Belgium, in 1848,[70] and in the quarter century that followed, countless variations and improvements were made to this safety device in European mining centers. Their complete reliability became all the more essential with the increase in the use of the cable to transport personnel as well as ore. The basic design of these safety devices was identical to that of the Otis elevator in the Crystal Palace. As a German mining engineer described it in 1868, "All known catch mechanisms so far follow the same principle: in the case of a cable break, the transport receptacle is designed to lock onto the rails or onto a special rod.[71] (In fact, the inventor of one of these devices, a mining technician named Philipp Lohmann, demonstrated the reliability of his catch mechanism in 1867 in exactly the same daring way as Elisha Otis thirteen years previously. He "was so convinced of the reliability of his invention that he placed himself and his wife on the platform and then severed the cable."[72] In contrast to the New York event, the spectacle in the municipal park in Essen did not become a date of world-historical significance but was consigned instead to oblivion, except for this mention in a 1902 history of mining in Westphalia.)

The Otis Company archives give no hint as to whether in the early 1850s Elisha Otis might have had knowledge of the achievements of European mining engineers. There is no documentary evidence of a relation between the beginnings of the elevator in New York—with the apparently singular invention of the catch mechanism—and the world of mining. In Germany, however, this relation is evident and frequent, and not just in the early dread of the suspension cable that hindered the introduction of passenger elevators. In the 1870s and 1880s, one can observe a productive relationship between underground and aboveground vertical transport, for during this time, building elevators also profited from the intensive efforts of mining engineers to improve the catch mechanism. One must again call to mind the fundamental difference in the number of subterranean and aboveground shafts in Germany. Around 1880, the highest elevator-equipped buildings did not exceed 80 feet, while the depth of shafts in the largest mines was already close to 2,600 feet. The cable-mounted ore baskets reached a speed of 26 to 33 feet per second at this time,[73] while even the most modern hotel passenger elevators still moved between floors at a speed of 1.6 feet per second.[74] Against the background of these comparative statistics, it is clear that the safety of aboveground elevator cabs could be quickly perfected. In the mines, the engineering challenge was to develop complex catch mechanisms that would gradually decelerate the furious plunge of an ore basket following a cable break so as not to endanger the stability of the guide rails or the safety of the miners. To reliably secure a building elevator moving at a speed twenty times slower, the techniques available at the time were completely adequate. In the *Zeitschrift für das Berg-, Hütten- und Salinenwesen* one occasionally finds evidence of the perspective of mining engineers on cab safety above ground. As professionals, they had a hard time taking this topic seriously. After witnessing the demonstration of an advanced catch mechanism developed explicitly for building elevators, one of them commented succinctly that the mechanism "may be appropriate for hotel elevators and shafts of negligible depth."[75] In the view of a professional mining engineer, aboveground elevator shafts were nothing but insignificant "shafts of negligible depth."

As a consequence of this wealth of knowledge about how to ensure the safety of ore baskets in mines, the focus of elevator accident prevention clearly shifted around 1880. The subsiding concern about a cab falling after a cable break was more and more overshadowed by another worry, namely, people falling into inadequately secured elevator shafts. Optimized catch mechanisms, even activated by nothing more than increased cab speed or excessive stretching of the cables,[76] ensured the safety of elevator use from the 1880s on. Statistics in construction journals and the brochures of elevator manufacturers both demonstrate that travel in an elevator was many times safer than travel by horizontal means of transportation,[77] and that even using a stairway carried greater risk for pedestrians.[78] In any event, all published reports agreed that in Europe before the First World War, there was in fact only a single elevator accident in which the passengers were killed explicitly by the fall of the cab, and this incident did not even involve the cable suspension so long regarded with suspicion. It was the otherwise highly reliable direct-hydraulic technique that precipitated the worst elevator accident in history in the Grand Hotel in Paris on February 24, 1878, a mishap in which three people died.[79] A broken casting connecting the piston to the undercarriage of the elevator at first caused the cab carrying the building superintendent, the elevator operator, and a guest to be pulled to the top of the shaft by the counterweight. There the cab's overhead suspension was ripped from its mounting and the cab plunged to the ground in free fall.[80]

The really dangerous part of an elevator installation, however, was less the cab itself than the access to it. The sliding doors that are obligatory today and "when they open disappear somewhere in the wall"[81] did not appear until after the Second World War; in the 1880s, manually operated hinged or folding doors of wire mesh on each floor still frequently misled careless passengers wishing to enter the cab into opening them and falling into the shaft. The Berlin elevator manufacturer Flohr boasted in a 1900 company publication of being the first to find a solution to this problem and portrayed the risky situation in the early years as follows:

> Until the year 1886 [when Flohr elevators were first equipped with a shaft door-locking mechanism], all elevators were manufactured with unsecured entrance doors. The frequent mishaps that resulted—people falling into the shaft through entrance doors that were too easy to open or being struck and killed by an arriving elevator—made the coordination of the shaft doors with the elevator cab an urgent necessity, so that they could open only when the cab had reached the same height as the doors, and on the other hand, would only allow the cab to resume its travel once they had closed.[82]

The reliable establishment of such "coordination" between cab and shaft doors represented the most urgent task of safety engineering in elevator manufacture in the early twentieth century. In the mechanically functioning hydraulic elevators of the 1880s and 1890s, this linkup usually consisted of a shackle that barred the door on the inside as soon as the cab left the floor in question. As one can regularly read in the news section of construction and engineering journals, however, this method was notoriously unreliable and led again and again to fatal falls into the shaft. This "most urgent problem" of elevator safety, "the elimination of the possibility of operating the elevator with the shaft doors open as well as the elimination of the possibility of opening the doors while the elevator is in motion,"[83] Kennedy, Sloane W. "The Vertical Railway." *Harper's Monthly*, November 1882 was not solved until the late 1890s with the advent of electric controls, for electric contacts established a reliable link between the door's locking device and the position of the cab, as Ludwig Hintz explained in his 1908 *Handbuch der Aufzugstechnik*:

> The principle of all these door-locking devices consists in installing contacts on the door that are connected to the power line of the cab controls or, less frequently, of the motor, in such a way that the contacts are only closed, thus completing the circuit, when the door is shut, and that when the door is opened, the circuit is broken.[84]

With the almost universal adoption of electrically powered elevators by the early twentieth century, all traces of this kind of accident disappeared. The threat to users of an elevator shaft becoming a deadly abyss in the middle of a building in the absence of a door-locking device was eliminated for good by the simple binary nature of an electric circuit: closed or open. For that reason, elevator fatalities in the twentieth century occurred primarily as workplace accidents. By the time of a 1911 congress for domestic hygiene in Dresden, Germany, a speaker could say, "As statistics show, elevator accidents can be traced without exception to recklessness or carelessness during installation or repair."[85] The only monograph on this subject ever published in Germany was intended only for potential elevator personnel. Georg Urban's *Unfallverhütung im Fahrstuhlbetrieb* (Accident prevention in elevator operation), published in the middle of the First World War and addressed to the large number of "young, untrained, and female workers"[86] in hotels and offices in wartime Germany, listed the dangers that could occur during installation, servicing, and repair of the machinery, when all safety devices were turned off. The eventuality that a passenger could be the victim of an elevator accident was hardly even mentioned in Urban's work. Its central concern (on fifty-two of its seventy-four pages), always with reference to workplace accidents, continued to be the improvement of the automatic locking devices for the shaft door. The protection of elevator workers prompted the author to invent a device that was destined to play a part in countless action and horror movies: the trap door in the ceiling of the cab. Apparently for the first time in the history of the elevator, Urban demanded that the "ability to open the roof" be obligatory, allowing installers and service personnel to work in the interior of the shaft without risk of accident.[87]

THE BREACH THROUGH THE BUILDING
ORGANIZING THE VERTICAL

A THEORY OF THE ELEVATOR SHAFT

An early essay on multistory office buildings spoke of the "simplicity of arrangement" that should be observed when organizing their spaces in the future. "From the point where the elevators deliver in each story," the author declared,

> the door of every office on that floor should be visible; or, at least the corridors leading thereto should be plain and unmistakable. Nothing is more distressing than a labyrinth of halls and passages, with endless spurs and unexpected twists and turns, ending in culs-de-sac, mere nothing, or quite impartially in important offices or janitors' dust bins. Plain, straight, coherent, giving an idea of the whole scope of the building at first glance—such should be the ideal to strive after in arrangement.[1]

This 1891 essay by the New York architect John Beverly Robinson clearly illustrated the transformation in the interior design of multistory buildings that went hand in hand with the introduction of the elevator. The stairway as means of access to the various levels had to now compete with a vertical shaft cutting a breach through the center of the building; this in turn had far-reaching consequences for the floor plans of new buildings since, as Robinson insisted, the linearity of the transport channel was to be applied to the entire organization of interior space. In office buildings equipped with elevators, the old winding corridors and labyrinthine stairwells replete with blind corners and dead-ends were re-placed by a clear distribution of space comprehensible at a glance. "From the point where the elevators deliver in each story," all confusion ends. As Louis H. Sullivan wrote in his famous manifesto of 1896, "The Tall Office Building Artisti-cally Considered," the multistory office building was to have "an indefinite number of stories of offices piled tier upon tier, one tier just like another tier, one office just like all the other offices—an office being similar to a cell in a honey-comb."[2]

In the debates on office building design that began about 1880 in the United States and thirty years later in Germany, we see the question of the transparency of spatial organi-zation coming to the fore again and again. The floor plan of each story was to be organized as simply as possible, a specification that, in the wake of the introduction of steel frame construction, quickly led architects to dispense en-tirely with permanent divisions into individual rooms. As Alfred Wiener wrote in 1912 in the longest German treatise on office buildings, "Each floor of the building is initially treated as a single large space, which can then be divided into as many individual spaces and rooms as needed and sized accordingly."[3] There is no doubt that the increase in building height at the end of the nineteenth century was in-separable from an increasingly geometric configuration of the floor plan, a hollowing-out process that led one Ameri-can architectural critic to note, as early as 1899, "There is . . . more of conformity and homogeneousness among the twenty-story buildings than there used to be among the five-story buildings."[4] The elevator is responsible for both of these developments. Its tractive force enabled the upper reaches of a building to be colonized, while the strict linear-ity of its movement ensured the rearrangement of vertical space in the building's interior. For the first time, people had access to a means of transportation that enabled them to take *the most direct route* from one level to another. While even the most uncomplicated stairwells represent a de-tour, a more or less winding and branching divergence from the vertical, the elevator channel—in the form of a closed or at least screened-in shaft—cut a plumb swath straight through the building.[5] This shift had considerable implications for the image of the multistory building, since the elevator established a distribution system whose boundaries, openings, and closings were precisely determinable, in contrast to a system of stairways. From then on, the elevator lobby constituted the unmistakable nodal point of each floor, from which, according to Robinson, "the door of every office on that floor should be visible." It was therefore logical that the interior design of the office building could restrict itself to providing continuous routes of circulation. For although "the arrangement of individual rooms does not need to be planned before the building is built," as Alfred Wiener wrote, "a number of spaces and facilities for general use do need to be laid down from the outset. These are primarily all arrangements for traffic on and between the separate floors of the building: vestibules, entrance halls, large corridors, stairwells, elevators, paternosters. . . . In modern office buildings, the siting and physical form of spaces and facilities for traffic circulation receive special attention."[6] The stringency of vertical organization led to a similar stringency in the horizontal.

The elevator's early history is also interesting for the extent to which the formerly insignificant architectural element of the "shaft" evolved in importance. Only two or three decades separate the first factory freight lifts—pieced-together, free-standing iron racks accessible from all four sides—from the continuous, partially closed shafts of New York "elevator buildings" that were soon being designed as the core of the structure. In that short time, a fundamental reorientation took place: no longer was the elevator a mobile rack adapted to fit preexisting surroundings. Now it was an integral component of the building, which in turn determined the shape of the floor plan. We must note the historical turning points at which the verticality created by the elevator became visible and the apparatus was transformed from a mere addition into a dominating swath cut through the building. In the United States, we can date this turning point to 1875 and the completion of an office building with a special claim to the designation "elevator building": the editorial offices of the *New York Tribune*. Although the Equitable Life Building of 1870 was the first to be equipped with elevators, it still concealed the fact of its seven stories behind windows that extended across two stories each. And the three passenger elevators of the Western Union Company's headquarters, completed shortly before the Tribune Building, ran between only some of its floors.[7] The floor plan of the ten-story newspaper building, however, was for the first time incisively oriented around the elevators' channel. The two public elevators, placed side by side, constituted the first "elevator bank" in history and regulated the heavy traffic in the rented office spaces on the middle floors. "There are some large buildings in this city," boasted a piece in the *Tribune*'s in-house organ shortly after the building opened, "in which two elevators are placed at opposite ends of a long hall so far apart that the impatient passengers who miss one and go to the other are very apt to miss that one too."[8] The centralized elevator bank, on the other hand, was logistically much more functional. Another sign that access to the building was now concentrated in the elevators was the novel installation of an express lift on the other side of the entrance hall, a cab in an enclosed shaft that travelled nonstop directly to the editorial offices on the upper floors.

To be sure, this emphatic siting of the elevator shaft, which occurred for the first time in the Tribune Building but in the course of only a few decades became a basic principle of all multistory office and residential buildings, was above all a strategy to prevent fire and accidents. On the one hand, the disappearance of the elevator behind enclosing walls was a reaction to devastating fires in which free-standing wood-frame elevator shafts contributed to the swift spread of fires. On the other, it responded to a frequently occurring accident of the early years, when passengers would lean out of unenclosed cabs and collide fatally with stairwell pillars. This is why the engineering literature on elevator construction between 1870 and 1900 dwelled constantly on how to improve the enclosure and clearly demarcate the shaft. This development also quickly reached Germany, as is evident from relevant passages in the first set of regulations governing elevator construction in the German Reich, issued for Berlin and its suburbs in April 1893. Section 1, "Production of Elevators: Elevator Shafts or Tracks within Buildings," stipulates that "elevators connecting separate stories within building interiors must as a rule be enclosed by solid walls with openings only for the necessary access doors and skylights."[9] Exceptions to this rule applied to elevators retrofitted in stairwells. In these cases, "a shaft with solid walls is not necessary as long as the channel is enclosed by wire mesh with maximum interstices of 0.4 inches and moreover, all parts of the elevator are adequately enclosed to prevent injury."[10] In an architectural manual that appeared shortly before the Berlin regulations went into effect, this compulsory enclosure of the shaft was already described in detail: "The platform serving to convey passengers must be enclosed in such a way that no one can be injured by extending a part of his body out of the cab. . . . To this end, an iron frame is mounted around the edge of the rectangular platform of the elevator. As a rule it is sheathed on all four sides with solid walls, less often with narrow-gauge wire mesh."[11]

These excerpts from regulations and manuals allow us to discern a revealing historical confluence. The cultural assimilation of the elevator, the metaphoric "fitting in" of the means of transportation, was synonymous with the literal fitting of the initially ill-defined shaft into the vertical dimension of the building. As long as there was no clear demarcation between elevator and stairwell, the new apparatus represented a potential danger; hazardous overlap of the two regions led on many occasions to limbs being crushed or amputated.[12] By the end of the nineteenth century, however, the elevator had achieved its final form. At the same time the disappearance of the cab behind the walls enclosing the shaft signaled the end of the defining pictorial representation of the new conveyance. The illustrations and photographs of luxurious elevator cars appearing in company prospectuses, advertising brochures, and technical manuals before the turn of the century became impossible as soon as there was nothing more to be seen of the cab except for its entrance door. A remark in a special publication in honor of the fiftieth birthday of the elevator manufacturer Flohr illustrated this iconographic disruption: at the end of an opulent twenty-page gallery of "predecessors"[13]—gorgeous wrought-iron Flohr elevators in open stairwells—came this succinct statement about the latest models: "The elevators themselves cannot be represented pictorially since they are located in walled-up shafts. Naturally, the decoration of such elevators is limited to the cab interiors, of which I shall present several types on the following pages."[14] One could say that the early history of the elevator lasted as long as there were still photographs of cab exteriors. The real Age of the Elevator began with the end of its representability (simultaneous with the introduction of floor indicators above the entrance doors and in the cab interior). From then on, the elevator's location was only indirectly perceptible to its occupants and those waiting to board.

How strongly floor plan configuration was focused on the elevator's conduit from the 1870s on was particularly apparent in the changing status of the stairwell in American buildings. In the course of only one or two decades, this traditional means of vertical access was pushed into the background, downgraded from a grandiose structural element occupying the center of a floor to a mere escape route. In the first multistory office buildings in New York, the stairwell was accorded the same location and relevance as the new means of conveyance. On all floors there was a "combined stair and elevator lobby."[15] When the establishment of steel frame construction in the early 1880s enabled buildings to rise to twelve or fourteen floors, this brief period of

Interior lobby with elevator, 1858–60 Seventh Avenue (112th Street–113th Street), New York City. Photograph by Wurts Brothers. Courtesy of the Milstein Division of United States History, Local History and Genealogy, New York Public Library, and the Astor, Lenox, and Tilden Foundations.

Elevator corridor to entrance, Warner Brothers Company, 90 Park Avenue, New York City. Courtesy of the Library of Congress.

View of three sets of elevator doors in the new Chicago Daily News building, 400 West Madison Street. Photograph by *Chicago Daily News*, negative DN-0089017. Courtesy of the Chicago History Museum.

equal treatment came to an end, a change documented by the carefully archived floor plan modifications of the Equitable Life Building. In the course of remodeling and adding extra floors in 1887, the space-consuming main stairway rising through all stories was removed and replaced by newly configured elevator shafts with a total of ten cabs. A stairwell was installed in a side wing of the building solely to meet fire escape requirements.[16] This 1887 renovation of vertical access in the Equitable Life Building is one of the oldest surviving examples of the relationship of elevator to stairway that from then on was obligatory in multistory American commercial and residential buildings. The appearance of a new space known as the "elevator lobby," now the only visible distribution point for vertical conveyance on each floor, ushered in the disappearance of the stairwell. As early as 1893, a New York architectural critic remarked as if in hazy recollection of bygone times, "Stairs in a twelve-story office-building are an untrodden tribute to the weary past, and, like those of the cloud-piercing apartment-house, are likely to be used merely as interior fire escapes."[17] The American stairwell survived in the twentieth century as a forgotten rear view, the "dead appendage of a living building,"[18] as Klaus Mann once called it in the novel *Der Vulkan,* the story of an affair in a New York hotel for émigrés. In order not to be found out, the lovers mostly meet among bags of trash on the "almost forbidden stairway."[19]

As is still evident today, the stairwell was not so thoroughly replaced by the elevator shaft in Germany. However, the elevator was already being discussed in the 1880s, as in Franz Reuleaux's report on the safety standards of the Otis hydraulic elevator: "The advantage of elevator technology in general has been so accepted in the United States that in large buildings, the elevators are no longer simply welcome aids to traffic, but an essential, decisive element. . . . They are no longer sited like an afterthought in some obscure corner and seldom used, but are as open and accessible as possible."[20] In Germany, however, legal limitations on building height to five stories ensured that well into the 1920s, the installation of elevators, whether retroactive or part of the original plan, was always conceived of as merely an addition to the stairways. The formulations in architecture and engineering manuals around 1900 revealed that the traditional conception of the elevator as a mere extension of the actual transport system, that is, the stairs, was still unchallenged. "A passenger elevator in a building should be sited in such as way," recommends the manual previously cited, "that persons wanting to use the elevator will not have to traverse other rooms before entering it." The shaft "should be located either in the stairwell or in its immediate vicinity."[21] A 1908 introduction to elevator technology still stated, "Like the stairway itself, the elevator to be used in its place should be easy for a stranger to find."[22] To be sure, the fact that the stairwell continued to be regarded as the stable reference point for vertical movement within buildings began to come under fire at this time. Under the rubric "Miscellaneous" in the Prussian *Zentralblatt der Bauverwaltung* (Official gazette of the construction administration) of December 1907, one can read this lovely passage:

> Elevators are now coming more and more into use even in Germany's public buildings. But it must be deemed curious that not only where the elevator is retrofitted in a building, but even when the elevator installation is intended from the first, the stairway is still regarded as the main connection between different floors and the elevators are treated as secondary. It is different in the United States of America, where the elevator constitutes the main connection between the various floors. There, it is easy to find the elevator and one can use it to reach any floor and all the rooms on that floor.[23]

Despite such remarks, the stairwell remained the primary space for vertical movement in early twentieth-century German commercial and government buildings. Not even in high-rise buildings of the late twentieth century did the demotion to neglected fire escape occur to the same extent as in American buildings.

The organization imposed on multistory buildings by the elevator shaft, a process completed around 1890 in the United States and around 1930 in Germany, was finally expressed in a complete equalization of vertical movement. Whether one's ride in the cab is up or down makes no difference at all with respect either to the energy expended by the passengers or to the value of those two directions. While Gaston Bachelard's *Poetics of Space* still devotes pages to the imaginative difference between one's direction on a stairway—"We always *go down* the one that leads to the cellar. . . . We always *go up* the attic stairs, which are steeper and more primitive"[24]—exactly the opposite goes for the ride in an elevator. It is no accident that elevators are used as a metaphor precisely to epitomize the lack of difference between up and down, their mutual cancelation. German sportswriters apply the term "elevator team" to a soccer club that shifts back and forth between leagues, playing one year in a higher league and the next in a lower one. It is remarkable,

Elevator bank. From Kerstin Englert and Alfred Englert, *Lifts in Berlin* (Berlin: Jovis, 1998).

however (and typical of its gradual integration into the building), that in the early years, the elevator's current metaphoric lack of direction was not yet firmly established. On the contrary, there is much evidence to show that well into the 1920s, at least in Europe, there was a clear directional priority—namely, upward—already etymologically manifest in the words *elevator, ascenseur,* and *Aufzug* (literally "up-pull"). In 1892, Philipp Mayer began the first comprehensive monograph on the elevator in German with the astonishing sentence, "Under elevators we understand those lifting mechanisms employed in multistory structures by means of which organic and inorganic material is transported in a vertical direction, *especially upward.*"[25] And in the section on safety precautions, this statement appears: "Although in general there is no special need to use the elevator for descent as well, that possibility must in any event also be taken into account."[26] Statements like this give us an idea of how fundamentally the perception of this means of transport changed in the course of the twentieth century. A universally understood metaphor in the sportswriting jargon of recent decades would have still been puzzling at a time when the new apparatus was just beginning to gain acceptance. Statistical information as well as literary works document the fact that at first, the downward and the upward rides were by no means equal undertakings. Thus, a 1908 article on elevators mentions that a survey of passengers using paternoster lifts in Hamburg "applied only to those riding upward; it yielded an annual average of ten million persons." The statistician in charge "assumes that only 3/4 of that number also use the elevator to ride downward."[27] Likewise, Paul Fechter's 1926 novel *Der Ruck im Fahrstuhl* (The lurch in the elevator), whose main figures are constantly riding the elevator to their apartments on the upper floors of a Berlin tenement house, lets us know incidentally, in subordinate clauses, that in the morning the residents prefer to "run down the stairs."[28] The fact that around 1900 the use of the elevator for riding downward was still something unusual and even potentially threatening was drastically illustrated by the second case study in Freud and Breuer's *Studien zur Hysterie* (*Studies on Hysteria*). Breuer explained a sudden neurotic episode in the patient "Emmy v. N." as follows: "When asked, relates that the pensione in which the children are living here is located on the fifth floor and can be reached by elevator. Yesterday she asked the children to use the elevator to descend as well and is now reproaching herself that the lift is not completely reliable."[29] Although the patient's story later is interpreted as having been made up to divert attention from more compelling catalysts, its truth content from the point of view of the history of technology lies in the fact that in 1890s Vienna, it could obviously make a neurosis-promoting difference if you wanted to use an elevator "to descend as well."

If one sets out to trace the conditions under which the privileging of the upward ride began to fade, it's not enough to refer vaguely to the public accustoming themselves to the new means of transport. The incipient lack of direction of elevators can be precisely dated to a specific change in its controls. With the advent of electric push-button controls

Old elevator. From Kerstin Englert and Alfred Englert, *Lifts in Berlin* (Berlin: Jovis, 1998).

around 1900,[30] there was now a single contact in the cab available for each floor, independent of whether the passenger was located below or above that floor when he boarded the elevator. With the crank and lever controls obligatory in the elevators of the 1890s, there was still a necessary connection between the operation of the controls and the direction of travel. One can observe the importance of the change in the engineering commentaries at the beginning of the twentieth century, such as this comment in a catalog of the latest elevator models: "The remarkable thing about these designs is that the elevator controls use the same push button regardless of the direction of travel. The passenger does not have to figure out first whether from his location he needs to set the elevator in motion upward or downward. He simply presses the button that corresponds to the desired floor."[31] Push-button controls were the technical prerequisite for the equalization of vertical transport by elevator. Just as from then on, no distinction between upward and downward travel was necessary to set the cab in motion, the motion of the cab itself knew no difference.

ARCHITECTURES OF LINEARITY

The elevator shaft's important role in the structure of commercial and residential buildings becomes even more manifest when one considers how verticality was organized when this element was not yet imaginable. To make clear the whole scope of the changes at the end of the nineteenth century, we can compare the remarks of John Beverly Robinson, Louis H. Sullivan, and Alfred Wiener about the interior design of modern office buildings to a passage from one of the most successful and infamous novels in the history of German literature. In Gustav Freytag's *Debit and Credit* (1855), the principal setting of the novel, a multistory building housing the Schröter grocery concern, is characterized as follows:

> The building itself was an old, irregular one with additions, little outbuildings, and courtyards, replete with walls, small staircases, mysterious passageways where no one suspected them, corridors, niches, deep closets, and glass partitions. The whole structure was the centuries-old product of human ingenuity intent on making it as difficult and incomprehensible as possible for future generations.[32]

This description could be the model for a historical tradition that constitutes the gloomy background to John Beverly Robinson's plea for "coherent" traffic patterns. Before the late nineteenth century, there was no linear traffic corridor through buildings. And even if in Berlin the central stairwell "has already developed all its essential features in the floor plans of better apartment houses built since the end of the [18]30s,"[33] according a chapter to the voluminous 1877 chronicle *Berlin und seine Bauten* (Berlin and its buildings), interior coherence was still compromised by problematic overlaps. For example, the same chapter refers to an 1871 census of Berlin residential units showing that in multistory tenement houses there were still a total of 1,176 "entresols"—mezzanines of extremely dubious livability—as well as a considerable number of residential buildings in which the main corridor of each floor ran right through the middle of all the apartments.[34] Such sources show that, especially in Europe, building structure around 1880 was still characterized by excrescences in both vertical and horizontal directions and by a lack of clarity about where to draw the line between one floor and another, as well as between private and public spaces. The art-historical study *Das Berliner Wohnhaus* (Residential architecture in Berlin), published in 1917, offers a concrete example of this state of affairs. Examining the floor plan of a residential building of the early nineteenth century, the author notes,

> Typical for the time is also the addition of a mezzanine in a side wing. The ground floor of the wing was used to house stalls or small apartments. The latter, however, had such low ceilings that between them and the second floor there was room for a so-called entresol. On the stall side, it contained rooms that could be used as additional space, as needed, by the ground-floor apartments of the main building. A stairway leading no farther than to the floor level of the entresol was built next to the passageway connecting the main building to the wing. The primary stairway of the wing was located at the far end.[35]

This description clearly reflects the incoherent vertical structure of early multistory residential buildings. The text even gives the impression that the convoluted spatial organization has seeped into its complex sentence structure. The floor still cannot be clearly identified as a structural feature of verticality, a difficulty that the historian Clemens Wischermann described in a very similar way for the poor residential quarters of Hamburg and other Hanseatic towns in the middle of the nineteenth century. In these neighborhoods in the city centers, known as *Sähle* or *Gängeviertel*, "the greatest possible number of tiny rented rooms, often opening onto alleys only two or three yards wide, would be jammed behind the buildings on the wide main thoroughfares, or entire conglomerations of small living quarters on rear courtyards would often be connected to the street by only one narrow passageway through the front building."[36] The division into stories did not even occur in these jumbled neighborhoods with barely enough room for separate entrances to individual apartments, where movement between levels was mainly via crooked stairways. Wischermann drew attention to a telling administrative detail: the category "floor" did not even exist in Hamburg residential statistics before 1846, complicating the inclusion of all the inhabitants of the *Sähle*.[37]

It was a crucial characteristic of multistory buildings early in the era of European urbanization that their amorphous verticality had not yet found an adequate form. The hodgepodge of entresols, back stairways, and dead ends got in the way of the clear differentiation and classification of spatial units. We must examine the elevator shaft precisely with respect to its creation of improved comprehensibility. In this context, it is instructive to turn our gaze toward comparable construction projects that have received much more attention from historians. Looking back beyond the advent of the elevator's vertical breach, we see that primarily horizontal breaches were opened up around the middle of the nineteenth century in the form of railroad tracks, boulevards, avenues, canals, and subway tunnels. It is no exaggeration to call the decades between 1820 and 1880 the Age of Alignment. Perhaps one could even say that the project of modernism expressed itself in architecture and urban planning as a practice of opening breaches. The cultural and political implications of this practice have been researched from many perspectives. In particular, Haussmann's reorganization of Paris (begun in 1853, the year the E. G. Otis Elevator Company was founded) has been the object of well-known analysts from Friedrich Engels to Walter Benjamin and Sigfried Giedion to Richard Sennett.[38] Recently, the Zurich historian of technology Daniel Speich has used psychohistorical categories to describe the taming of ramified and potentially rampant landscapes with the principle of linearity. His study of the straightening of the Linth, a river in eastern Switzerland whose flooding in the late eighteenth and early nineteenth centuries conjured up the threat of a natural disaster, concentrates on portraying two parallel developments, and analyzes the extent to which the taming of a landscape is always connected to the civilizing of the social order. The river project was a battle against both the riverside flood-plain marshes and the immoral behavior of the people who lived beside them. As the "wild flood plain with its meandering streams . . . [was] regulated into a geometrically ordered, cultivated landscape,"[39] the scattered bands—whom the construction supervisors at first referred to as "half-human"—developed into a domesticated unit. Thus the successful regulation of the river not only prepared "the ground for the technical and industrial modernization of the nineteenth and twentieth centuries" by bringing in its wake the construction of railroad tracks and telegraph lines along the river,[40] it also became an early foundational myth for the establishment of the Swiss Confederation in 1848. At the end of his work, Speich stresses that "the regulation of the Linth provides an excellent introduction to the genesis of some primary principles of modernism."[41]

But what precisely constitutes the connection between works of civil engineering and changes in the history of thought? What is the political function of linearity? To answer this question, one can turn to Michel Foucault's reflections on "disciplinary space" in the eighteenth century, when the creation of the greatest possible clarity and transparency became the most important principle of spatial organization in such institutions as barracks and factories. In a much-cited passage from *Discipline and Punish*, he wrote that such institutions must "avoid distributions in groups; break up collective dispositions; analyse confused, massive or transient pluralities. . . . One must eliminate the effects of imprecise distributions, the uncontrolled disappearance of individuals, their diffuse circulation, their unusable and dangerous coagulation."[42] Against this background, nineteenth-century breaches in the landscape and above all in town planning become comprehensible. The replacement of a meandering stream or street with a dead-straight riverbed or boulevard tames the possibility of Foucault's "collective dispositions." As the myth of the regulation of the Linth proved, the barbaric "half-humans" of the flood-plain marshes became trustworthy citizens living beside a canal.

This disciplinary impulse of linearity can be observed with particular clarity in Georges Eugène Haussmann's urban renovations under Louis Napoleon. Nine times between 1827 and 1851, the convoluted streets in the old center of Paris became the scene of barricades and street battles.[43] The demolition of ten thousand buildings was therefore planned not just as a hygienic measure, but from the beginning also as a strategic defense against future civil unrest. Contemporary commentators already described Haussmann's three major road construction projects—the disentanglement of the dense network in the city center, the creation of broad boulevards radiating toward the city limits, and the streamlined connections between thoroughfares and secondary streets—in terms of their political function. Thus the German historian Theodor Mundt, in his 1858 *Skizzen aus dem französischen Kaiserreich* (Sketches from the French Empire), described the evisceration of the Ile de la Cité, in which fifteen thousand houses were demolished:

Wherever the folk clumps together in resistant masses, the authorities find dangerous terrain from which at any moment they can be attacked. For that reason, Louis Napoleon has undertaken the reconstruction of the Cité according to the most radical plan possible. For in this infamous part of the city, which has always been a real labyrinth of misery and unrest, from now on almost all dwellings will disappear and only public buildings will remain or be built.[44]

At the end of the reconstruction project, only three large structures remained on the Ile de la Cité, and the square in front of Notre Dame Cathedral had grown to forty times its former size. It is important to take note of Mundt's diction, especially with regard to the masses "clumping together," clumps that would be broken up by Haussmann's breaches and the integration of the Ile de la Cité into the network of new boulevards. Again, it is linearity's job to sort people out. No wonder Foucault can write, "Discipline organizes an analytical space."[45] The breach, originally a term from military strategy, was an urgently needed instrument for this task. It entered into the fray against the impermissible heterogeneity that occurred in various metaphoric guises in the mid-nineteenth century: as a "swamp" in hydrologic engineering or a "primeval forest"—a frequent metaphor for Paris in the Second Empire[46]—in town planning. In the space of seventeen years, an architecture of transparency was imposed upon Paris as a guarantee of that "distribution of individuals in space" that Foucault calls the basic task of disciplinary society.[47] (Haussmann himself was so thoroughly devoted to linearity that he even had his own birthplace torn down to make room for one of the great arterial boulevards, which he then named "Boulevard Haussmann."[48] The swath itself, not the house it displaced, became the memorial to its creator.)

The corridors that were cut through landscapes and cities in the mid-nineteenth century are related to each other. Haussmann repeatedly emphasized in his memoirs how much his plans for the boulevards owed to the idea of railroad tracks; both function as "large arteries" for the circulation of traffic in the city.[49] From 1841 on, Paris was the official hub of the rail network, and the primary purpose of some of the newly conceived boulevards was to connect the train stations as directly as possible.[50] In turn, the construction of tunnels for the London underground, begun in 1863, followed Haussmann's general principles.[51] The history of architecture documents how many European metropolises broke up and straightened out their centers on the model of Paris—Vienna for the world's fair of 1873, for example, or Rome in the 1880s. Thus we see that in the early years of urbanization, the organization of space was highly focused on the creation of straight, horizontal lines. Of significance for the history of the elevator is the extent to which, in the second half of the nineteenth century, this tendency began to have marked influence on the vertical structure of buildings as well. The incipient hygiene movement referred to large tenement houses in Germany with the familiar metaphors of amorphousness: their inhabitants were present in "abnormal density," their corridors filled with "swampy air" that must be ventilated.[52] In this sense, the elevator shaft cut a breach through the levels of a building in the same way the boulevard did through the streets of the city. It eliminated the proliferation of entresols and secondary stairways, setting in motion a vertical Haussmannization. But how exactly did the elevator-induced reorganization of multistoried buildings function? First of all, the category of the "floor" had to be stabilized. The elevator did not invent the category, but it did define it with hitherto unknown clarity. The *Sähle* in Hamburg, the entresol dwellings in Berlin, and the counting house described by Freytag in *Debit and Credit* all make clear that until the middle of the nineteenth century, the transitions between the vertical layers of a building could be confusingly labeled. The elevator, however, established the principle of floors clearly separated from each other, for it goes only to the "first," "second," "third," or "fourth" floor, eliminating any deviations or intermediate entities. The history of how multistory buildings are imagined cannot overlook the importance of this change. The fantasies of buildings without boundaries like the ones still elaborated in such early twentieth-century novels as *Golem*, by Gustav Meyrink, or *The Trial*, by Franz Kafka,[53] came to an end in the age of the elevator, for the vertical swath with its regularly spaced openings tamed and distributed the interior space with nothing left over.

We need to investigate the elevator from precisely this perspective, as a vehicle for improved comprehension of multistory space. In commercial and residential buildings equipped with elevators, each spatial unit is assigned a precise location. In comparison with the featureless jumble of living quarters in the slums of earlier decades, there is a pronounced "partitioning" of space.[54] This aspect of comprehensibility emerges with particular clarity when we examine how the inhabitants are identified to the outside world. It is more than a coincidence that, at least in Europe, the establishment of the elevator occurred at the same time as the introduction of the bank of doorbells at the building's entrance. The convention of representing the human fabric of a building's interior by a list of names at the entrance began at the end of the nineteenth century and presupposed utter clarity about how the spatial units were distributed. Thus an 1897 manual titled *Haustelegraphie* (Building telegraphy) recommended newly conceived "pull contacts for 4 floors, ground floor and stories II-IV," which were to be

> installed at the building entrance with wires leading up to each floor. The pull contacts of genuine bronze possess small removable windows with panes of glass behind which either the name of the tenant or the floor and room number are inserted. . . . The main door is equipped with an electric door opener. When a signal is sent to any floor, the main door can be opened *without leaving the apartment* by depressing a button.[55]

This description is one of the earliest mentions of a bank of doorbells in a multistory building. Its existence, however, depended on the possibility of representing verticality. How could such a bank have existed in the Hanseatic *Sähle* or a building in Meyrink's Prague ghetto? The unchecked proliferation would not have been representable to the outside world, especially not in the form of that orderly listing of the names that imitates the order of the apartments, from the very first so characteristic of banks of doorbells. In a building organized by its elevators, however, a miniature image of the interior distribution can be assembled and installed at its threshold with no trouble at all.

If the process of modernization is conceived from a topographical perspective as one of disentanglement, then the appearance of the bank of doorbells was an important event. It ensured the organization of diversity; there was complete congruence between sign and signified. Every person in a multistory apartment building was now identifiable at the entrance to the building. The bank of doorbells produced addressability and, for the identification of an individual dwelling, had a significance similar to the introduction of house numbers a century earlier for the entire building. The possibility of such a representation of multistory space, however, is linked to the establishment of the elevator and the image of verticality within the building that it generated. Even if not every tenement house in 1850 was laced with mezzanines and blind corners, only the conduit of the elevator introduced a regularity of floor structure and a more precise identification of location that from then on determined even the floor plans of elevatorless stairwells (there is no multistory apartment building of the last eighty years whose inhabitants were not represented by a bank of doorbells). At issue is the connection between an architecture of linearity and the creation of that form of modern individuality characterized by precise ascertainability. Georg Simmel described this relationship in his *Soziologie* using the example of house numbers: "The numbering of urban buildings," he wrote,

> means in a higher sense the localization of individuals, since it provides a mechanical method for finding them. The nature of this findability is obviously quite different from the medieval designation of special streets and quarters for particular classes and professions. . . . In contrast to the latter, the system of house numbering is eminently unhistorical and schematic—on the one hand

much more individualized, on the other much more indifferent to the individual as a person. In this respect, too, the inner, sociological essence of city life expresses itself in spatial language. The more pure the development of city life, the more rationalistic it reveals itself to be—especially in its repression of everything idiosyncratic, accidental, sharply angled, or crooked in the layout of streets in favor of what is straight as an arrow, uses established geometric norms, and follows general laws.[56]

It is remarkable how seamlessly Simmel's comparison of two concepts of individuality—one "monumental" and the other "documentary," to use Foucault's terminology[57]—meshes with a comparison of two conceptions of space. Monumental individuality corresponds to the "sharply angled, or crooked"; documentary individuality to "what is straight as an arrow." Thus we see once more the political impulse toward linearity in the nineteenth century. The breach as a correction for everything random and organic is the architectonic signature of modernism pure and simple.

THE VOID BETWEEN FLOORS

The elevator can be understood as a disciplinary element in the history of the building to the extent that it makes verticality accessible and distributes spaces. We must not forget, however, that the conduit it opened up caused a second fundamental change in the interior structure of the building that had nothing to do with greater transparency (that "predilection for perspectives"[58] Walter Benjamin attributes to Haussmann's boulevards), and even in some sense contradicted it. For there is something connected to the linearity imposed by the shaft that could be called the fragmentation of the building. Thus the elevator created not only new visibilities but also new invisibilities. In order to describe this "obscuring" function of the apparatus, we must take a closer look at the stabilization of floor configuration already discussed. The discontinuous points at which the elevator stops, the restriction of accessible space to the "first floor," "second floor," and so forth, transformed the tiers of the building into discrete units; whatever lies between those units in some sense no longer exists. In the vocabulary of signaling technology, the transition from stairwell to elevator could be described as a transition from the analog to the digital principle. According to Michel Serres, "In information technology, an analog signal is one that delivers its information continuously in a proportional relationship. . . . In contrast to the analog technique, digital technologies reduce the information to a series of whole numbers."[59] Precisely this structural shift applied to vertical access to buildings in the decades around 1900. Ascent in an open stairwell appeared as a continuous process. In the elevator building with its "discrete samplings, at equal intervals to the greatest extent possible,"[60] the region between the floors is forgotten space (so utterly nonexistent that it costs the protagonist in the most famous of all elevator stories, Louis Malle's film *Elevator to the Gallows*, his head because he has no alibi for the hours he has spent trapped in the shaft[61]).

It is telling that in the early history of the elevator, this element of discontinuity became more pronounced as push-button controls were developed. The mechanical forms of control by cable, steering wheel, or crank still moved the cab up and down in a continuous process. The movement of the cable or wheel controlled by the elevator operator bore no specific relation to the floor to which the cab was headed. The advent of electric push-button controls, on the other hand, not only caused the equalization of travel direction discussed above, but also created the impression that individual floors are distinct units from the way they appear on the control panel. From then on, each stopping place was assigned a button with the corresponding number, and pushing one of the buttons conveyed the passenger (thanks to the automatic precision stop mechanism introduced at the same time) to the exact threshold of the desired floor. It is not surprising that a 1909 booklet for elevator operators pointed out in what seems now an almost tautological formulation that the new control system needed "a number of push-buttons in the cab that corresponds exactly to the number of possible stops."[62] But precisely this seemingly obvious correspondence had decisive implications for the perception of multistory buildings around 1900. The elevator with the electric push-button controls and enclosed shaft, which became obligatory at the beginning of the twentieth century, transformed the multistory building irrevocably into a series of separate platforms. It engendered a fragmentation of verticality whose irritations Rem Koolhaas thematizes in *Delirious New York* in connection with the earliest skyscrapers. He reproduces a contemporary illustration showing a fictitious eighty-four-story high-rise in cross-section. Every level of the building, outfitted with a country estate, trees, and animals, constitutes an autonomous cosmos all the way out to its very edges. "On level 82 a donkey shrinks back from the void, on 81 a cosmopolitan couple hails an airplane."[63] Each of these floors, Koolhaas writes, "is treated as a virgin site, *as if the others did not exist.* . . . Incidents of the floors are so brutally disjointed that they cannot conceivably be part of a single scenario. The disconnectedness of the aerial plots seemingly conflicts with the *fact* that, together, they add up to a single building."[64]

It's also possible to trace this disruption in the image of the building in literary history. What influence did the reconfiguration of verticality caused by the elevator shaft have on the narration of texts that take place mainly in multistory residential buildings? We can find out about the pre-elevator age, for instance, from two novels in Zola's Rougon-Macquart cycle whose main characters are the inhabitants of large tenement buildings: *L'Assommoir* (1877) and *Pot Luck* (1882). Gervaise, the heroine of the first novel, set among the working class of Paris, is introduced to the family of her future husband, Coupeau, in one of the early chapters. The two of them enter a seven-story tenement building located on the street where Coupeau has grown up. At this point, the gigantic building complex, which will be the main setting for the novel, is described in this way:

> The Lorilleuxs lived on the sixth floor—staircase B. Coupeau told
> her with a laugh to keep tight hold of the iron railing and not let
> it go. She looked up, half shutting her eyes, and gasped as she
> saw the height to which the staircase wound. The last gas burner,
> higher up, looked like a star trembling in a black sky, while two oth-
> ers on alternate floors cast long, slanting rays down the intermi-
> nable stairs.[65]

The passage makes clear how explicitly the multistory
building is perceived as a unity; it can be surveyed in its
entirety from the ground floor all the way up to the "star
trembling in a black sky." This homogeneity is evident in
Zola's frequent use of organic metaphors to describe it.
Gervaise was "as interested in the house as if it were a living creature," he writes at one point, and when she reaches
the seventh floor and looks back down, "the smells, the
turbulent life of this great house, seemed to rush over her
in one tremendous gust."[66] With the first ascent to the top
floor, the tenement house and all its inhabitants (who will
have a decisive influence on the young marriage in the
course of the story) are displayed as a completely open,
interactive space, an openness that befits the portrayal of
the relationships among them. We can see that the elevatorless stairwell in a multistory dwelling has specific nar-
ratological implications. If the various tenants and their
embroilments are to constitute the content of the novel,
they must come into regular contact with each other. The
stairwell, as a continuous "spiral" through the building,
guarantees such contact. All the characters live beneath
the same "black sky."

This connection between vertical access to the building
and the narratibility of its inhabitants' stories is revealed
even more trenchantly in Zola's *Pot Luck*. The later novel,
about the secret intrigues and affairs among the inhabitants
of a luxury apartment building in Paris,[67] begins with the
arrival of the main protagonist, a young provincial named
Octave Mouret, for whom a family friend has arranged a
rented room on the fifth floor of the building. One of the

first scenes in the novel describes how this friend, who lives on the fourth floor, accompanies Octave to his new room:

> Then, as they slowly climbed the stairs, he mentioned the names of the various tenants. On each floor there were two sets of apartments, one overlooking the street and the other the courtyard, their polished mahogany doors facing each other. He began by saying a word or two about Monsieur Auguste Vabre. He was the landlord's eldest son, and that spring he had taken the silk shop on the ground floor, and also occupied the whole of the entresol. Then, on the first floor, the landlord's other son, Théophile Vabre, and his wife lived in the apartment at the back, and in the one overlooking the street lived the landlord himself, formerly a Versailles notary, but now living with his son-in-law, a judge at the Court of Appeal.[68]

Considering that the six hundred pages to follow will be about nothing but Mouret's amorous and commercial relations with individual inhabitants of the building, this first ascent of the stairway has a special function in the economy of Zola's narrative, for in addition to introducing the protagonist to his new dwelling, it also gives readers an initial orientation. They gain insight into the configuration of the novel's cast of characters. The participants in the intrigues to come already pass in review on its opening pages.

Thus the stairwell appears as the armamentarium of a narrative tradition whose aim, like Zola's here, is to present the multistory dwelling as a microcosm. The question is whether such a panoramic novel about the fabric of relationships within a tenement house is still possible in the age of the elevator. There is a reason why no representatives of this genre are to be found in the twentieth-century literature of America or Europe. Perhaps it is not too much of an exaggeration to say that novels like *L'Assommoir* and *Pot Luck* could only have been written in the brief period between 1870 and 1920, the period in which there were already multistory apartment buildings but the elevator was not yet universally established as the means of access. The reason for the disappearance of this genre has to do with the walled-in shaft running through the building. If the path to one's own floor is no longer associated with an ascent through all the lower floors, if one's knowledge of the building is restricted almost exclusively to that floor (as has been the case in elevator buildings for decades), then stories derived from the interaction of all the various tenants will necessarily peter out. The image of the multistory building that had been developing for a century in the United States and for at least half a century in Europe represented a completely different configuration. In place of the hollow tower and the seething organism, one is now confronted with a stack of unconnected levels. This abstraction has had a concrete effect on novels that present the story of a building. In recent decades, literary images of multistory buildings must take into account the inhabitants' ignorance of events on floors other than their own. A recent example is Paul Maar and Nikolaus Heidelbach's popular German picture book *Der Aufzug* (The elevator), which tells the story of a little girl who meets a mysterious dwarf. We are told at the beginning of the book that Rosa "lives with her parents in a high-rise, way up on the ninth floor. Every morning when Rosa goes to school, she gets in the elevator, pushes the button that says 'G,' and rides down. Every afternoon, when Rosa comes home, she pushes the button that says '9' and rides back up."[69] Here, the fragmentation of verticality is explicitly visible. In the child's imagination, the building consists of nothing but the ground floor, her own floor, and the connecting element of the elevator cab. To make this abstraction concrete, the first page of the book has a picture of a child's hand pushing a button on the elevator's control panel. The fantastic element of the story is introduced one night when the girl discovers a dwarf who has made the cab into his living room and invites her on a tour of the entire building. The travel time between floors suddenly lasts not mere seconds, but long enough for the dwarf to serve her cake and raspberry wine. And when they finally reach one of the other floors and the door slides open, a fantasy-landscape is spread out before them. On the seventh floor Rosa meets the Seven Little Goats, the Seven

Swabians (both from the Grimm brothers' fairy tale collection) and six of the Seven Dwarfs (the seventh being her tour guide). A week later they travel to the third floor, where they encounter "triplets on a three-speed tricycle," the Three Wise Men, and the Three Miller's Sons.[70] What, then, are the floors of a twentieth-century high-rise? Not communicating components of a spatial totality, but mere push buttons on an elevator's control panel. Their existence is so tied to the numeral on the button that in the imaginary order of a picture book, that numeral has programmed their very appearance. There are no longer other tenants on the various floors with whom in naturalistic novels one could have quarrels or affairs, but rather incarnations of the floor number itself. This is exactly what makes it possible for the elevator to become a magic machine in the literature of the twentieth century. It engenders imaginary spatial levels because it conceals the real ones.

FROM ATTIC TO PENTHOUSE

THE VERTICAL HIERARCHY OF BUILDINGS

GRAND HOTELS

Gabriel Dan, the protagonist in Joseph Roth's 1924 novel *Hotel Savoy*, is on his way home to Vienna after spending several years in Russian POW camps. He arrives in a Polish town and takes a room in a hotel—on the sixth floor above ground level, where the prices are lowest. After a few hours' sleep he sets out on a tour of the other floors. As he closes the door of his room behind him, he finds a notice tacked to it by the hotel manager, Kaleguropulos:

QUIET IS REQUESTED AFTER 10 PM NO RESPONSIBILITY CAN BE TAKEN FOR VALUABLES LEFT IN THE ROOM. THERE IS A SAFE IN THE HOTEL. . . . I go along the corridor to the main staircase and take pleasure in the handsome square flagstones of the hotel passage, in the clean red stone and the steady echo of my footsteps.

I walk slowly downstairs. From the lower floors come voices, but up here everything is silent. All the doors are shut, one moves as if it were an old monastery, past the doors of monks in prayer. The fifth floor looks exactly like the sixth, one could easily confuse them. Up above and here, too, a standard clock hangs facing the stairs, but the two clocks do not tell the same time. The one on the sixth floor says ten past seven, on this floor it says seven, and on the fourth floor it says ten to seven.

Upon the flagstones on the third floor lie dark red carpets with green borders and one no longer hears one's footsteps. The room numbers are not painted on the doors but mounted on little porcelain signs. A maid passes with a feather duster and a wastepaper basket. They seem here to pay more attention to cleanliness. This is where the rich live, and the cunning Kaleguropulos lets the clocks run slow, because the rich have time.

On the mezzanine the two wings of a door were standing wide open.

This was a large room with two windows, two beds, two chests of drawers, a green plush sofa, a brown tiled stove and a stand for luggage. Kaleguropulos' sign was not to be seen on the door—perhaps the residents at this level were allowed to be noisy after ten o'clock, and perhaps the management did take responsibility for valuables—or did they already know about the safe, or did Kaleguropulos inform them personally?

A scented woman with a grey feather boa rustled out of a neighbouring room. This is a lady, I say to myself, and walk close behind her down the last few stairs, admiring her little polished bootees.[1]

There is perhaps no other passage in European literature of the time that so vividly describes the vertical structure of the traditional grand hotel. The interior of the building is revealed as if in cross-section; as he descends from top to bottom, Dan records floor by floor the subtle changes in the facilities, from the nature of the flooring to the standards of hygiene, from the font of the room numbers to the time shown on the clocks. It is no accident that Joseph Roth describes the new guest's foray through the hotel in such detail, for the hierarchical order of the floors reflects the post–World War I social divisions that he is portraying. Like the personnel of the novel—on the one hand the profiteers who have salvaged or even enlarged their fortunes, on the other the war's impoverished victims—the Hotel Savoy, their common dwelling, is also divided into two halves. The building's demarcation line runs between the third and the fourth floors. Those who live below it continue to be provided with the standard symbols of luxury. The floors above, however, lead by stages to the hotel's wasteland. The novel returns insistently to the leitmotif of this threshold, speaking repeatedly of the distinctions in hotel service. In the case of breakfast, for instance, on the upper floors,

> a floor waiter came, wearing a green baize apron. His rolled up sleeves revealed his muscular forearms, dark with curly hair as far as his elbows. Evidently maid service was only for the first three floors. The coffee was better than might have been expected, but what was the use of that without a maid in a white cap? This was a disappointment and I wondered whether there were any possibility of moving to the third floor.[2]

Shortly after his arrival, Gabriel Dan discovers that some guests even live a floor above him. The attic story, actually the Savoy's steamy laundry, is even more sparsely furnished, without even so much as a "standard clock" on the wall. It houses a separate society of people thrown together by their shared destitution: a vaudeville dancer on her way to Paris, a consumptive circus clown and his wife and child, and finally, in the worst room in the entire hotel, a once prosperous factory owner named Fisch who now ekes out a living predicting winning lottery numbers for other hotel guests. ("Many people have become rich through Fisch's dreams and live on the first floor of the Savoy. Out of gratitude they pay for his rooms.")[3] The inhabitants of the attic floor are cut off from the normal life of the hotel. No room service comes to them; they prepare their own meals on illegal alcohol stoves. In the consciousness of the hotel employees, these guests do not exist, as evidenced by the fact that they don't even know their names: when the circus clown Santschin calls for a doctor, "'Number 748 has suddenly fallen ill,' say the floor waiters. There were no names whatever on the top three storeys of the hotel. Everyone was known by room numbers."[4]

In June 1926, two years after the publication of Roth's novel, the Ritz Tower, the tallest apartment house in the world, opened in New York. The forty-one-story building on Park Avenue, commissioned by the wealthy journalist Arthur Brisbane and designed by Joseph Roth's namesake Emery Roth, the chief architect of the New York skyline, was an "apartment hotel," that is, it consisted of condominium apartments but with services typical of a luxury hotel. The architectural historian Steven Ruttenbaum described the building in his biography of Emery Roth:

> The second and third floors contained numerous maids' and servants' quarters; these rooms were separated from the tenants' living area, as was traditional in large single-family dwellings. These floors also housed private vaults for the tenants, a separate one for each apartment. The fourth through the eighteenth floors contained suites of two to four rooms connected to the elevators by means of a double-loaded corridor. . . . On the nineteenth and twentieth floors was located one of the most unusual duplex apartments in the city. Consisting of eighteen large rooms, it was designed specifically for Brisbane. The double-height living room was the most noteworthy feature of the apartment. It measured 20 feet high and 20 feet wide, and it ran the entire length of the Park Avenue frontage for 70 feet. . . . A narrow terrace surrounded the entire apartment at the nineteenth-floor setback, providing a sweeping panorama of the city in every direction. . . . Of the three passenger elevators in the building, one was designed specifically to stop at the nineteenth and twentieth floors for Brisbane's sole use. . . . The floors above Brisbane's apartment, from the twenty-first level to the top, contained apartments of four to twelve rooms each. They consisted of single-floor and duplex suites of one to four bedrooms, each with its own bath. Floors 21 through 24 were arranged with two single-floor apartments per level; floors 25 through 32 offered two duplex suites in each two levels; and floors 33 to 37 were designed with one apartment per level. The most unusual feature of the duplex suites was a large (16 feet wide by 40 feet long) double-height studio/living room with doors at each end leading to terraces set within the corners of the tower. The entrance to these apartments was gained through a single story foyer, above which was built a balcony overlooking the living room one floor below. These duplex studio apartments were designed for tenants who desired such unusual and luxurious space.[5]

Thus we see two cross-sections through hotel buildings of the 1920s. Both represent a continuous change, an increase in luxury from floor to floor, but what distinguishes them from each other is the direction of movement. Gabriel Dan's foray through the Hotel Savoy—which is modeled on a mid-nineteenth-century grand hotel of the same name in Lodz[6]—proceeds from top to bottom, beginning on an unadorned upper story and ending with a reverential peek into the rooms of the *bel étage*. Ruttenbaum's description, on the other hand, begins with the lowest floors, where the servants' quarters and storage rooms for the residents are located, and from there lists the various strata of the apartment hotel in ascending order. What these two lengthy descriptions illustrate is a fundamental transformation in the vertical structure, a reversal of the hierarchic order. The best rooms have migrated from below to above, the most modest from above to below. One could say that the Hotel Savoy and the Ritz Tower stand on either side of an epochal watershed, the four decades between 1890 and 1930 (although in Europe it developed less quickly and consistently than in the United States). During those decades, a momentous shift occurred in the material and symbolic ordering of multistory buildings, in particular a shift in the significance of the upper stories, to which we will now turn our attention. The focus will be on two aspects of the process: one is the multifaceted nature of the readjustment (which occurred not just in hotels but also in tenement houses and commercial buildings), the other is the special role of the elevator, for it is no exaggeration to say that the introduction of this conveyance was the prerequisite for the recodification of verticality around 1900.

There can be no doubt that the hierarchical structure of buildings is inseparable from the problem of access. In the traditional grand hotels of Europe, for example, the reason the rooms became worse and worse the farther up they were was quite simply that only the most lowly guests and the hotel personnel could be expected to climb all those stairs. The elevator freed the upper stories from the stigma of inaccessibility and lent them an unheard-of glamour instead. At the same time, it resolved the old symbolic dissonance between vertical hierarchy and social hierarchy that survived into the first years of the twentieth century. There is a lovely passage in *Hotel Savoy* in which Gabriel Dan muses on this architectural paradox:

> Those who lived on high were in the depths, buried in airy graves, and the graves were in layers above the comfortable rooms of the well nourished guests sitting down below, untroubled by the flimsy coffins overhead.
>
> I belong to those who are buried on high. Do I not live on the sixth floor and shall I not be driven by Fate onto the seventh? To the eighth, the tenth, the twentieth? How high can one fall?[7]

In the course of the twentieth century, hotel guests "buried on high" slowly but surely disappeared. Once the elevator established itself, the pyramid of society could be accurately reflected in the structure of multistory buildings as well, although we must not lose sight of a certain understandable delay. For even if we recognize the reversal of vertical order as an effect of the elevator, the construction costs of retrofitting the traditional grand hotels ensured that the installation of the new conveyance reorganized their interior space only little by little. In contrast to America, where hotels at the beginning of the twentieth century were built from the start around the core of the elevator shaft, there was a period of transition in Europe. A provisional, retrofitted elevator was already part of the better floors (as it is in the novel *Hotel Savoy* as well), but the ingrained, traditional hierarchy of floors remained in place. The Paris Hotel Saint James and Albany, where Thomas Mann's eponymous hero Felix Krull begins his job as an elevator operator, presumably shortly before the turn of the century, is still in this transitional phase.[8] The hotel has five stories above the ground floor, the first four of which are occupied by the guests, while the fifth contains cramped dormitories for the staff. Very similar to the Hotel Savoy, the attic floor in Mann's novel is described as a separate region of the building, as shown not least by the fact that the two modern passenger elevators go only as high as the fourth floor. Upon his arrival, however, Krull is conveyed to one of the dormitories by the service elevator located at the back of the building, which goes all the way to the fifth floor. That meagerly furnished floor, with its "ill-lit, carpetless corridor,"[9] reminds Krull of the terrors of the halls in the barracks he had hoped to escape in the grand hotel in Paris. When he finally begins work the next morning and reenters the luxurious region of the hotel with another employee, his descent is clearly reminiscent of the corresponding passage from *Hotel Savoy*: "We walked down a flight of stairs to the fourth floor, where the corridors were much wider and had red carpets. There he rang for one of the guest elevators that came up that high."[10] Once again we get the details—the wider corridors and red carpets—that constitute the traditional demarcation line in the grand hotel of the nineteenth century. Although a guest elevator is already in service in the Saint James and Albany, only the prestigious floors have access to it. The attic floor, the hotel's drab backside, can be reached only by clandestine conduits: the back stairs or the service elevator.

Such was the situation in Europe around 1900. In the luxury hotels of New York, on the other hand, the avant-garde of twentieth-century hotel culture, conditions had changed, as the construction of the Ritz Towers shows. The new hierarchical order was most consistently realized, however, in another New York building, the Waldorf-Astoria Hotel, opened in 1931, whose two towers were long the hallmark of the Manhattan skyline. These towers, which rose from the twenty-ninth to the forty-third story, constituted from the beginning the hotel's unique appeal to which the American journalist Ward Morehouse devoted an entire book.[11] Below the demarcation line of the twenty-ninth story, the Waldorf-Astoria, although expensive, was accessible to everyone; above the line began an exclusive region of suites of as many as twelve rooms with private butler service. For many years, the Towers was reserved exclusively for politicians, diplomats, and other prominent long-term guests. "The Towers is really a kind of vertical Beverly Hills," writes Morehouse, "a hotel within a hotel."[12] Here too, the upper floors were separated from the rest of the hotel, but now for the opposite reason. No longer did they serve to house makeshift extra rooms or dormitories for the personnel, but were instead an enclave of the elite. Whereas the shabbily dressed Gabriel Dan was immediately recognized by suspicious hotel employees as an inhabitant of the upper floors, Morehouse writes that Nicholas Racz, an early manager of the Waldorf-Astoria, "could spot the people who 'belonged' in the Towers at first glance."[13] This reversal was also evident in the changed configuration of the elevators. In the Waldorf-Astoria it was no longer the upper but the lower floors that had no access to the best elevator service; the express elevators for the Towers went directly to the twenty-ninth floor. No longer were the austere quarters for personnel kept hidden away on the upper floors: now it was the inscrutable sphere of power that was sequestered there. Not infrequently, politicians preferred to conduct important negotiations there rather than in the official institutions of the city.[14] In this regard, Ward Morehouse relates a revealing anecdote about postwar American foreign policy. At the beginning of his presidency, Dwight Eisenhower was forced to break with the tradition of his predecessors and give up the presidential suite in the Towers because his wife, Mamie, suffered from acrophobia. The decision to stay on one of the lower floors, where the hotel personnel was housed, threatened to become a political issue, because the president would be too far from the prestigious region of the hotel during the great United Nations conferences, for instance.[15] In order to at least ameliorate the negative effects, Eisenhower reserved a suite on the eighth floor, the only floor below the Towers where the express elevator was able to stop.[16]

The appearance of the elevator and its intervention in the structure of multistory buildings wrought a change above all in hotel culture in Europe, a culture that had already experienced a great advance beginning in the second half of the nineteenth century.[17] One can assess the significance of this event in the precise traces it has left behind in the tourist guidebooks' descriptions of hotels during the decades before and after 1900. In various editions of the Baedeker guides, for instance, the infiltration of the momentous invention into hotels can be followed in detail. Into the 1880s elevators were not mentioned at all, either in the introductory texts about a region's hotels in general or in the lists of amenities at individual hotels. The prominent mention of the new invention in the recommendations of subsequent editions proves its enormous significance. In the 1896 edition of the London guide, for instance, the hotels on Piccadilly Circus "include some of London's most elegant and expensive hotels, with electric lighting, lifts, etc."[18] In the 1892 guide to northeast Germany and Denmark, the hotel Hamburger Hof was described as a "superb building with elevator and every convenience."[19] In 1896, the Grand Hotel de Rome in Berlin was "in the best location, with 120 rooms, elevator, electric lighting, bathhouse."[20] The order in which things were mentioned deserves attention. In their recommendations of the most luxurious hotels of the time, the Baedeker editors gave the existence of an elevator highest priority, even higher than other epoch-making innovations such as electric lights or central heating. In some guides—those for Belgium and Holland (1891) and Austria-Hungary (1898), for instance—the names of the best hotels in major towns are accompanied only by the phrase "with passenger elevator."[21] It is exactly from such marginal, abbreviated entries that one can glean what the establishment of the elevator meant in the history of the hotel. And when the 1893 North America guide made more extensive remarks about the new invention, there was a sense of awe at the exotic apparatus: "Access to the rooms on the upper floors is significantly improved by the splendidly functioning 'elevators' (lifts)."[22] You can read the author's sense of wonder in his use of scare quotes, which disappeared in subsequent editions. In 1893, however, they were the typographic precipitate of innovation. Just as the passengers still mistrusted this means of transportation and anxiously gripped the railings in the cab, the author was not yet at liberty to use the term without cautiously enclosing it in quotation marks.

The period of adjustment, however, did not last long. From the Baedeker guides one can also gather how quickly the elevator entered the everyday life of the hotel; it took about twenty years. The assimilation process occurred in stages. At first, in the editions shortly after the turn of the century, the presence of elevators was still explicitly mentioned, although no longer separately for each individual hotel, but rather in the introductory commentary to the list of recommendations. Thus the Paris guide of 1900 stated, "The large first-class hotels are of course equipped with all modern conveniences, spacious dining rooms, smoking rooms and lounges, guest elevators, electric lighting, central heating, baths, often luxuriously appointed."[23] This wording can be found with almost no variation in most of the Baedeker guides for European metropolises between 1900 and 1910, but during the following decade, a change began to make itself felt. In the 1911 guide for northern Italy with Ravenna, Florence, and Leghorn, for instance, there was no mention of elevators at all in the luxury hotel category, but for several second-class hotels one finds descriptions such as this: "more modest, without elevator and central heating."[24] Expectations had already shifted by 1911; a feature worth mentioning in a second-class hotel was now not the presence of an elevator, but its absence. A decade later, the question of whether the modern conveyance belongs to a hotel's amenities had disappeared entirely from the discourse of the guides. In the editions of the 1920s, all specificities about luxuries had been removed from the standardized introductory sentence about the hotels. Now there was only the generalization, "The large first-class hotels in the metropolises offer the usual international conveniences."[25] In the hotel business, the elevator had become such a matter of course that its presence required no special mention.

The Baedeker guides provide evidence not just of the gradual establishment of the new technical apparatus, but also of its accompanying effect on the hierarchical structure of the hotels. The elevatorless order—the privileging of the lower stories—was still clearly evident in the early editions, as in this advice from the 1862 guide to southern Bavaria regarding guest services in Munich hotels: "If one needs information about anything, rather than approaching the subordinate staff it is better to turn to the hotel proprietor himself or the maître d'hôtel, since the former is occasionally available only to the guests on the *bel étage*."[26] In 1883, the authors of a guide book for hikers in Switzerland advised them to seek out the "inexpensive small hotels" rather than "the grand hotels in the latest style, where the better rooms are reserved for families or guests who can be expected to book in advance, while single travelers, especially in the high season, must climb to the fifth floor or get a small room giving onto the courtyard for the same price."[27] The vertical hierarchy of the hotels was especially evident whenever the Baedeker guides included a list of prices for the various floors in their recommendations. Thus the 1883 guide to central and northern Germany listed these prices for Berlin luxury hotels: "On the upper floors and facing the courtyard 2–2½ marks, ground floor and second floor 4–7 marks."[28] The price list for rooms in the luxury category in the 1885 edition of the Paris guide shows that the simplest rooms on the fifth and sixth floor would cost five francs, those on the second floor ten francs.[29] The most detailed information was provided by the fifteenth German-language edition of this guide, published in 1900, in the table listing the room prices for the two luxury hotels Elysée Palace Hotel and Hotel Terminus:

ELYSÉE PALACE HOTEL:	HOTEL TERMINUS:
Entresol: 12–20 F	2nd floor: 10–18 F (facing courtyard 8–12 F)
2nd floor: 8–40 F	3rd floor: 9–16 F (facing courtyard 7–10 F)
3rd–5th floor: 7–10 F	4th floor: 7–14 F (facing courtyard 6–9 F)
6th floor: 6–9 F	5th floor: 6–12 F (facing courtyard 5–8 F)
	6th floor: 5–7 F (facing courtyard 4–7 F)[30]

This table is one of the few detailed price lists still extant from the turn of the century. It is a valuable document, for the vertical and horizontal order apparently still obligatory for European hotels in 1900 would soon be a thing of the past. The fact that the rooms on the street side of the hotel were in every case more desirable and expensive than those facing the inner courtyard began to change with the increase in street traffic. The shifts in relationships among the various floors were a result of the elevator: the lists of differential prices gradually disappeared from the guidebooks, doubtless because from about the 1920s on, it was no longer possible to posit a direct connection between the floor and the quality of the rooms. The following edition of the Paris guide from 1905 dispensed with this kind of statistic. The formulation "Rooms are priced according to floor," basically repeated in the introductory note to all the early guidebooks, began to disappear in the editions of the 1920s and was gone completely by the 1930s. From that point on, rooms were differentiated by other criteria, such as whether they had a private bath. The hotels' vertical hierarchy disintegrated thanks to the elevator, whose explicit mention as a criterion of luxury disappeared from the guidebooks at precisely the same time that the lists of room prices became obsolete. By the 1920s, although the history of European hotels had not yet resulted in a total reversal of the hierarchical order as in the cities of the United States, one can at least speak of a leveling process.

GARRET ROOMS, 1839: POOR POETS AND ELOPING COUPLES

In his 1957 work *The Poetics of Space*, an attempt to construct a "psychology of the house," Gaston Bachelard introduced the idea of a "consciousness of verticality."[31] The house, he wrote, "differentiates itself in terms of its verticality" and can be divided into various levels from the cellar to the attic, each with specific semantic characteristics.[32] Precisely this "consciousness of verticality" is a touchstone for an examination of the elevator in the history of domestic life. How did the perception and use of the rooms change because of the conveyance? What connections can we make between the history of technology and the semantics of spaces? The vertical extension of buildings proceeded in an identifiable sequence into the twentieth century, as we have seen from the history of the hotel. But in order to answer more or less adequately the question of the elevator's influence on the development of the "consciousness of verticality," we must broaden our investigation to include not just hotels, but other types of buildings as well. We need to analyze the structure of tenement and office buildings before and after the introduction of the new conveyance. Not surprisingly, Gaston Bachelard entitled the first chapter of his book "From Cellar to Garret." As the upper reaches of a building, attics and garrets were obligatory locations well into the twentieth century, both in one-family houses and—beginning in the second half of the nineteenth century—in multistory tenement houses as well. Until recently, these rooms have received almost no attention from historians; with the exception of Bachelard's (actually quite limited) interest, they are overlooked in works of cultural history although they repeatedly play a role, especially in literature and painting. Even if no compendium of literary motifs and themes grants them an entry, there are remarkable connections among the narrative and dramatic texts whose topography is structured by garrets. Thus to describe the vertical organization of late nineteenth-century buildings, we may find it useful to turn to literary images of the building and to the regularly recurring functions of garrets before the appearance of the elevator.

In the course of the twentieth century, these locations disappeared. It would be difficult to find a text from the last fifty years that is set in the present but takes place in an attic or garret room. Their sharply defined semantics, however, survive in clichéd metaphors such as the "artist's garret," which continue to remind us of a certain connection between the dwelling type, the economic situation, and the orientation of the artwork. Where are the ur-scenes of this paradigm to be sought? Even today, without any doubt, the most enduring representation is Carl Spitzweg's 1839 painting *The Poor Poet*.[33] It presents the iconographic unity of the garret and artistic isolation in its most condensed form. All the details—the dying embers in the tile stove, the umbrella patching a leaky ceiling, the empty change purse hanging from the wall, the candle-end, the empty ink bottle on the floor—draw our attention to the material want of the solitary poet, declaiming his verses from his bed. Art historians emphasized that the painting's composition seized upon a "recent cliché"[34] and followed a contemporary "convention of the iconography of poverty."[35] In fact, the garret room and its poetically ambitious inhabitant belong with other motifs popular in early nineteenth-century European painting that illustrate a withdrawal from the world. Besides the scattered insignia of squalidness, Spitzweg makes this clear above all in the structure of the room. The bed is placed in its darkest possible corner. The window at the left, while serving as vanishing point, seems blocked off from the viewer, admitting hardly any light into the room. Looking out, one can barely catch sight of snow-covered roofs across the way.

In the same year *The Poor Poet* was painted, the Romantic writer Ludwig Tieck published a novella entitled *Des Lebens Überfluss* (Life's excess), in which the structure of space evinces a palpable similarity to Spitzweg's canvas. The novella tells the story of the socially unacceptable love between the bourgeois Heinrich and Clara, the daughter of a country squire. When their love letters are discovered, they flee across the border into the neighboring principality, marry in secret, and go into hiding in the capital city. They live clandestinely in the "narrowest and darkest street of the little suburb"[36] "in a little house"[37] whose garret they have rented under an assumed name. Tieck's novella, the "late summing up" of the Romantic era,[38] casts an ironic

Carl Spitzweg, *The Poor Poet*, 1839.

light on the essentialism of the Romantic concept of love, its mania for the natural that condemns even the slightest cultural embellishment of life as a falsifying "excess." (Not surprisingly, the eponymous word occurs fourteen times in the course of fifty-four large-print pages.) In a variety of ways, Tieck elaborates the situation of the couple, who have taken the precaution of cutting off all contact with the outside world. For months Heinrich and Clara don't even leave their room (a servant girl who has come along on their flight procures the necessities for them). They live in utter poverty; their only contact is with each other. They even lack books, paper, and ink, but Heinrich has kept his old diary, which he reads from back to front to recapitulate the history of their escape. They don't experience this situation as isolation, however, but think of themselves as "Adam and Eve in Paradise."[39] The authenticity of their love grows in proportion to the intensity of their outward deprivations. Like the course of the plot, the almost parodic tone of the novella indicates that at the end of the era, Tieck was interested in the latent autism of Romantic inwardness. With regard to the present chapter, however, the question of topography is decisive. What location does Tieck choose to tell his story of withdrawal? Just like Spitzweg in the most famous painting of the Biedermeier period, he chooses a garret. In the early phase of European urbanization, poets and painters who wanted to illustrate seclusion within a city had recourse to attic rooms. The lighting alone offered them good opportunities. Thus the "poor poet" lies in near darkness, far from the narrow window, which doesn't afford much of a view in any case. The description of the view in *Life's Excess* is like a reminiscence of Spitzweg's painting:

> The builder of this little house must have been in a strange and almost unimaginable mood, for beneath the windows of the third floor the lovers inhabited there extended a fairly wide tile roof that made it completely impossible for them to look down into the street. If this roof completely cut them off from all contact with other people, even when they opened the windows in the summer, so did the smaller house across the street from theirs. For it only had apartments on the ground floor, and so they never saw windows or figures standing by them, but only the vast roof, black with smoke that began nearby and then angled up and away from them. . . . It is not easy for people in live in as complete an isolation as these two had achieved here.[40]

Thus we have the garret in 1839, an isolated room with the power to excite the imagination of its inhabitants. Twenty years earlier, E. T. A. Hoffmann, one of the first contemporary authors to make city life the object of his stories, had already recognized this correlation. The last tale published during his lifetime, "My Cousin's Corner Window," tells of an ailing poet whose only pleasure is observing a market square in Berlin from his attic lodgings and conjecturing about the biographies of the passersby. "It is necessary to mention that my cousin lives in a small room with a low ceiling, high above the street. That is the usual custom of writers and poets. What does the low ceiling matter? Imagination soars aloft and builds a high and cheerful dome that rises to the radiant blue sky."[41] Even if the view from this attic window has no obstacles to take into account, Hoffmann is already emphasizing the connection between the height of the dwelling and the power of imagination, a connection reinforced by Tieck's characters. The upward flight of imagination in the garret is expressed in Heinrich's aspiration to make their solitude ever more absolute, until at last it occurs to him to dismantle the staircase between the attic and the ground floor and use it as fuel for their stove. This is the story's clever climax: their withdrawal from the world culminates in the gradual disappearance of the only stairway. A means of access is transformed into a means of survival, a connection into kindling. Exchange with the outside world is sacrificed for the comfort of the immobile body, a principle that the "poor poet" also takes to heart by burning his own works in his stove, thereby eliminating contact with his potential readership.

This extinguishing of literary and architectural means of communication exemplifies the fact that garrets are locations of precarious self-absorption. When Heinrich in *Life's Excess* finally admits to his wife where the fresh firewood is coming from, he prepares her for the fact "that for the time being, even more than before, we will have to be enough company for each other. For how would an invitation to an afternoon coffee ever reach you up here? No, I'm all you need and you're all I need."[42] To be sure, this insular existence is abruptly brought to an end when the landlord returns from a spa, unnoticed by his tenants in the garret. After discovering that the stairway is missing, he notifies the police, but at the decisive moment the lovers are found and rescued by a well-to-do friend of Heinrich's. This last plot twist has the gesture of a moral lesson. Heinrich, the enemy of the stairs, owes his liberation to a steadfast connecting link: an old volume of Chaucer's works he had sold to an antiquarian book dealer after their flight. To its flyleaf he had entrusted their story as well as the address of their hideout. His friend, who had given him the book as a present, happened upon it in another antiquarian bookshop and thus learned what had happened. At the end of the story, he hands it back to him with the well-founded remark that the book is "amazingly enough the stairway that has brought us together again."[43] The epoch of emphatic self-isolation has been overcome, both in the life of the hero and in the biography of his creator.

THE HYGIENISTS' BATTLE AGAINST
THE TENEMENT HOUSE

Spitzweg's painting and Tieck's novella illustrate the semantics of the garret on the threshold of a new era in which how people live would be profoundly reconfigured. Beginning in the 1840s or 1850s, in the wake of urbanization, a completely new form of construction became established: the multistory tenement house. The historian Clemens Wischermann described its increasing presence in Hamburg, for example: "Within a few years, the previously unknown tenement clearly becomes the standard for new home construction; this type of dwelling accounts for almost the entire increase in housing since the 1850s."[44] Heinrich and Clara's romantic attic room was still located in a building of only three stories in which the landlord also lived. The Biedermeier urban scenes of Spitzweg's early works also typically consist of narrow buildings of at most four stories. Around the middle of the nineteenth century, these conditions were fundamentally transformed, as a disconcerted contemporary of Spitzweg's recorded in his memoirs: "In place of well-built bourgeois dwellings for individual families, there arose on the linear streets barracks-like apartment cubes that piled story upon story, inhabited in place of families by groups of people, layered one above the other and alienated from their fellows."[45] In the largest German cities, statistical records of the distribution of apartments on various floors reveal that while a fourth floor was almost unheard-of in the 1840s, that was where the majority of the population was living a scant half century later.[46] Between 1860 and 1880, the recorded average number of inhabitants per building multiplied in almost all German cities. The epoch-making transformation of European cities began in Paris under Louis Napoleon and Haussmann. Accomplished in barely twenty years, the metamorphosis of Paris was unmatched in extent and political energy. Nevertheless, all the rapidly expanding metropolises of continental Europe modeled their construction practices on the changes occurring in Paris. In the 1860s and 1870s, the construction of wide boulevards and ring roads between inner and outer districts, lined with continuous rows of multistory apartment buildings, emerged as the predominant principle of spatial expansion, a development that the urban reformer Rudolf Eberstadt, one of the most prominent German critics of tenement buildings, described at the beginning of the twentieth century as a pan-European contamination: "Paris was the widely admired modern metropolis. . . . Monumentality—grandly proportioned streets, squares, and building facades—became the fashion in city planning, adopted and further elaborated in Cologne and Berlin, in Amsterdam and Vienna. In continental urban construction, 'cosmopolitan' became synonymous with grand buildings and outward display."[47]

As soon as the first mass tenement houses were built, they came under criticism. As early as the 1840s, there were scattered studies of living conditions among workers' families in large cities, where they were housed in the newly built multistory buildings.[48] It is fair to say that the so-called housing question, an object of much academic and political discussion in the late nineteenth and early twentieth centuries, is inseparably coupled to the beginning of urbanization and the establishment of what the Germans called *Mietskasernen*, "rental barracks."[49] From the beginning, the indeterminate density of habitation within the buildings, their crowded multiplicity of apartments and lack of large courtyards and gardens were regarded as problems, and the consequences for the inhabitants' physical and moral well-being were analyzed. This was the beginning of a long-running debate about the relative merits of mass-occupancy tenements and the British model of single-family houses.

One cannot exaggerate the role played by discussion of urban housing in the birth of the "public health" or "hygiene" movement gaining momentum in Germany in the second half of the nineteenth century. In the tradition of the "Complete System of Medical Policy" elaborated by the German physician Johann Peter Frank (1745–1821), but under the new conditions of urbanization, the public health movement attempted to influence not just the construction of slaughterhouses and morgues, the preservation of food, and the suppression of prostitution, but also the planning of sewers and the paving of streets. The establishment of what Foucault called a "bio-power," which "exerts a positive influence on life, that endeavors to administer, optimize, and multiply it, subjecting it to precise controls and comprehensive regulations,"[50] can be precisely traced in the hygiene movement, which arrived relatively late in Germany.[51] In the name of "public health," it sought to control urban living conditions in the most diverse areas, its touchstone being always the legitimacy and transparency of paths of circulation (be they for foodstuffs, sewage, or people). Acting hygienically meant establishing reliable channels and avoiding obstructions. In Germany, two factors accounted for the coalition of physicians, politicians, architects, and economists in an organ such as the *Deutsche Vierteljahrsschrift für öffentliche Gesundheitspflege* (German quarterly for public health), the hygienists' "central forum for discussion."[52] One factor was the problematic living conditions in the rapidly growing cities (Berlin doubled its population to a million between 1862 and 1876); the other was the susceptibility of the densely populated districts to the cholera and typhus epidemics that led to record-breaking mortality rates in the cities.[53] Against this backdrop, it is understandable that hygiene came into focus as the science of prophylaxis. Given the transformed housing conditions in the cities, what was at stake was the creation of circumstances that would prevent the spread of future epidemics. As the great Berlin pathologist Rudolf Virchow wrote in 1868, "The great progress made by modern healthcare lies in preventing more and more illnesses. We must therefore direct our attention to the living conditions of the population."[54]

In order to ensure the most reliable prophylaxis possible—"such as inoculation against smallpox"[55]—the hygienists concentrated their attention from the beginning on so-called building hygiene, that is, the effort to correct inadequacies in the development of urban housing and above all, establish guidelines for the creation of new mass rental housing. As James Hobrecht, city planner and mayor of Berlin in the 1870s, stated in his pathbreaking work of 1868 entitled *Über öffentliche Gesundheitspflege* (On public health), "In the most important respects, our dwelling place creates the conditions for the weal or woe of our existence. Depending on circumstances, it either gives or withholds irreplaceable sources of life: air and light. Its qualities have such continuous and lasting effect on our health that it must be the chief object of attention for the concerned eye of public health care."[56] Hobrecht emphasized that "from the point of view of sanitation" there were as yet absolutely no legal regulations in the building codes for dwellings and thereby identified a gap whose closing would be one of the most important concerns of the Deutscher Verein für öffentliche Gesundheitspflege (German Public Health Association), which grew out of the quarterly journal *Deutsche Vierteljahrsschrift für öffentliche Gesundheitspflege* in 1873. In the 1860s and 1870s, as continuous rows of multistory tenements began to be built, there was no legal structure in place to deal with the new construction practices. Existing building codes (Berlin's, for example, was from 1853) addressed only questions of fire prevention and until the middle of the century focused primarily on single-family bourgeois residences. In

Berlin, where the new neighborhoods planned in 1862 on the model of Paris created the conditions for the wholesale construction of mass tenements,[57] there were no legal restrictions on the number of floors. In the 1870s, buildings sometimes reached seven stories in height. This was the situation facing the incipient German hygiene movement at the time the German Reich was founded in the wake of the Franco-Prussian War: in metropolises like Hamburg, Danzig, Breslau, Dresden, Munich, and above all Berlin, the concept of the mass tenement building was already established. The lack of regulations controlling the density of development or the number of stories ensured that living conditions in the vast, overcrowded buildings became increasingly dire. Thus hygienic criticism focused on living conditions in the tenement houses, which were identified as the breeding ground for repeated cholera and typhus epidemics, as well as the spread of tuberculosis beginning in the 1890s.

Dwelling-place hygiene is especially concerned with two areas: promoting and overseeing expanded sewer systems and sanitary facilities in the tenements, and combating increases in the number of stories. All the basic questions of public health—how to accurately document and then lower the high mortality rate in the big cities, how to identify the connections between urban living conditions and the occurrence of certain diseases—were from the beginning tied to the question of the vertical location of apartments. For example, one of the most frequently repeated demands of the *Vierteljahrsschrift* was the standardization and accurate completion of death certificates. In this discussion, the information value of the floor of the apartment was repeatedly emphasized.[58] The value of knowing the floor where the deceased lived should not be underestimated as one important piece of evidence in the "mortality statistics" that the hygiene movement used to formulate its diagnoses and recommendations. The head of the Berlin Municipal Office of Statistics, Hermann Schwabe, presented the data from the capital at the second annual meeting of the Association for Public Health:

> The mortality rate is lowest in the *bel étage*, where 21.6 of every thousand inhabitants die annually. Above and below it, the rate increases: 22 of every thousand on the ground floor, but 25.3 in the basement. Continuing upward, mortality is 21.8 per thousand on the third floor, 22.6 on the fourth floor, and 28.2 from the fifth floor up.[59]

This listing is eloquent in several respects. First of all, it reflects the vertical order that remained in effect in mass tenements into the twentieth century, with its center on the second floor, the so-called *bel étage*, and a continuous decrease in value the closer one approached the outer limits of basement and garret. This hierarchy was extensively documented in the essays and manuals of the housing reformers, and also clearly reflected in the precise statistics of rental prices, which unanimously document that in the time between the founding of the German Reich in 1871 and the start of the First World War in 1914, the most expensive apartments were on the second floor, the moderate-priced ones on the first, third, and fourth floors, and the much cheaper ones in the basement or on the fifth floor or higher.[60] As early as the Berlin census of 1867, this structure was being described in the drastic terminology eagerly adopted by the hygienists: "One can . . . describe the apartments on the first three floors as normal, those in the basement or on the fifth or higher floor as abnormal."[61]

The fact that around 1870, apartments were already being discussed in the categories of pathology suggests that the hierarchical order of the tenement houses had consequences beyond simply a certain distribution of income level. As Schwabe's statistics made clear, at stake was the existential danger of certain "abnormal" dwelling levels. It was above all infant and child mortality in the large cities, already identified in the first volume of the *Vierteljahrsschrift* as "one of the most important topics for public health to address," that was repeatedly connected to floor of the dwelling.[62] For differing reasons, apartments in the basement and on the upper floors were the most problematic areas of the tenement building, those in the basement because of their dampness and darkness, those on the upper floors because of their stuffiness, lack of protection against the heat of the summer months, and difficulty of access. From the beginnings of public health to the high-water mark of the housing policy debate before the First World War, the condemnation of apartments on the upper floors did not cease. Rudolf Virchow, for example, also exploited the statistics mentioned by Schwabe in his 1873 report *Reinigung und Entwässerung Berlins* (Purification and drainage of Berlin) and attempted to clarify the salient mortality rates: "Among the conclusions that clearly emerge from the analysis of conditions in dwellings on the upper floors, we must mention above all the number of stillbirths. Their frequency in the women who must climb up so high is frightening."[63] In contrast to 1.3 stillbirths per thousand among the inhabitants of the *bel étage*, among inhabitants of the fifth floor or higher the rate was 1.7. "These numbers," Virchow wrote, "speak for themselves."[64] But the focus was not just on excessive stair-climbing for pregnant women, but also on the fact that children and older people living five or six stories up went outside much less often. In 1886, the Berlin hygienist Hermann Wasserfuhr wrote, "because of the difficulty of stair climbing, apartments just under the roof condemn their inhabitants—especially weak or sickly persons—to much more indoor air than is the case for families living on the lower floors."[65] And that was so dangerous precisely because the temperature and air quality became worse the higher one climbed in the tenement house. Precarious access lengthened the time spent in precarious rooms, a vicious cycle the housing reformers tried to break by demanding that housing construction be reoriented on the English model of the single-family house. "If children and baby carriages have to be carried up and down three or four flights of stairs every time one goes outside, it becomes a rare occurrence. In small houses spread out over more area, going in and out of the house is so easy it can be done numerous times per day."[66]

The unhealthiness of some floors of a tenement house had become such an urgent problem by the end of the nineteenth century that the newly founded health insurance funds commissioned surveys on the connections between living conditions and susceptibility to illness.[67] The largest and longest-running among them was conducted by the Berliner Ortskrankenkasse für den Gewerbebetrieb der Kaufleute, Handelsleute und Apotheker (Berlin health insurance fund for merchants, tradesmen, and apothecaries)—after 1914 renamed Allgemeine Ortskrankenkasse (General health insurance fund). From 1901 until 1920, an annual report was published on the living conditions of members who had fallen ill (mainly from tuberculosis). Extensive questionnaires and photographs documented in detail their living conditions, and the question of floor number always appeared as a separate category in the forms, which offered the options "ground fl.," "_____ floor," "attic," and "basement apt."[68] For the housing inspectors as for the statisticians of mortality, the vertical location of the apartments played a central role, a fact still reflected in the title of the 1982 reissue of Berlin photographs from 1901 to 1920: *Hinterhof, Keller und Mansarde* (Rear courtyard, basement, and attic).[69] Almost without exception, the chronically ill in the tenement houses lived in the locations featured in this title, and eighty years later, it was symptomatic of the vertical organization of apartment buildings around 1900 that a book title meant to attract maximum attention continued precisely this identification of above and below. Until about 1920, basement and attic apartments were both condemned in hygienic discourse.

It is instructive to observe the success of the public health movement in the nineteenth century as it strove to eliminate dwellings in these locations. A glance at the revision of urban building codes, for instance, shows that from about 1880 on, hygienic demands were transformed into judicial facts. The initial failure to regulate the number of stories was corrected, as one can see from the revised building codes of Munich (1879),[70] Vienna (1883),[71] Prague (1883),[72] Berlin (1887),[73] and Breslau (today's Wroclaw, 1892).[74] All these regulations had been supplemented with almost identically worded clauses restricting to five the number of stories in new apartment buildings, and the influence of the hygiene movement on the change in the law frequently received explicit mention. Thus the introduction to the new Prague building code referred to the annual meeting of the Public Health Association in 1875 and expressed gratitude for the "food for thought"[75] that it had provided "in the area of sanitation."[76] The annotator of the Breslau building code, on the other hand, lamented the relative tardiness of the revisions of 1892: "A large number of apartment buildings of more than six stories owe their existence to this fact."[77] Thus the vertical increase in building size, occurring in a virtually unregulated environment in the early phase of urbanization, was prohibited from the 1880s on, and tough restrictions on the habitability of the attic story were formulated. The Berlin building code of 1853, for instance, gave no attention to this question. By 1887, on the other hand, article 37 specified that apartments were permitted only as high as the fifth floor.[78] Wording added in 1897 added the explanation that "attic rooms" above that level were not to be regarded as "rooms meant for long-term human habitation."[79] By the end of the nineteenth century, laws were in place in Germany that prohibited rental apartments on upper stories, at least in newly constructed buildings. The regulations in some other European metropolises were even stricter. According to the revised statutes of 1883, within the city limits of Vienna and Prague, "the installation of dwellings in attic rooms is forbidden without exception."[80] Only small single-family houses at the edge of the city were not affected by this regulation: "Living spaces in attics are permitted only in single-family houses and villas."[81]

Why is it necessary to include these hygienic and judicial attacks on upper-story dwellings in a history of the elevator? Because they are imaginable only in an era whose image of the apartment building did not yet include the still largely unknown conveyance. From about 1910 or 1920 onward, the battle against the fifth floor was largely abandoned. In the diction of the public health movement, one could say that the upper stories became "normalized" (and beyond that, even glorified). But how exactly shall we describe the elevator's reprogramming of "apartments on abnormally high floors"?[82] What influence did the technical apparatus have on the arguments of the hygienists? One could say that it played both a direct and an indirect role. For one thing, the elevator quite simply made it possible for the inhabitants of the upper floors to avoid the hardship of climbing stairs and so ensured that pregnant women no longer had to "climb up so high" and children "going outside" was no longer a "rare occurrence." Thus the elevator directly put an end to many of the public health objections by making vertical access to all the apartments in a tenement building equally available. For another thing, however, it indirectly set something in motion that is more difficult to localize. One could call it a change in the "imaginative potential" of the top floor. For as the elevator became established, it is remarkable that even those unhealthy aspects of apartments on the upper floors that remained unresolved by the installation of the new conveyance lost their urgency. We must wonder why the hygienic ambition of a "pathology of the upper stories" in the early twentieth century subsided, although the heat and stuffiness of the apartments in fact continued. Without ignoring other relevant factors such as techniques of thermal insulation or air conditioning, we are still left with the suspicion that beginning in the second decade of the twentieth century, a changed perception of upper-story dwellings—a new "vertical consciousness"—was created by "the elevator" as a concept of the collective imagination, as well as by the organization of newly constructed apartment buildings with their rooftop gardens and penthouses. It is no accident, for example, that in his famous chapter about spaces in *The Structure of the Artistic Text*, Yuri Lotman chose the following examples of "binary semantic opposition" in nineteenth-century novels:

> The world is divided up into rich and poor, natives and strangers, orthodox and heretical. . . . In the text, these worlds, as we have said, almost always receive spatial realization: the world of the poor is realized in the form of a poor suburb, the slums or *attics*, while the world of the rich is realized as Main Street, a palace, or the *dress circle of a theatre*.[83]

In the age of the elevator, Lotman's binary oppositions could no longer be maintained. The scope of this transformation in the early twentieth century becomes especially clear when we reflect that from the beginning, hygienic discourse about the upper stories included both physiologic and moral aspects. Along with the quality of the rooms, the behavior of their inhabitants was always simultaneously subject to scrutiny as well—the day laborers, messenger boys, widows, and proletarian families who populated "the two extremes of dwelling location"[84] (especially the upper stories, since the relatively well-to-do proprietors of ground-floor shops often lived in the basements beneath them). Numerous hygienists leave us in no doubt that the unacceptably high mortality rate on the upper floors had to do not only with the unhealthy conditions of the apartments or with the poverty of the renters, but often with irregularities in their family life. Thus Carl Flügge, one of the most vehement advocates of the single-family house, speculated that the high rate of infant mortality on the attic story could be connected to the fact "that there are, for example, usually more bottle-fed or more illegitimate children there who are more likely to succumb to gastro-intestinal illnesses."[85] The ease with which the connections between apartment location, family composition, and disease susceptibility were posited here demonstrates how the top floor was still being interpreted in the early twentieth century. The appearance of the elevator severed these connections. Beyond the creation of healthier access, it domesticated an entire region of the building in both an architectonic and an ethnologic sense, as it were. It engendered a completely different upper-story "ethic." For this reason, the decades-old association of basement and attic was radically split apart beginning in the 1920s. As a concrete result of the hygiene movement, the basement as a dwelling level disappeared from the cities. The top floor, on the other hand, entered its heyday.

THE SEMANTICS OF THE ATTIC AROUND THE FIN DE SIÈCLE

The problematic status of the upper stories that emerged in hygienic and judicial discourse at the end of the nineteenth century was also discernible in literary images of apartment buildings. To better understand the topographical structure of texts in which attics play a central role, one must bear in mind that in the 1880s, the revised building codes in Berlin and Prague prohibited attic apartments "without exception." Four major literary works from turn-of-the-century Europe use attic rooms as settings: Henrik Ibsen's play *The Wild Duck* (1888), with the photographer Hjalmar Ekdal's strange attic studio whose back room is revealed to be an artificial nature preserve; Robert Musil's short novel *Young Törless* (1906), set largely in the secret attic hideout of a group of military school students; Gerhart Hauptmann's play *The Rats* (1911), set in the attic of a Berlin tenement that the failed theatrical director Hassenreuter has converted into a costume rental agency; and finally Franz Kafka's novel *The Trial* (1914), with its famous court offices in attic rooms on the outskirts of a city. What function do these locations have in their respective texts? How does their artistic deployment relate to contemporary hygienic caveats with regard to buildings? Over and above the obligatory bleakness and poverty of these attic rooms, we can perhaps define seven characteristics they share:

STUFFINESS

When one recalls that poor air quality was one of the most important arguments of public health advocates against the attic region, a story like *Young Törless* sounds almost like an experiment to prove their thesis. At one point the boys are entering their secret hideout: "From inside the attic came a breath of warm, stale air, like that in small hothouses. . . . On one side of them were some large water-tubs for use in case of fire. It was obvious that the water in them had not been changed for a very long time; it had a sweet, sickly smell. The whole place was oppressive."[86] The mention of the climatic conditions in attics always signals the importance of their effect on those present. The lack of fresh air is exactly the reason for the "oppressive" atmosphere. This same association is also established in *The Rats* when Hassenreuter's mistress, arriving in the attic for a secret rendezvous, immediately notices that the air is "a bit heavy."[87] And in *The Wild Duck*, before a decisive conversation with his wife about whether their daughter was actually fathered by another man, Hjalmar Ekdal sends the girl out of the apartment with the words, "All these fumes in here aren't good for you; the air here under this roof is bad."[88] In attics, both the climatic and the communicative conditions are oppressive; sluggish circulation befalls both oxygen and fresh, independent thought. Especially those still unaccustomed to the stuffiness of attic rooms must fear loss of control.

This constellation is a frequent theme in Kafka's *Trial*. When Josef K. is overcome by dizziness during his first visit to the court offices, a woman who works there says,

> "Well, you see then, it's nothing at all unusual. The sun beats down on the attic beams and the hot wood makes the air terribly thick and stifling. That's why this isn't such a good location for the offices, in spite of the many other advantages it offers. But as far as the air is concerned, on days when the traffic of involved parties

is heavy you can hardly breathe, and that's almost daily. . . . But in the end people get quite used to the air. When you come here the second or third time, you'll hardly notice the stuffiness at all."[89]

Helplessness in the face of the impalpable court is demonstrated by the fact that the accused's ability to breathe is literally reduced. In the attic, Josef K. begins to stagger, although, as he says, he is "an official myself and I'm used to office air" (75). In his office on a lower floor, however, with its "huge plate-glass window" (66), the climatic conditions are completely different, as is repeatedly emphasized. Obviously the location of the court even changes the body's constitution, for we learn that since the lungs of the court officials have grown used to the stuffiness of the attics, they can no longer cope with conditions outside the offices. When Josef K. is helped to the exit by two workers after his attack of vertigo, as he bids them farewell he notices "that they were unable to bear the comparatively fresh air from the stairway, accustomed as they were to the air in the offices of the court. They could hardly reply, and the young woman might have fallen had K. not shut the door as quickly as possible" (79). Something similar happens to Musil's Törless, who has been so thoroughly initiated into attic existence by his comrades Reiting and Beineberg that he can no longer stand the "vigor" and "man-of-the-world confidence" of the boys returning from vacation (133). The outside world "shamed him, who now cared only for the stuffy air between four narrow walls" (133). Thus the climatic conditions in the attic create a disturbance in perception repeatedly emphasized in *The Trial*. The atmosphere in the court offices give rise to *Schwindel* in both of its senses in German: dizziness and deception. Both Josef K.'s balance and his sense of reality are put to the test. The location of the court engenders vertiginous sensations as well as illusions. That's why the oppressive atmosphere is referred to throughout the novel every time Josef K. comes into contact with the court, and above all when he visits the studio of the painter Titorelli. One could say that in the attic, the subject's sense of self is endangered. Lack of access to the free circulation of breathable air drastically increases the feeling of being at the mercy of powers already acclimatized to it. In this respect, it is not surprising that the experiments in hypnosis practiced on the weak-willed Basini in *Törless* take place in the attic. Conditions there are declared "favorable" as the boys prepare the hypnosis session: "the stale air, the foul, brackish smell emanating from the water-tubs, all this generated a feeling of drowsiness, of never being able to wake up again, a weary, sluggish indolence" (147). There can be no doubt that the stuffiness of the attic threatens to blur the border between reality and illusion.

UNCANNINESS

The attic twilight is above all the product of insufficient lighting. In place of the equally spaced windows typical of the apartments and offices on lower floors, the garrets under the eaves contain only slanted skylights, isolated "small windows," or no source of natural light at all. Vision is obscured in these locations. Thus according to the first stage direction in *The Rats*, the "prevalent gloom" of Hassenreuter's windowless costume collection makes it hard "to decide whether the place is the armour room of an old castle, a museum of antiquities or the shop of a costumer" (325). When Hassenreuter's daughter has an attic assignation with her lover, she experiences the riskiness of moving from daylight into the twilight of the attic. Unexpectedly, she stumbles upon the cleaning lady:

> WALBURGA: Why, dear me! Who is here? [She has cried out and is about to run away]. . . . But you do look like a ghost, Mrs. John.
>
> MRS. JOHN: How do you say I looks?
>
> WALBURGA: Oh, it just seems so when one comes out of the vivid sunlight into the darkness, into these musty holes. It seems as though one were surrounded by ghosts. (339–40)

In Hauptmann's drama, this comment is to be understood literally, for the inhabitants of the former cavalry barracks are convinced that the ghost of a soldier who hanged himself from the roof beam is still haunting the two-story attic.

When Hassenreuter discovers some costumes missing from his collection (they are being used for the clandestine delivery of the servant girl Pauline's illegitimate child on the attic's second floor), he summons the concierge, who immediately suspects the undead soldier. Everything that advances the plot (which revolves around Mrs. John's purchase of Pauline's infant) takes place in the attic: the first conversation between Mrs. John and Pauline in which the terms of the purchase and handing over of the child are settled; the acquaintance of the servant girl with Mrs. John's brother Bruno, her subsequent killer; and finally the death of a second infant whom Mrs. John has stolen from a neighbor's apartment in order to show it to an official as Pauline's child. It almost seems as if this location becomes a kind of catalyst for the spreading tragedy. In the words of a famous interpretation, the "dark, uncanny atmosphere" of the attic contaminates the other rooms and irrupts "directly into the sitting rooms of the upright bourgeoisie."[90]

The uncanniness of upper-story rooms unfolds precisely in contrast to the well-lighted "sitting rooms" on the floors below, the classrooms of Törless's boarding school, Josef K.'s office, or the villa of the merchant Werle in *The Wild Duck*, whose rooms are "brightly lit by lamps and candelabra" (393). Like the stuffy air, the diffuse light also ensures that the familiar coordinates of reality become confused. Thus when Törless would return from the attic room, "what he also liked was afterwards coming back into the daylight, walking among the other boys, and being back in the midst of their jollity, while he could still feel the excitements of solitude and the hallucinations of darkness trembling in his eyes and ears" (48). Especially in the case of Kafka's *Trial*, the question often arises whether one can really trust one's eyes in the sphere of the attics or whether they produce "hallucinations" instead. From the beginning, the action of the novel occurs on the threshold between reality and illusion, in the "twilight that falls between dream and wakefulness," as Gerhard Neumann puts it.[91] The focus is on the "anxious question of whether the hero of the novel awakens from a dream into the reality of a world of laws or on the contrary, whether he steps from the world of wakefulness into the realm of bad dreams."[92] The entire novel is obviously organized by the "riskiest moment" when Josef K. wakes up in the morning, as suggested by his often-quoted first defense plea, which Kafka excised from the first chapter.[93] You could say that *The Trial* plays out the consequences of an unsuccessful act of waking up, the fate of a man whose presence of mind at the moment of opening his eyes was not sufficient to negotiate the precarious transition between the spheres. What is the consequence of this fluid borderline for the spatial structure of the novel? It gives rise to that impenetrable labyrinth of attic offices of which it's impossible to say whether it is a hitherto overlooked part of the familiar environment or in fact a completely different world.

EVOCATION OF THE PAST

One of the German words for attic is *Speicher*, which also means storehouse, warehouse, or granary. This points to one of the attic's primary functions, the conservation and storage of objects. The furniture of the attic stands unresolved between eras, belonging neither completely to the past nor to the present. Although not in immediate use, it hasn't disappeared or been destroyed either. Whoever shifts a great part of his existence to an attic like Ekdal in *The Wild Duck* or Hassenreuter in *The Rats* is reacting to some flaw in his present biography. In the attic, a happier phase of one's life survives. That's why the rooms in which Harro Hassenreuter gives acting lessons and runs his costume rental are furnished in the spirit of his earlier triumphs. Photographs of him as leading man, laurel wreaths, and red ribbons bearing texts extolling his art hang from the walls. Besides the three hundred crates full of old costumes, the only thing left over from better days is a love affair with one of his former actresses. The retreat to the attic as evocation of the past appears even more radically in Ibsen's *Wild Duck*. In the topography of the play—the confusing domicile of the Ekdal family—a photography studio in the attic that connects the rooms for living and working to a sort of artificial wilderness with trees and small animals, is the antithesis of the imposing villa of Old Ekdal's former business partner, Werle. An unsuccessful real estate speculation accounts for the course of their contrasting biographies: Werle survives the mistake unscathed, while Ekdal, "a broken man, beyond any help" (405), after serving a long term in prison, is being cared for in the attic apartment by his son Hjalmar and daughter-in-law Gina, formerly a maid in the Werle household. As he does so often, Ibsen stages the eruption of a long-concealed conflict in *The Wild Duck*, putting the crumbling pillars of bourgeois existence to the test. In this play it is Gregers, Werle's recently returned son, who takes it upon himself to reveal that the familial happiness of Hjalmar Ekdal is based on lies. Apparently, Hjalmar and Gina's fourteen-year-old daughter, Hedvig, is in reality the product of Gina's affair with her former employer, Werle, who had arranged for Gina to approach and quickly marry the son of his sometime business partner so that he would think the child was his. *The Wild Duck* plays out the catastrophic effects of revealing these facts after fifteen years of concealment. The Ekdals' delusional order—both the old man's long-standing mental imbalance and the festering lie of his son's marriage—finds its exact counterpart in the spatial order of the play: the pretend wilderness of the attic, whose décor is supposed to remind Old Ekdal of a more intact phase of his biography. For the former "tremendous hunter" (423) Ekdal, the artificial forest stocked with wild animals has the same significance as the framed theatrical photographs and laurel wreaths for the director Hassenreuter. They compensate for their present incapacitation with an elaborate attic reenactment of their past.[94] As in *The Rats* (and to a certain extent also in *Törless*, where the schoolboys indulge in spiritistic fantasies in the attic room decorated to look like a thieves' den), the attic functions as a surrogate space where present reality can no longer intrude. This sealing off becomes explicit when Gina and Gregers talk about the attic's furnishings—the cupboards full of old books a sailor once left behind:

> GINA: And then there's . . . a huge clock with figures that are supposed to come out. But the clock doesn't go anymore.
>
> GREGERS: Even time doesn't exist in there—with the wild duck.
>
> (436)

Clearly, the eponymous bird is introduced as a sort of heraldic animal of this illusionary world; it lies wounded in the attic just like its human inhabitants. Thus it is only logical that Hedvig commits suicide at the end of the play after Gregers has suggested euthanizing the bird. Annihilating the damaged "symbol of illusion and the lie they are living"[95] is equivalent to annihilating the damaged family itself.

Bearing in mind this temporal overlapping in attics, we return to the question of their uncanniness. For you don't need to have your entire biography tied up in attic rooms like Hassenreuter or Ekdal to know that what is stored there is never entirely stashed away for good. Even in those seldom-visited attics that serve as real storage rooms without being remodeled as places of permanent exile, it can happen at any time that the past forces its way into the present and supposedly superfluous objects prove to be significant. What a remarkable inventory of putatively lost paintings, documents, and posthumous works could be drawn up from the "sensational finds" discovered in attics in the nineteenth and early twentieth centuries (and continue to be made occasionally right up to the present). This location seems so predestined for the appearance of forgotten things that one would think the oppressive atmosphere actually brought them into existence rather than just preserving them. In the images of fantasy literature, this latent independent life of the attic plays a recurring role. The borderline between animate and inanimate material is called into question. One must entertain the possibility that there are still remains of life hidden among the objects, that the whole mixture might begin to ferment. The conditions in attics are ideally conducive to the creation of monstrous entities. We need only think of perhaps the most famous of them all, the Golem of Prague, the figure of clay that, according to an old Jewish legend, Rabbi Loew both called into being and laid to rest in the attic of the Old New Synagogue.[96] The latent threat of this location results precisely from the close relationship between what is one's own and what is foreign; the monstrous thrives on the formerly familiar. To that extent, the "uncanniness" of the attic paradigmatically confirms the most famous definition of this concept. In his 1919 essay "The 'Uncanny,'" Sigmund Freud famously begins with the semantic ambivalence of the word *heimlich* (originally "belonging to the house, secure, snug," but currently "secret, concealed") and he explains why the same adjective can mean two diametrically opposed things by defining the uncanny as "that class of the frightening which leads back to what is known of old and long familiar."[97] In the logic of language and of emotions the same rules apply. The uncanny, Freud says, "is in reality nothing new or alien, but something which is familiar and old-established in the mind"[98] and the prefix *un-* in the German *unheimlich* ("uncanny") is "the token of repression" of what was once familiar.[99] There is good reason to apply it to a space that is defined by its function of storing the old-established. An uncanny atmosphere dominates the attic because the objects jumbled there preserve some hint of an incompletely processed relationship to their owners.

INACCESSIBILITY

Musil describes in detail the location of the secret attic room in *Törless*. To get there, the boarding school boys have to climb to the third story of the building.

> From there on the stairs became narrow and went up, in short flights at right-angles to each other, to the attics. And—as old buildings are often whimsical in plan, with an abundance of nooks and crannies and unmotivated steps—this staircase actually went a considerable way above the level of the attics, so that on the other

side of the heavy, iron, locked door, which blocked the way further, it was necessary to go down again, by a flight of wooden steps, in order to reach the floor of the attic.

What this meant was that on this side of the attic door was waste space some yards high, reaching up into the rafters. In this place, which hardly anybody ever entered, old stage-scenery had been stored, dating from school theatricals in the remote past. (45)

The imperfect "logic" (in the quote above "whimsical" is a translation of the original "unlogisch"—illogical) of old buildings results in the attic region's double remoteness. For one thing, it is located on the highest and most inaccessible level of the building. For another, this level itself is complexly ramified, divided into different chambers, fragmented stairs, and subsidiary levels. Musil describes precisely how much caution and concentration are required each time the three boys enter their dark hideout, protected as it is by snares stretched across the path. The ritualized ascent to the attic region leaves no doubt that it is not accessible to just anyone. Only at the end of a convoluted and booby-trapped path do the boys reach their chamber, where Beineberg and Reiting hatch their plots, keep a diary, and hold séances.

It is especially the obscure approaches to attic rooms that make them locations of voluntary isolation, a situation we see repeated in the dramas of Hauptmann and Ibsen. Hassenreuter's lover once remarks that his costume collection is reachable only by "questionable ways" (351)—in the original "auf Schleichwege" (on secret paths, surreptitiously)—and thus fortunately completely inaccessible to his asthmatic wife. When they hear a pistol shot from back in the artificial wilderness in *The Wild Duck*, Hjalmar says to a startled Gregers, "We're very lucky in the way the loft is placed—nobody can hear us when we're shooting" (440). There, as in Musil's boarding school building, the attic is not simply a single lofty room, but an "illogical" (in the Wilkins and Kaiser translation, "whimsical") network. Hauptmann's stage directions mention "an adjoining room" and "stairs" (325);

Ibsen describes the imitation wildlife sanctuary behind the studio as "an extensive, irregular loft room with many nooks and corners, and two separate chimney shafts ascending through it" (425). And of course, the labyrinthine complexity and inaccessibility of the attic rooms in Kafka's *Trial* are of special significance. Josef K.'s disorientation already begins during his first progress through the outer corridors of the court ("'Surely you're not lost already,' asked the court usher in amazement" [72]), even before he learns from his lawyer, Huld, that the remoteness of the offices only increases the more influential their official inhabitants are. "The gradations and ranks of the court are infinite, extending beyond the ken even of initiates. The proceedings in the courts of law are generally a mystery to the lower officials as well; therefore they can almost never follow the progress of the cases they are working on throughout their course" (118). From a certain point on, not even the lawyers have access to the seats of power: "The trial has entered a stage where no further assistance can be given, where it is being handled by inaccessible courts of law, where even the defendant is no longer within reach of the lawyer" (121). Scholarship on *The Trial* has clearly established that the power of the court can be neither located physically nor slotted into a hierarchy. There is no legitimizing authority to which all statements are referred as evidence, just as there are no rooms in sight to which the work of all the others leads. The "highest court, which is totally inaccessible to you and me and everyone else" (158) as Titorelli says to Josef K., ensures a constant fragmentation and shifting of responsibility that express themselves in the topography of the novel in two primary ways, both in the steadily increasing inaccessibility of the center of power and equally in a certain kind of expansion of the sphere of the court that one could call the "dissolution of space."

LIMITLESSNESS

Among the vexing characteristics of the architectonic order in *The Trial* is the fact that the attic court offices are interconnected in completely unexpected places. What is true of the confusing personnel structure ("'So many people are connected with the court!' said K. with bowed head" [134]), is also true of the topographic structure. The reach of the institution cannot be determined. The threshold between its inner and outer aspects is constantly shifting. This uncontrollable proliferation of rooms is most conspicuous during Josef K.'s visit to Titorelli, "who lived in a suburb that lay in a completely opposite direction from the one with the law court offices" (139–40). The ascent to the painter's attic studio is explicitly described as an approach to a space that marks an end point: "The stairway that led to him was particularly narrow, extremely long, without a turn, visible along its entire length, and ended directly at Titorelli's door" (141–42). Nothing about its location in the city or in its building suggests that the studio could be a component of an extensive series of rooms. However, in the course of their conversation, Titorelli mentions a "second door" (155), barely visible behind the bed. Josef K. decides to leave through it, since the usual exit is blocked by the girls listening outside the door to the stairwell. As K. "looked through the open door" he is brought up short.

> "What's that?" he asked the painter. "What do you find so surprising?" he asked, himself surprised. "Those are the law court offices. Didn't you know there were law court offices here? There are law court offices in practically every attic, why shouldn't they be here too? In fact my atelier is part of the law court offices too, but the court has placed it at my disposal." (164)

Thus the "topography of power"[100] precisely mirrors the endless ramifications that also characterize the judicial process according to Titorelli and Huld the lawyer. Under the best of circumstances, indictments can be continuously "postponed" but never end in a decisive dismissal. As Huld tells him,

> "Try to realize that this vast judicial organism remains, so to speak, in a state of eternal equilibrium, and that if you change something on your own where you are, you can cut the ground out from under

your own feet and fall, while the vast organism easily compensates for the minor disturbance at some other spot—after all, everything is interconnected—and remains unchanged." (119–20)

Like the series of trials, the series of rooms is never-ending. But in the context of this chapter the important question is this: in a European novel written in 1914, why is the attic the best possible setting for such a fantasy of limitlessness? Apparently it is exactly the upper regions of residential buildings whose comprehensibility cannot be guaranteed. In the imaginative ordering of a turn-of-the-century building it is still possible that in its remotest corners, just under the roof, an uncontrolled growth could begin, that rooms and corridors could proliferate unnoticed, overrun the walls dividing rooms and then those dividing buildings as well, establishing an extensive, ramified system. Kafka's novel is perhaps the most impressive evidence of a topographic imagination belonging to the age just before the final establishment of the elevator. The new conveyance put an end to precisely the remoteness of the upper stories, that is, the prerequisite for producing such fantasies of unlimited growth. To the limitlessness of the attic—the horizontal proliferation at the top of crooked wooden stairways—the elevator shaft opposes the clearly defined channel described in chapter 1.

ILLEGITIMATE RELATIONSHIPS

What kind of social relations emerge in the four attic texts? In Ibsen's play, the attic rooms are inhabited by a family whose blood relationships are in question. Hauptmann makes the attic the location of several love affairs as well as the place where the housemaid Pauline gives birth to her illegitimate child. Kafka houses his unofficial court offices in attics, and in Törless, the attic room is introduced as the secret hideout of a group of schoolboys. Bastards, foundlings, secret lovers, and clandestine organizations: attics are always places of suspect relationships. They are the place for assignations forbidden in legitimate spaces—the marriage bedroom or the authorized office. Whereas the airy penthouse suites of late twentieth-century hotels will become the preferred location for honeymoons—the place where the privileged consummate their marriages—the attic story of elevatorless buildings around 1900 is where you cheat on your spouse. Thus on that Whit Sunday in Hauptmann's Berlin tenement, two pairs of secret lovers get in each other's way: Hassenreuter and the Viennese actress, his daughter Walburga and her tutor. Dubious familial relationships, illegitimate sexuality: the attic is the focal point not just for unmarried lovers and pregnant housemaids, but for the family in *The Wild Duck*, whose conjugal existence has been contrived by their child's actual father, and in *Törless*, for the homoerotic experiments of boarding school boys.

In the topographic structure of Musil's story, the attic has an especially important function because it represents an explicit counter-world to the school's official study hall, refectory, and dormitory. Its atmosphere is even capable of steering the course of one's thoughts in unusual directions, as Törless remarks after listening to Beineberg's spiritualistic musings:

> "Would you talk just the same if we were sitting downstairs among the others, who are doing their geography or history or writing letters home, where the light is bright and the usher may come round between the desks? Wouldn't this talk of yours seem a bit fantastic even to yourself there, a bit presumptuous, as though we were not the same as the others, but were living in another world?" (144–45)

One of the most remarkable aspects of the story's composition is that it consistently takes spatial and psychic systems into simultaneous account. Discovering a hidden level of the building means discovering a hidden layer of one's own consciousness, and by overstepping the boundary between legitimate and illegitimate space, the schoolboys inevitably also overstep the one between secure and insecure identity. The "confusions" of Musil's title character (the original title is *Die Verwirrungen des Zöglings Törless*—The confusions of the pupil Törless) are topographically predetermined. The "narrow, winding passages of sensuality" (140) and the "weird alleys" (173) that Törless's imagination invades have their exact correspondence in the spatial structure of the school. Again and again, Törless's erotic and cognitive crises (such as Kant's "walls in the dark" [114]) are described in metaphors that also apply quite literally to the difficulty of getting one's bearings in the attic. Especially in the conversation with Reiting in which he first learns about the humiliations Basini is subjected to in the attic, Törless realizes that ruptures in life histories and in buildings are congruent. Because, Törless reasons, if it is possible that the intact biography of a fellow pupil can be destroyed from one day to the next, then

> this narrow little room was possible. . . . Then it was also possible that from the bright diurnal world, which was all he had known hitherto, there was a door leading into another world, where all was muffled, seething, passionate, naked, and loaded with destruction—and that between those people whose lives moved in an orderly way between the office and the family, as though in a transparent and yet solid structure, a building all of glass and iron, and the others, the outcasts, the blood-stained, the debauched and filthy, those who wandered in labyrinthine passages full of roaring voices, there was some bridge—and not only that, but that the frontiers of their lives secretly marched together and the line could be crossed at any moment. (56)

The borderline between an existence grounded in the office and the family—the "transparent and yet solid structure, a building all of glass and iron"—and the porous world of the attics is suddenly breached. What is true of the "confusions" of the schoolboy Törless goes for the bank clerk Josef K. as well, at least for one pillar of this metaphoric building. Until his arrest, glass and iron are also the defining materials of the rooms he occupies day in and day out. The bank building is repeatedly described as having a flight of exterior steps, and its offices have large windows through which K. can gaze down onto the town square. The location and architectonic design of the bank display all the insignia of an imposing institution—things the arrestee at first also expects of the "court." Thus when K. is first summoned to "a street in a distant suburb" (36) one Sunday for his first examination, he tries to "recognize the building, even at a distance, by some sign he hadn't visualized precisely" (38), but the absence of any official emblem, as well as the unusual location and business hours, awaken some initial doubts about the legitimacy of this institution. Finally, with his discovery of the offices "where tenants who were themselves among the poorest of the poor tossed their useless trash" (65), he loses almost all respect for the court. "Now K. could see why they'd been ashamed to invite the defendant to these garrets for the initial interrogation, and chose instead to pester him in his lodgings. What a position K. was in, after all, compared to the judge who sat in a garret, while he himself had a large office in the bank, with a waiting room" (65). Comparable to the topographic structure of *Törless*, the attic rooms of *The Trial* are introduced as a counter-world to official spaces. In contrast to the city's "Palace of Justice," for instance, the offices of this court have no clear entrances or identifying marks. Kafka's novel sharpens the confrontation of the two institutions by introducing the lawyer Huld, who in his first conversation with K. and his uncle mentions that he already knows about the case and obviously stands between different judicial authorities.

> "You move in those legal circles," K. asked. "Yes," said the lawyer. . . .
> "With whom should I associate, if not my professional colleagues?" the lawyer added. It sounded so irrefutable that K. didn't even answer. "But you work at the court in the Palace of Justice, not at the one in the attic," was what he wanted to say, but he couldn't bring himself to actually do so. (101)

The "court in the Palace of Justice" and the "one in the attic" stand for two different forms of justice in the novel: the public and the hidden, the legitimate and the illegitimate, the central and the peripheral. (It is indeed remarkable that

Kafka and his family were themselves witnesses to the incipient recodification of the upper stories by the elevator, as one can read in Klaus Wagenbach's travel book about Kafka's Prague. In 1907, due to his father's expanding business, the family moved into one of the "newly built luxury apartment buildings" in the Old City, which meant a "definitive rise in social prestige." It was "a new building with an elevator, where the family lived on the top floor with a view of the Moldau."[101] Perhaps Kafka sited his elevatorless tenements in "suburban streets" seven years later because the success of the new invention was already perceptible in the center of Prague. In the better neighborhoods the top floor was no longer a place "where tenants . . . tossed their useless trash," but rather the luxurious refuge of upwardly mobile retailers of ladies' notions.)

IDENTIFICATION WITH THE CELLAR

According to Gaston Bachelard, the "psychology of the house" is characterized by a

> polarity of cellar and attic, the marks of which are so deep that, in a way, they open up two very different perspectives for a phenomenology of the imagination. Indeed, it is possible, almost without commentary, to oppose the rationality of the roof to the irrationality of the cellar. A roof tells its *raison d'être* right away: it gives mankind shelter from the rain and sun he fears. . . . Up near the roof all our thoughts are clear. In the attic it is a pleasure to see the bare rafters of the strong framework. Here we participate in the carpenter's solid geometry.
>
> As for the cellar, we shall no doubt find uses for it. It will be rationalized and its conveniences enumerated. But it is first and foremost the *dark entity* of the house, the one that partakes of subterranean forces. When we dream there, we are in harmony with the irrationality of the depths.[102]

It would be a stretch to say that Ekdal, Törless, and Josef K. take any pleasure in seeing "the bare rafters of the strong framework" in the attic, and their thoughts "up near the roof" are anything but clear. These texts are remarkably unanimous in presenting the attic and the cellar not as a polarity, but rather as closely related spaces. On a building's highest level, the connotations of its lowest level return. Hedvig calls the attic "the depths of the sea" (438), Hassenreuter speaks of his "catacombs" (344), and Törless thinks of himself as "deep inside a mountain." In their book on Kafka, Gilles Deleuze and Félix Guattari draw our attention to the "almost subterranean offices" in *The Trial*.[103] Thus in the topographic structure of these novels and plays we can discern the same association of especially lofty and especially lowly rooms that is also decisive for the hygienic overseers of tenement buildings.

Bachelard's invocation of the attic as a place of rationality has to do with the fact that, as he says himself, his phenomenological approach has only one kind of building in mind, namely, residences with no more than three levels: cellar, ground floor, attic. "One floor more, and our dreams become blurred. In the oneiric house, topo-analysis only knows how to count to three or four."[104] But to do justice to multistory tenement houses or "illogically" ("whimsically" in the English translation) labyrinthine boarding school buildings, topo-analysis would unavoidably have to learn how to count to five, six, or even seven. Bachelard's semantics of the attic, first published in 1957, is restricted to the exurban architecture of the single-family house. Accordingly, he denies urban dwelling places phenomenological consecration.[105] He dismisses those lofty attics and garrets that determine the collective image of this type of room and its reflection in literature and painting in the second half of the nineteenth century. These attics, however, contradict Bachelard's analyses in all respects. They are refuges of irrationality, cellars turned on their heads. It is no accident that the theater historian Joachim Hintze, in his comprehensive study of interiors in modern German drama, connects the two ends of the vertical axis when describing those interiors that represent significant "contrasting scenarios to the prosperity of the bourgeois way of life" in turn-of-the-century plays: "Although they appear in various guises—as cellars, flophouses, or attics—these types of settings form a semantic unity that banishes them to the periphery of society."[106] The upper reaches of buildings at the turn of the nineteenth to the twentieth century are the opposite of the rationality Bachelard attempts to invoke. They evoke instead associations with imprisonment or even death, as the remark from Roth's *Hotel Savoy* about the residents of the upper floor suggests: "Those who lived on high were in the depths, buried in airy graves."

PENTHOUSES, ROOF GARDENS, AND THE EXECUTIVE SUITE

By the beginning of the twentieth century, the hasty and un-considered building practices of the first phase of urbaniza-tion had been eliminated in central Europe. Strict control over vertical growth had been imposed by precise limits on building height as well as the so-called *Staffelbauordnung* (graduated building code) adopted in numerous towns to lower both building height and population density in newly built suburbs.[107] The building codes in Vienna and Prague, for example, left no doubt as to the reputation of the up-per stories: "In a four or five story building with a main stairway there are also one or more auxiliary stairways, the latter may also be used as the main stairway to the two highest floors."[108] The line of demarcation in buildings is clearly drawn, just as we have seen in Joseph Roth's and Thomas Mann's depictions of hotels. In the first years after the turn of the century, however, when the elevator was still largely unknown in tenement buildings, a complete reor-dering was already being depicted in promotional material such as a 1910 brochure from the Berlin firm Moosdorf and Hochhäusler:

> As we enter the building Am Treptower Park 24, a passenger eleva-tor, operated by the concierge but which residents may also oper-ate themselves, takes us up to the fourth floor in just a few seconds. Here a painter friend of ours is planning to pitch his tents (as he

modestly expresses it) after his wedding. Nine rooms with access to extra space in the attic as well as a rooftop garden will constitute the magnificent domicile of this modern Raphael—rooms, each more beautiful than the last, furnished with the most refined amenities. . . . One can see across the Treptow Park all the way to the tower and Bismarck Lookout on the Müggelberge.[109]

We can assume that this brochure is promoting one of the very first penthouses in Germany. The singularity of such an apartment in 1910 is especially clear when we reflect that the war against the fifth floor was still being waged. At the International Congress for Residential Hygiene held in Dresden the following October, for instance, top-floor apartments continued to be directly connected to high urban rates of infant mortality.[110]

Yet, beginning in the second decade of the century, there were increasing indications of a revalorization of living spaces on upper floors. From its inception, the new Berlin magazine *Bauwelt* (Construction world), whose first issue featured what amounts to a programmatic advertisement of an elevator company on its flyleaf,[111] was a leading advocate of liberalized building codes, as demonstrated by the title of its very first editorial, "The Seventh to the Ninth Floor: A Challenge for the City Center."[112] In the years before the First World War, the magazine regularly reported on the construction of new luxury apartment buildings like the one on Treptow Park. For example, the summer 1910 issue carried an article entitled "Villa Apartment on the Fifth Floor" about a nine-room apartment in the Charlottenburg neighborhood that could be reached via a "self-operated elevator."[113] One year later, the notice of "Luxury Apartments on the West Side of Berlin" in a building under construction at Kurfürstenstrasse 87 announced,

The building will contain two eight-room apartments on each of its four floors. . . . There are also extensive facilities for the children of the house. A gymnasium has been installed on the top floor. Rooftop gardens have also been planned as playgrounds. In addition to the most modern passenger elevators for the residents, elevators will be installed in the rear stairwells for service personnel. This is the first time that elevators in this form and for this purpose are being constructed in Berlin.[114]

At the end of 1911, the magazine laid out its fundamental principles in the article "Apartment with a Rooftop Garden," which focused primarily on a newly constructed building at Kurfürstendamm 70. After praising the luxurious interior décor of its eight- to ten-room apartments, the author noted that "the building attracts attention especially with its singular application of the new motif 'rooftop garden,' which has been evident for quite some time in certain areas of the 'new west' of Berlin, but seldom in such an energetic configuration."[115]

Compare the direction of such articles and advertisements with the frightening images conjured up just a few years earlier—and to some extent, at the same time—in the publications of the hygienists and housing reformers. In 1901, the physician Robert Dölger explained once again in the *Vierteljahrsschrift für öffentliche Gesundheitspflege*, "why we hygienists must be opposed to large buildings." It is on account of the upper stories, "because stale air, tainted by the breath of the residents, by odors from the kitchen or the water closet, rises from the lower stories to the upper ones and it is impossible that the air even in the corridor or the stairwell, which supplies the upper floors as well, can remain clean."[116] By contrast, how did the company Moosdorf and Hochhäusler promote its apartments? It too used the vocabulary of the hygienists, stressing the increasing difficulty of finding a healthy apartment in the big city of Berlin:

> The home gardens that used to be so frequent have been almost entirely replaced by factories or rear buildings. A spot of grass in the courtyard or by the front door is a rarity! Yet how important a bit of nature is for the modern big-city dweller! Since he can't avoid the nerve-wracking hustle and bustle of the metropolis in his everyday work life, he must think about securing a little "happy corner" for himself, where he can withdraw from the heat and burden of the day.[117]

This sphere of quiet, brightness, and transparency is offered by the apartments with rooftop terraces on the fourth and fifth floors, and the brochure makes clear from the outset that the elevator is the decisive prerequisite for the existence of these apartments by beginning its description of them with the statement that the conveyance reaches "the fourth floor in a few seconds." It is clear from the construction and marketing of such apartment buildings around 1910 how effectively the elevator intervened in the hygienic and aesthetic discourses of urbanization and transformed the image of the apartment house. If Dr. Dölger described the vertical dimension of the tenement building as an increasingly clogged canal in which the stale air threatened to collect just beneath the roof, the elevator, rooftop terraces, and expanded top floors created a kind of exhaust system. It is surprising therefore that in their tracts the health advocates almost never mentioned the significance of the elevator in the development of urban housing. In 1912, in one of the first German histories of the hygiene movement, Wilhelm Gemünd recapitulated the success of his discipline and above all of "healthful technologies on which the hygiene and convenience of the modern residential building primarily rest, e.g., the various forms of central heating, plumbing, flush toilets, drainage."[118] There is no mention of the technical apparatus that makes these conveniences available on all the floors of a building. The elevator, too, was a healthful technology, and not just because it replaced the ascent of the stairwell, which posed risks "especially for the feeble, those suffering from cardiac and pulmonary diseases, convalescents, girls and young women especially during menses,"[119] but also to the extent that the elevator reshaped the conditions of the large apartment building, both meteorologically and socially.

From about 1910 on, it was the upper stories of new buildings that attracted the most attention. Detailed description replaced the obfuscation noted by a contemporary hygienist with respect to early Berlin housing censuses: "Externally and internally, everything is avoided that would draw attention to the fact that an apartment is being rented on the top floor."[120] In promotional brochures for the new two-story luxury apartments, everything possible was done externally and internally to draw attention to the fact that an apartment was being rented on the top floor. Pre–First World War Berlin offered a perfect venue for observing the European birth of a type of dwelling that would later come to be called a penthouse. Gradually, in the week-to-week reports of the construction industry journals, a hierarchy of apartments began to emerge that would become anchored in the collective imagination in the following decades and achieve a social significance that remains unassailable to the present day. A particularly nice example of this occurs in the film *Pretty Woman*. The businessman Edward Lewis (Richard Gere) brings the hooker Vivian Ward (Julia Roberts) to his hotel for the first time, where he has rented the penthouse suite as usual. The first thing Vivian does is to walk out onto the large terrace, where the following conversation takes place:

VIVIAN: Wow, great view! I bet you can see all the way to the ocean from out here.

EDWARD: I'll take your word for it. I don't go out there.

VIVIAN: Why don't you go out there?

EDWARD: I'm afraid of heights.

VIVIAN: You are? So how come you rented the penthouse?

EDWARD: It's the best. I looked all around for penthouses on the first floor, but I can't find one.[121]

This is the situation in 1990: a wealthy entrepreneur has to suppress his acrophobia because the only appropriate place for him to stay is the penthouse. The social class-consciousness of a late twentieth-century businessman, however, harks back to the early years of the century, when brochures like that of Moosdorf and Hochhäusler were at work for the first time on a typology of the penthouse inhabitant. Not for nothing was the artist who was "planning to pitch his tents . . . after his wedding" in Treptow described as a "modern

Raphael." There was hardly another painter who embodied the sovereignty of art so well. Everything in the prospectus signaled an exalted atmosphere: the professional success of the tenant, his well-ordered private life, his view of the "Bismarck Lookout." In the interplay of artistic lifestyle, economic standing, and living conditions, the painter occupied a position directly opposed to Spitzweg's and Tieck's poor poets. The unworldly garret of 1840 had been transformed into the urbane rooftop terrace apartment of 1910.

Of course we cannot forget that this recoding of verticality at first applied only to the dwellings of the most well-to-do. One can gather this, for example, from a table of real estate values published in 1908, which listed five building categories in Berlin and its surroundings, from "manorial" to "constructed with little care and inferior materials."[122] Only the first category included the element "elevator" as an obligatory amenity. The descriptions in magazines like *Bauwelt* left no doubt that the newly built apartments were among Berlin's most luxurious. Siegfried Ascher's statistical study *Apartment Rents in Berlin from 1890 to 1910* vividly showed what an exception elevator installations were in Germany before the First World War. It's not just that the criterion "elevator" did not even appear in the apartment statistics until 1905.[123] The same study listed 782 marks as the average annual household income in Berlin,[124] which makes clear the exclusiveness of this means of transportation, whose production and installation were estimated at 10,000 marks.[125] According to Ascher, of 554,619 households in Berlin, between 1890 and 1910, only 1,579 had access to elevators.[126] By comparison, in the same period, 318,543 households had running water.[127] In these years, it was not yet imaginable that the elevator would one day be a self-evident component of new multistory construction. Nevertheless, the emancipation of the upper floors was beginning.

In American metropolises like Chicago and New York, of course, there were luxury apartments on the upper floors much earlier than in Berlin. In the well-documented history of housing in Manhattan, the beginning of the multistory "apartment house," which would all but eliminate the single-family house within half a century, is dated to the year 1869.[128] Moreover, the second such house ever built—the eight-story Stevens House of 1870—was already equipped with an elevator.[129] We will discuss the development of the New York apartment house in chapter 4. In the present context, it is revealing that for a surprisingly long time even in New York, the floors directly beneath the roof were considered unrentable and were used as laundry rooms or employee housing. The architectural historian Elizabeth Hawes quotes from a chronicle of the Dakota Building, erected in 1884 on the then largely unbuilt Upper West Side and planned as one of the first apartment houses for decidedly well-to-do tenants. The initial design of Henry J. Hardenbergh, the architect of the ten-story building, situated

> the largest apartments in the lower two floors ... because elevators were still something of a novelty and not entirely trusted. ... Also, Hardenbergh reasoned that lower-floor living would seem more familiar to New Yorkers who were accustomed to living in town houses. The eighth and ninth floors were to be used exclusively as laundry rooms, service and storage rooms, and servants' rooms.[130]

For the builder himself, however, an eighteen-room apartment had been planned on the seventh floor "in the hope of popularizing upper-story-living."[131] But in New York City this hope was at first in vain. At the beginning of the twentieth century, servants' quarters in new luxury apartment houses were as a rule still located just beneath the roof.[132] "In the first decade of the twentieth century," writes Elizabeth Hawes, "only architects and artists seemed to want to live at the top of the buildings,"[133] an astonishing diagnosis when one considers that at the same time, the first rooftop terrace apartments were being built in the well-to-do neighborhoods of Berlin. Thus the history of the penthouse did not necessarily begin in the city where the first multistory apartment houses were located, as one might expect.

Even if apartments in prewar Berlin were not permitted any higher than the fifth floor, the fact that the largest and most expensive of them were directly under the roof, surrounded by terraces, obviously happened sooner than it did in New York. A glance at the façades of New York apartment houses erected before the 1920s shows that the highest floors are not designed to stand out. Around 1915, for instance, before war and economic crisis interrupted construction activity for several years to come, the buildings of Emery Roth, the most active New York residential architect in the decades around 1900, still presented utterly regular façades, just as the apartments within followed no vertical hierarchy.[134] An apartment house on West End Avenue "originally contained a total of thirteen apartments, one per floor. Each had nine rooms."[135] In the 1920s, however, this inner and outer uniformity was ruptured, and increasing emphasis was placed on the upper stories. The English word "penthouse," which up to then had designated any sort of "appendage" or after-the-fact addition, now was redefined as a luxurious rooftop terrace apartment, the meaning it would have in German from the beginning when it was adopted from English.[136] So even if the phenomenon may have had European predecessors in Charlottenburg and Treptow, the origin of the word in its present meaning was obviously New York in the early 1920s. In these years, the first apartment houses with the most exclusive apartments on the top floor were built. In 1922–1923, Emery Roth built the fifteen-story twin buildings Myron Arms and Jerome Palace at Broadway and 82nd Street, and it was for these buildings that Roth's biographer Steven Ruttenbaum introduced the word "penthouse" for the first time.[137] Ruttenbaum provided this description of an almost identical apartment house built only a few months later:

> What made it special, however, was the penthouse apartment he designed at the top for himself and his family. . . . One of its special features was a terrace wrapped around it on all sides. . . . Roth took a great deal of pride in the apartment, for it symbolized the

fulfillment of his . . . youthful aspirations for a house with a garden, even though it was atop a city building."[138]

Historians of New York architecture are unanimous in designating the 1920s as the turning point in vertical design. Elizabeth Hawes, for instance, identifies Roth's Ritz Tower of 1925, with its numerous rooftop terraces and the two-story "duplex" apartments on the top floors, as the watershed: "It effected a new attitude toward an aerial city and an aerial home. . . . Penthouse and terrace apartments became fashionable and proliferated; style-conscious tenants staged parties on terraces and planted gardens in the air."[139] Manhattan, too, had a modern Raphael with a brand-new wife: "Alfred Stieglitz and Georgia O'Keeffe took a top-floor apartment at the thirty-four story Shelton Hotel and sketched the sights from the window."[140] No apartment house of the 1920s was still designed in the uniform style of the previous decade. The most prestigious apartments were routinely situated on the top floors, a fact reflected in the exterior design of many buildings, with their upper stories a series of receding stepped terraces. Interestingly enough, this characteristic physiognomy of the most luxurious apartment houses between 1920 and 1930 also owed its existence to a restriction in the building code, the Setback Law of 1916, which attempted to mitigate the threat of decreased sunlight posed by multistory buildings. The law stated that the height of a new building could exceed the width of the street only if from that point on, its higher stories successively receded. At any rate, the significance of the new type of apartment was best illustrated by a column about recent apartment houses in the *New Yorker* magazine, which was founded in 1925. The column was alternately entitled "Duplex" and "Penthouse."[141] Thus early on, there was a conviction that the sound of the word "penthouse" would help to raise circulation; forty years later, it was still responsible for the success of a men's magazine.[142]

Although penthouses did not take hold in New York until the 1920s, the transformation of the upper regions of buildings had already been under way there for quite some time in the form of roof gardens. In 1883, four decades before the earliest rooftop terrace apartments, the Casino Theatre was erected at Broadway and 39th Street. In the summer months, its rooftop became the venue for concerts and operettas. The conductor and impresario Rudolph Aronson hoped to import to New York the European tradition of open-air concerts in gardens and parks, but was stymied at first by real estate prices in crowded Manhattan until he made a virtue of necessity, as he related in his memoirs:

> Why not utilize for garden purposes the roof of the building I hope to erect and thus escape the enormous cost of valuable ground space? In other words, I mentally transported the Ambassadeurs from the ground floor of the Champs Elysées in Paris to the roof of a building on Broadway. Already, I christened it in my mind the Roof Garden.[143]

The success story of New York roof gardens as venues for concerts, vaudeville, and dances lasted from the 1890s into the 1920s, as Stephen Burge Johnson writes in his study *Roof Gardens of Broadway Theatres*. The region of the roof attracted interest not as a place to live but rather as a place to be entertained, inviting precisely the "long-term human occupation" that the revised European building codes prohibited. Johnson's description of the Casino Theatre and the other Broadway rooftops, most of which opened in the 1890s, re-creates the excitement these buildings engendered. Their façades and gardens were among the earliest locations in New York to be illuminated by electric lights, making the new theaters identifiable as attractions even from a distance.[144] But the central novelties were the concerts sixty-five feet above street level, at an elevation offering not only "the coolest, most comfortable breezes" in New York's summer heat, but also "a view of the city that no one had ever seen."[145] Such amenities made the roof gardens the center of social life during their first years of operation. The opening of Madison Square Garden's rooftop in 1892, for example, was attended by 3,500 guests, which led a contemporary reporter to write that New Yorkers were "roof garden daft."[146] All the customary connotations of the upper reaches of buildings in the late nineteenth century were contradicted by the sunlight, coolness, and panoramic views from the open rooftop. In contrast to the secluded attic where one wallows in memories and solitude, Aronson's rooftop concerts, following the dramatic performances in the theater below, opened up a contemporary and explicitly accessible space. As Johnson writes, "A large elevator near the main entrance carried patrons to all levels, including the roof."[147] In his description of the heyday of roof gardens at the turn of the century, the historian of the roof gardens leaves us in no doubt that it was the elevator that made the vertical relocation of cultural events possible:

> Within twenty years of Aronson's idea New Yorkers were to make common use of their rooftops. Strengthened foundations, the use of steel, and the development of the elevator allowed easier access to the upper story of ever taller buildings. Hotels, apartment buildings and even schools made their rooftops into gardens, playgrounds, or refreshment areas. But in 1881 [the year construction began on the Casino Theatre] the elevator was still an oddity, used only in a few commercial buildings and as a novelty ride. Without it, rooftops with any clear view were inaccessible, and the tallest building of any kind in a neighbourhood was likely to be a church or a theatre.[148]

The elevator was the technical prerequisite for the Broadway roof gardens, and the question of accessibility in fact determined their entertainment offerings. Johnson describes in detail how the performance focus shifted several times during their thirty years of existence—from concerts to vaudeville and circus performances to the large dances of the 1910s. Although for a short time at the turn of the century complete plays were on the program, they were not a success because the elevators could not handle the simultaneous arrival of the entire audience, and waiting for them cost too much time. Vaudeville, on the other hand, lacking a continuous plot, resulted in "constant traffic to and from the roof" and became established as the preferred genre.[149]

In 1913, the German author Bernard Kellermann published a hugely successful science fiction novel entitled *Der Tunnel* (*The Tunnel*), which was translated into twenty-five languages and sold over a million copies. It narrates the construction of a railroad tunnel under the Atlantic connecting America and Europe. The decisive negotiations on the project take place in the roof garden of the fictitious thirty-seven-story Hotel Atlantic in New York. There Mac Allan, the engineer who initiated the tunnel project, has assembled a group of entrepreneurs and bankers to persuade them to underwrite the construction. The novel emphasizes that Allan has chosen this site for its symbolic value, since its elevated location illustrates the engineer's own rise from impoverished beginnings. The easily persuaded captains of finance "knew that at twelve years old he had been a stable boy in a coal mine who in the course of twenty years had worked his way up from a subterranean depth of 2,500 feet to the roof garden of the Atlantic. That was something."[150] Roof gardens were the summits of both buildings and biographies, a congruence Stephen Burge Johnson also notes. Practitioners of such dubious arts as dancing or vaudeville saw their reputations immediately enhanced when their performances gained literal elevation; according to a 1902 newspaper article quoted by Johnson, "Until the stage went up with the elevators vaudeville may be said to have stood on the ragged edge of society."[151] Social acceptance began with the move to the roof. Here the symbolic ordering of verticality no longer included an affinity between its highest and lowest extremes. "Coal mine" and "roof garden" appear in Kellermann's novel as decidedly antonymous, not synonymous locations as they are in Hauptmann's play *The Rats* when Hassenreuter calls his attic rooms "catacombs." What has already been said with regard to the earliest penthouses is also true for the public roof gardens: they freed the upper region of the building from the suspicion of seclusion. A comparison between the contemporaneous novels *The Trial* and *The Tunnel* would bring out these symbolic shifts. Two topographies: uncontrollably proliferating attic rooms as the seat of an illegitimate court on the one hand, the well-ventilated and easily accessible environs of the roof garden (one of the invitees has even landed his plane there[152]) as the meeting place of legitimate power on the other. "She would never forget this moment," declares *The Tunnel*'s narrator about Allan's wife, Maud, "how they all were sitting there in a circle! The *names* she had been hearing since she was a little girl, names whose very sound conjured up an atmosphere of wealth, power, genius, daring, and scandal."[153]

While roof gardens also became an element of numerous New York apartment buildings shortly after the opening of the Casino Theatre in 1883,[154] interest in the novelty in Germany had to make do mostly with utopian novels about the American metropolis. According to the magazine *Bauwelt*, for instance, the first roof garden in Berlin was not dedicated until 1909, and even then as part of a sanatorium in Charlottenburg.[155] The rarity of this event in Germany, thirty years after Aronson's invention, led a reader of the magazine to write a melancholy letter to the editor:

> Why can't we have roof gardens as well? How refreshing it would be to dream away warm summer evenings on the roof of one's building—high above the noise of the streets, under the twinkling stars! What an amusing sensation it would be for our cafés to elevate their guests up onto the roof in the summer, where strings of colored lights cast their romantic beams. . . . In the middle of the city, where expensive real estate no longer allows space to be wasted on gardens, the roof garden with arbors and walls of ivy could provide a modest surrogate for the lost paradise of the private garden.[156]

This suggestion from a *Bauwelt* reader, whose use of the neologism *emporliften* ("elevate" up) suggested the significance of the elevator for the success of the project, ignited an exchange of opinion in the magazine on the "burning question of roof gardens for Berlin," but the fire died down after only a few letters.[157]

Obviously the idea of roof gardens did not take hold in Berlin except for the terrace gardens of luxury apartments, a missed opportunity that would be criticized a few years later, during the war, for unforeseen reasons. Suddenly this location gained positive attention "from the standpoint of public health."[158] Construction industry journals now publicized the idea of building convalescent centers with roof gardens for returning soldiers. They were also promoted as playgrounds for children. The rooftop region, for half a century the object of the most vehement hygienic attacks, was now introduced as a location for the "promotion of good health."[159] "After all, it must be admitted," declared the Prussian *Zentralblatt der Bauverwaltung* (Central journal of building inspection) in 1915, "that roof gardens in Berlin are not yet as widespread as would perhaps be desirable for public health."[160] And the rooftop region, opened up and freely accessible, also induced a shift in ethical considerations. No longer were latently promiscuous relationships or "illegitimate children more susceptible to gastro-intestinal diseases"[161] at issue, but rather the rooftops' beneficial influence on mankind: "Perhaps moral advantages would also result from the integration of roof gardens into neighborhoods with many children, since the children would not be as exposed to all the influences of city life as when the street is their playground."[162] What would have been impossible in the debates between 1870 and 1900 now appeared in these wartime pleas; the rooftop region of tenement houses had become an important element in the strategies of public health advocates. Now, in a reversal of the decades-old argument, "for the prevention of infant mortality in tenement houses . . . the utilization of the buildings' roofs is recommended."[163] The fact that there were no roof gardens in Berlin was regretfully recorded and attributed to the strictness of the building code. Thus the hygienic discourse of 1915 came into conflict with that of 1887, when the law restricted the vertical extension of buildings to six stories. The installation of a roof garden (and the sublayers necessary to protect the building from rain and heat) would exceed that limit. In the age of the elevator, public health advocates ran up against out-of-date principles. Whereas the collective image of the rooftop region had already been transformed, the law was still at the stage of early urbanization.

The "refreshing" prospect of public roof gardens in Berlin continued to be a vain hope despite an increasing number of advocates—at a time when their history in New York was already winding down. Stephen Johnson describes how in the years after the turn of the century, it was primarily legal disputes about whether roof gardens were to be officially regarded as theaters that began to cause economic problems for their proprietors. The increasing number of rooftop vaudeville and theater performances led officials to decide that roof gardens needed the more expensive theater license rather than just a concert license. The former involved both stricter fire regulations and a prohibition on the sale of alcohol.[164] As a consequence of this decision, roof gardens began to cancel their shows. Despite their brief and regionally restricted existence, the early New York roof gardens marked a decisive turning point in the history of the elevator and the imaginative ordering of verticality. For the first time, they presented the rooftop region, if you will, as a location of unfettered circulation—of people, of air, of social energy. The roof garden proprietors were so conscious of the effect of their location that some of them even heated the elevators in order to heighten the refreshing effect of emerging onto the rooftop.[165] No one fainted anymore beneath the roof like Kafka's defendants. Stuffiness was even artificially induced during the brief elevator ride so that the pleasure of cooler air could be enjoyed to the full. One thing, however, remains to be said: however antithetical the relationship between attic and roof garden may have been, it was not a pure dichotomy. We must not forget that the program on the Broadway rooftops often had an experimental character. Contested forms of performance were given a trial run to see whether they could also play in the big street-level

Broadway theaters during the winter months. In addition, rooftop cabaret and freak shows caused recurring scandals and lent the roof gardens a louche and illegitimate air also characteristic of the attic. One wonders to what extent the rooftop region of buildings was always an invitation to dubious productions and destabilized identities, no matter how easy it was to access, no matter whether an elevator was present or not. After all, implicitly or explicitly, there's playacting going on in the attics of *The Rats* and *The Wild Duck*, and of *Young Törless* and *The Trial* as well. But such constants are less obvious and harder to pin down than the semantic transformations set in motion around 1900 by improved access to the rooftop region.

In Germany, the emancipation of the upper stories, the creation of a few roof gardens and penthouses *avant la lettre*, coincided with the first calls for a relaxation of height limitations in the building codes. The united front formed during the last quarter of the nineteenth century against the unlimited vertical growth of the cities was beginning to crumble. Periodicals such as *Bauwelt* offered a forum for the proponents of multistory buildings. From the inaugural editorial of its first number on, the prewar issues of *Bauwelt* repeatedly took up the cause of legalizing additional stories. On the one hand, the goal was to increase the allowable height, at least of commercial buildings, from five to eight or nine stories—"ensuring, of course, the preservation of all hygienic aspects."[166] On the other hand, the continuing prohibition of rooftop additions above the fifth floor (even the penthouses in Wilmersdorf and Charlottenburg were not allowed to go higher) was being put to the test. For almost a decade after 1914, however, these forays took a sudden change of direction. In the years of war and hyperinflation, while the editorial staff of *Bauwelt* still advocated the exploitation of higher stories, their pages no longer featured plans for high-rise offices or elegant penthouses, but rather suggestions for simply increasing available housing. In 1922, for example, there were regular appeals to Berlin landlords to begin enlarging their top floors "to alleviate the housing shortage."[167] Every three or four issues, the magazine published an extensive list of builders who had already answered the call. What made *Bauwelt*'s campaign possible was a bylaw to the Berlin building code issued in August 1918 that gave temporary approval to apartments above the fifth floor in order to combat the "shortage of housing."[168] After the first signs of a recoding of dwellings on the upper floors in the prewar years, from 1918 on the status of attic apartments as temporary emergency housing reestablished itself, an image that persisted until after the Second World War as the bylaw was regularly renewed.[169] What all the architectural debates about a liberalization of the building code could not achieve—permission to install dwellings on the sixth floor—was enabled by the consequences of the First World War. A history of the semantics of upper-story dwellings must thus bear in mind the ambiguous connotations of the top floor in the first half of the twentieth century. On the one hand, luxurious penthouses gradually came to outshine the decades-old images of the top story. On the other hand, housing shortages and economic instability ensured that the traditional image of the garret persisted in the interwar and postwar years.

An important milestone in the history of multistory architecture in Germany occurred during the economic crisis following the First World War, possibly as an enticement to increased construction: on January 3, 1921, by order of the Prussian minister of public welfare, the building code was modified to allow construction of high-rise buildings:

I have no fundamental objections to permitting the construction of multistory buildings (high-rises) for commercial and governmental purposes in locations where a need for them can be established. Such high-rises, however, are subject to review in each individual case in view of the deleterious influence on their surroundings through blockage of sunlight, etc., but especially with respect to traffic circulation and the preservation of an aesthetically satisfactory urban image. It is therefore not advisable to insert into the building code general guidelines for the permitting of such structures. It is advisable instead to grant permission only case by case and by way of a variance. Because of the importance of this issue for the general public, I must insist that plans for high-rises be submitted to me for my opinion before being sent on to the Board of Appeals.[170]

For the first time, the struggle to lift the restriction on building height, begun in the years prior to the First World War, had consequences reflected in the legal code. From then on, buildings of more than five stories could be planned, but the authorities continued to stress that this applied only to commercial and government buildings. The 1928 *Handwörterbuch des Baurechts* (Compact dictionary of construction law) demonstrated that in 1920s Germany, the high-rise was essentially synonymous with the commercial building. The entry for "high-rises" consists only of a cross-reference: "Cf. office buildings, multistory."[171] In 1928 the builders of the Europa-Haus, one of Berlin's first high-rises, decided on short notice to convert what was planned as an eight-story office building into a more profitable hotel, and the Welfare Ministry revoked their building permit, explaining that

as a basic principle, the ministry is not at all opposed to the construction of high-rise buildings in large cities, as is shown by the Welfare Ministry's permits for high-rises in Cologne, Hannover, Düsseldorf, Dortmund, and other cities. It is however a well-known fact that it continues to defend the position, widely recognized as correct by experts, that residential high-rises should not be permitted.[172]

The Europa-Haus was not completed until 1930 as a thirteen-story office building. In the history of German high-rise buildings, there were only three exceptions to this ruling during the 1920s: a ten-story luxury apartment building in Düsseldorf in 1927, a ten-story apartment building in Hannover in 1928, and two twelve-story apartment buildings in Düsseldorf in 1929.[173] In the last years of the Weimar Republic and during the Third Reich, air-raid ordinances put an end to construction of high-rise apartments altogether.[174]

In the more than thirty years between the beginning of the Great War and the end of the Second World War, multistory dwellings played too small a role to figure in contemporary building codes. In the revisions of the building codes, for example (in Berlin in 1925 and 1929, in Munich in 1927), the sections regulating the number of floors mentioned the possibility of a variance for office buildings,[175] but the restriction to six stories continued to be the rule: "In apartment buildings, however, more than six stories are never permitted."[176] One must also remember that the battle against "tenements" and the ideology of the single-family house, revived in the late 1920s, received a powerful impetus after the National Socialists came to power in 1933 and was now integrated into their racist argumentation. If one assumes that National Socialism arose basically as a logical consequence of biopolitical (and therefore hygienic) thought, one can find revealing support for this thesis in the area of building hygiene. For it is astonishing how easily the well-known objections of public health advocates to tenement buildings and their occupants could turn racist and anti-Semitic. Thus in 1937, the editor of the magazine *Der Neubau* (New construction) turned earlier essays that were free of explicit political utterances into a manifesto entitled *Rasse und Wohnung in der großen Agglomeration* (Race and residence in large urban areas). In it, he came to the conclusion that the single-family house was the typical "Germanic" dwelling, the tenement building typically "Latin." In summary, "The struggle against the Latin life style can only be won as a battle for one's own home."[177]

At what point was the elevator first mentioned in German building codes as an explicit component of multistory buildings? Although it was mentioned in the building-magazine portraits of luxury apartment buildings in Düsseldorf and Hannover,[178] there were no regulations governing the installation of elevators in the permits for high-rise buildings, not even for the numerous office buildings. The author of a 1928 article entitled "The Elevator in the Modern Apartment

Building" opined that "if in the future buildings grow even higher, the elevator will become a necessity and an integral component of apartment buildings"; this meant that it had not yet achieved that status and could be ignored by the building code.[179] A 1926 report on "guidelines for the construction of high-rise buildings," issued by the German Association of Cities and Towns, suggested that "an adequate number of safe and speedy elevators should be planned," but this recommendation had no impact on building codes.[180] In fact, not until after the Second World War, in the early 1950s, were binding regulations issued for the first time for the interior facilities of multistory buildings. In December 1954, a working group of the federal states issued "Guidelines for Supervising High-Rise Construction" in order to prepare the legal ground for the "constantly increasing number of building permit applications for the construction of high-rises," as the introductory text states.[181] This ordinance was adopted as an appendix to regional building codes,[182] and stipulated that "high-rise buildings must . . . be equipped with elevators."[183] Thus from 1954 on, every building in Germany with more than five stories had to contain an elevator, or more precisely, "Every residence must be accessible by at least one elevator with enough space to accommodate a stretcher as well as freight, with a cab measuring at least 3 feet x 7 feet. In residential buildings, the cabs must have doors."[184] In the history of vertical organization, that meant that from then on, the building codes themselves put an end to the hierarchical structure that had dominated hygienic discourse since 1870. The equalization of access to all floors in the multistory buildings of the Federal Republic of Germany was now prescribed by law. When we look back for a moment over the semantics of upper-story dwellings between 1840 and 1920, from the garrets of Spitzweg and Tieck to the pathologized fifth floor of tenement buildings to Kafka's and Hauptmann's attic rooms, we can say that the slow establishment of the elevator and its influence on the inner structure of new buildings reached a sort of conclusion in these government guidelines, which now explicitly allowed residential high-rises as well. To the extent that the equality of access to apartments became legally prescribed, the discourses and images of inaccessible, uncanny, upper stories where illegitimate relationships flourish gradually disappeared. The familiar residential high-rise of the last forty or fifty years is characterized by a certain vertical neutrality, unless—thanks to penthouses, roof terraces, and swimming pools—it obeys a hierarchy from high to low. The penthouse became the *bel étage* of the twentieth century.

Any discussion of the reconfiguration of upper-story spaces in the decades around 1900 must include a third variation in addition to the penthouse and the public roof garden, namely, the top-floor executive suite. Here the focus is not on domestic life or culture, but on work. The history of the office has been extensively studied in recent years.[185] These analyses have concentrated above all on the following aspects: the spatial concentration of government administration beginning in the early nineteenth century and the establishment of the word *Büro* (bureau, office); the transition from the old-fashioned, patriarchally run "counting house" to modern, highly differentiated business administration; Taylor's concept of "scientific management" and the variety of streamlined procedures in the early twentieth century; and finally the debate about the most efficient way to configure work space, which reached a high point in the 1960s with the concept of the "office landscape."[186] There is one question, however, that is either mentioned only in passing or neglected completely by all these studies: how the vertical hierarchy of space changed from the last third of the nineteenth century on with the development of the multistory building.

In order to characterize the typical spatial organization of a counting house that prevailed into the late nineteenth century, we can return to Gustav Freytag's economic bildungsroman of 1855, *Debit and Credit*. The hierarchic structure of commercial spaces in the mid-nineteenth century is exemplified by the detailed description of the counting house of the Schröter grocery concern, where the central character, Anton Wohlfahrt, is trained and finally becomes a partner. The general organization of the building is dominated by the commingling of working life and private life still characteristic of businesses in the nineteenth century.[187] The ground floor of the main building contains the business offices and on the floor above them the residence of the head of the firm, the "principal" in nineteenth-century terminology, and his family. There, the communal midday meal is also eaten. Bedrooms for the dozen or so employees are in the rear building. The hierarchy of the business spaces is purely horizontal in arrangement, as Freytag's first description of the counting house makes clear. When the young Anton Wohlfahrt arrives in the city following the death of his parents and prepares to enter the building with a letter of recommendation to the principal in his hand, he encounters a clerk at the entrance:

> With a brief gesture with his paintbrush handle, he directed Anton to the offices off the rear part of the main hallway. Hesitantly he approached the door. It cost him a great effort to decide to turn the knob with his hand—later, he would often remember this moment—and as the door silently opened and he saw the twilight of the great workroom, he was so fearful that he could hardly cross the threshold. His entrance attracted little attention. The pens of half a dozen clerks were hastily scribbling across blue sheets of letter paper to get down their final lines before the office and the post closed. Only one of the gentlemen sitting near the door stood up and asked in a cool, businesslike tone of voice, "How may I help you?"
>
> In reply to Anton's bashful explanation that he wished to speak to Mr. Schröter, a tall man with a lined face, a starched collar, and very English-looking demeanor emerged from the second office. Anton quickly pulled out his letter, said who he was, and explained in a solemn voice that his father had died and had sent Mr. Schröter greetings from his deathbed.

The principal welcomes his visitor and immediately hires him as an apprentice. "After these words," the novel continues, "he gave a slight nod and returned to the second office, where six more gentlemen were also bent over their sheets of blue paper."[188] Thus Wohlfahrt's first visit to the business runs its course as a progression through a series of rooms: entrance, central hallway, first office, second office. The series does not come to an end here, however, as the novel makes clear in a subsequent chapter when the apprentice learns of his accelerated promotion to full-fledged clerk. Schröter invites him for the first time into his private office: "On the following morning, the principal called the new clerk into the small room beyond the last office, the Holy of Holies of the business, and listened with a smile to Anton's expressions of gratitude."[189] The "Holy of Holies," the place of power and responsibility in a mid-nineteenth-century business, is at the far end of a horizontal line.

Our basic question—how much elevators transformed the vertical structure of buildings—is easier to answer for the office building than it is for the tenement. For the precise point at which the elevator enters the history of the office building is well documented, as are the consequences of its installation. It makes sense to first follow the development of the office building in New York before returning to the situation in Germany. In 1870 the Equitable Life Assurance Society of New York, the largest insurance company in America, inaugurated its new eight-story headquarters. As mentioned above, it was the first commercial building in the world to install elevators.[190] This building was Equitable Life's answer to the increasing lack of space in the business district of Manhattan; in the 1860s this crisis even led to brief consideration of moving the entire financial district uptown. Building higher than four or five stories was not yet widely recognized as a possibility. "When a ground-floor firm found its business really flourishing, it would expand sidewise, knocking passages through the walls of adjacent structures."[191] Finally Henry B. Hyde, the founder of Equitable Life, became the first to expand his business vertically (perhaps on the basis of his earlier friendship with Elisha Otis),[192] and the two elevators in his headquarters on Broadway reinvigorated the proliferation of the elevator, which had stagnated during the Civil War. It is manifest that unlike elevators in multistory residential buildings, elevators in commercial buildings led rather quickly to a reordering of verticality. The *New York Times* obituary for Hyde in 1899 already stated that the elevator in the Equitable Building "revolutionized the construction of office buildings throughout the city."[193] The founder of the company had to overcome his board of directors' opposition to the unusual height of the new headquarters,[194] not least because the cost of installing the two elevators was close to $30,000, a fifth of the total construction costs.[195] Hyde obviously took personal charge of renting out the fifth, sixth, and seventh floors (the insurance company at first occupied only the third and fourth floors), since it involved persuading people to move into office spaces whose location at the time was the equivalent of a social stigma. "Nobody but an occasional slave or a miserable bell ringer was expected to ascend regularly to the upper reaches," as an essay on the early history of the company has it.[196] Victor Hugo's Quasimodo thus strikes Civil War–era New York attorneys seeking office space as the typical denizen of an upper-story workplace. In the Equitable Life Building the hunchbacked outsider, alone among the tangle of stairways, is replaced by the self-confidant businessman, familiar with the advantages of an office high above the streets of the metropolis. Hyde, the same essay continues,

> persuaded Equitable's own attorneys . . . that it was their duty to establish themselves in the upper reaches of 120 Broadway. He then turned his winning eyes on other lawyers. . . . A decade or so later, the *Tribune*, proudly commenting on New York's transformation from a horizontal to a vertical city, declared, "The lawyers were the first to appreciate the upper floors, full of light and free of dust and far above the noise of the street; and bankers are now following their sensible example."[197]

By 1897, an article entitled "The Modern Business Building" confidently stated, "There are men called 'high livers' who will not have an office unless it is up where the air is cool and fresh, the outlook broad and beautiful, and where there is silence in the heart of the business."[198]

The image of a certain type of room has been burned into the twentieth-century imagination by countless films and television shows: the top-floor executive suite with wide windows affording a magnificent view of the city below. The view from the headquarters of the Equitable Life Building is a perfect example of an image that has become so self-evident that a popular book about the history of the office can contain the simple sentence, "In Europe as in America, the office of the CEO is usually a corner room with a beautiful view on the highest floor."[199] The famous architect George B. Post, technical advisor for the headquarters' construction, provided the most important impetus for upgrading the value of the upper floors: "Post, convinced of the wisdom of the decision to install passenger elevators, rented offices on the top floor of the Equitable Building for his own use, which he was able soon thereafter to sublet at a much higher rate of rent than what he had originally engaged himself."[200] Yet in 1870, the insurance company itself still took no part in a fundamental vertical reorganization; except for the offices of the corporate lawyers, its own offices—which occupied just under half the total floor space—were on the lower floors and still completely in the tradition of the nineteenth century. The custodian's apartment was on the eighth floor.[201]

In the history of office building architecture, the Equitable Building had to relinquish its title as the largest and most modern commercial building in the world soon after its opening. In New York and after 1871 in Chicago as well, insurance companies, newspapers, and communications firms built office buildings that were even taller and—unlike the building at 120 Broadway—did not attempt to conceal the number of floors with windows that extended across several stories. The eleven-story Tribune Building and the twelve-story Western Union Telegraph Building, both built in New York in 1875, were "much more visibly than the Equitable the products of the elevator," in the words of the contemporary architecture critic Montgomery Schuyler.[202] But it was obviously Equitable Life's ambition to keep up with the competition. Already in 1875 the building was enlarged by the addition of three more stories. In 1887, after the purchase of almost the entire block between Broadway, Cedar Street, Pine Street, and Nassau Street, a general renovation was carried out. The resulting twelve-story building—no longer the tallest, to be sure, but in the words of Henry B. Hyde "the best building in the world"[203]—perhaps deserves the title of the real birthplace of the top-floor executive suite. The vertical distribution of offices, still a combination of their own and those of other firms willing to pay the very high rents, had changed. The lower floors were still occupied by the insurance company, but a brochure on the internal structure of the building emphasized that the eighth floor offered the most attractive of all available office space:

> On this floor the arrangement of offices differs materially from that of the other floors. . . . The windows of the larger rooms will have window-seats and book-shelves on either side. The views from these windows will be especially interesting and extensive. The wood-work will be quartered oak, of attractive design and richly paneled, and the rooms will be particularly attractive.[204]

Moreover, the installations on the upper stories were led by the firm's founder himself, who in addition to the expanded executive suite on the fourth floor occupied two further offices, one on the eighth and one on the twelfth floor.[205] The in-house magazine of the rival Mutual Life characterized Equitable's twelfth-floor suite as "the highest and most sumptuous boudoir in town," a resentful reference to the illegitimacy of upper-floor rooms, an illegitimacy now dissipated by buildings like the Equitable Life.[206] In his office of 1887 at least, Henry B. Hyde figured as the pioneer of the concept of an executive suite, cementing the alliance between commercial success and lofty office by founding the exclusive Lawyers' Club with a restaurant and social rooms on the sixth and seventh floors of his building. It opened with 400 members and within a few years had grown to 1,400. Shortly after the Equitable Life Building opened, it had the "greatest concentration of lawyers to be found in any building in the city."[207] From then on, the sphere of power was irrevocably located in the upper regions.

Within twenty or thirty years, the criterion for rentability of office space in New York had been reversed, as noted by a later chronicler of Equitable Life: "The downtown tenant population had indeed followed the lawyers upstairs in the elevators, and thus ushered in the skyscraper era, but large blocks of space on the lower floors had then become unrentable."[208] Rents in New York also reflected the new hierarchy that became all but obligatory in the twentieth century. While an article of 1897 declared that the average annual rent was approximately eight dollars per square foot for ground-floor offices but only three dollars for offices on the top floor, this ratio was soon reversed.[209] By 1933, at the beginning of the Great Depression, the Sheridan-Krakow Formula (named after the two construction engineers who developed it) went into effect in an attempt to control the increasingly arbitrary nature of rents for commercial real estate. Under the supervision of Sheridan and Krakow, guidelines were developed for uniform and mandatory valuation of office space. The criteria were size, story, proximity to a corner of the building, and amount of direct sunlight. The benchmark against which variations were calibrated was an eighth-floor office of eighteen by twenty-five feet facing the street. Office rents were calculated based on their deviation from this standard.

> Percentage factors were adopted for variations. For instance, 1 per cent was added for each story above the eighth floor, and 1 per cent deducted for each floor below. . . . By adding and subtracting the percentage points of an office, say on the 20th-floor street front,

a rating of 120 per cent might be obtained. This signified that the space was worth 120 per cent of the standard eighth-floor area.[210]

Thus from 1933 on, the vertical hierarchy of offices in New York was officially codified. The eighth floor was the semantic zero point, and the value of space increased with each subsequent story.

It is evident that with the advent of the loftily situated executive suite, the relationship of space and power structures within a company changed fundamentally. The purely horizontal gradation of the nineteenth-century counting house offered the principal the privilege of privacy; his work was shielded from outside eyes, in contrast to that of his clerks in the front offices.[211] The executive suite of the twentieth century was distinguished by additional spatial factors. Commercial power in executive suites furnished with great expanses of glass was now associated with foresight, overview, and grandeur. One could say that the establishment of the elevator in office buildings and the new location of the executive suite made possible a modern variation of that well-known fantasy of insight that for centuries was to be gained only on a mountaintop or a tower. The history of this gesture has been written; consider the famous article by Joachim Ritter on Petrarch's ascent of Mount Ventoux in 1336 and the problem of modern subjectivity. Ritter asks whether the view of landscape from a great height precipitates insight into or obliviousness to oneself.[212] Literary history provides us with numerous examples of figures whose crises of identity take place at the top of towers and mountain peaks, from Goethe's Wilhelm Meister to Ibsen's master builder Solness and Professor Rubek. For the modes of representation of social power at the turn of the nineteenth to the twentieth century, it is important that this gesture—earlier confined to the ritual ascent of a mountain or tower—now suddenly also gained relevance within the everyday life of business establishments. Someone who has made it looks down on the world; the mountaintop and the top floor offer the same perspective. That was not always the case, as the hygienic discourse on the top story has demonstrated: the lofty regions of a building were at first rather thought of as the antithesis of the mountaintop experience of grandeur. In 1901, at a time when the lower offices in Chicago and New York were already going begging, the physician Robert Döl- ger wrote of the multistory tenements of Berlin:

> On the other hand we must also remember that the stairwells rep- resent conduits for bad air in general, and that the effect of climb- ing the stairs is necessarily the opposite of climbing a mountain wafted by good air, i.e., an ongoing slackening of energy that in- creases the higher the floor to which one ascends.[213]

The elevator made the highest floor the urban equivalent of the mountain peak—or something even more impressive, as Henry B. Hyde wrote during a trip to the mountains shortly after the opening of the Equitable Life Building: "I put my head at the base of a perpendicular rock six thousand feet high, and looked ever so far into the clouds; but somehow the sight did not impress me so much as when I saw the last cornice stone of the Equitable put in its place."[214] Foucault remarked incidentally that "sometime or other, the history of spaces must be written, which would be at the same time a history of power."[215] The birth of the top-floor executive suite would be an important chapter of that history.

In his investigation of American magazine advertise- ments from 1920 to 1940, the cultural historian Roland Marchand devotes a section to the motif of office windows. The image of the businessman looking down from the win- dow of his lofty office, the telephone within easy reach, was so widespread in the 1920s that it became a "visual cliché" for advertisers.[216] Marchand asks why it was telephone com- panies like AT&T who emphasized the connection between having one's own personal telephone (in offices of the first half of the century still a great privilege) and the view from the window:

> Both the telephone and the window-with-a-view symbolized pres- tige and power. Their combined presence adequately distinguished the executive, even the junior executive, from the mere salesman.

The telephone placed the protagonist among those men in the firm whose rank entitled them to an individual extension. . . . The window was even more symbolically significant. To command a view not only suggested high status within the firm (secretaries and mere salesmen almost never appeared next to large windows with views, except when they came into the boss's office); it also conjured up that ineffable sense of domain gained from looking out and down over broad expanses.[217]

As an AT&T advertisement from the 1930s announces, the deployment of the telephone promises these "broader horizons" by providing a more efficiently structured business and increased profits. The promise of increased scope is underscored by the businessman's open view of the city. Communicational and optical superiority, the association suggests, are inseparable criteria for success. The former is ensured by the right telephone service, the latter by the right office location. The images analyzed by Marchand, with their recurring panoramic views through unframed expanses of glass, are a precise illustration of the new semantics of the executive suite. An upper story and an optimal connection to the outside world now formed a new alliance unknown in the early years of multistory buildings, as Spitzweg's and Tieck's dark garrets and solitude-seeking inhabitants attest.

The way the window was employed to profile the successful businessman could also be seen in the design of the view from his window. Marchand distinguishes two popular motifs: the early 1920s favored a view of the boss's factory—set in a rural landscape—from his office in the administrative building; the view of the city skyline from a skyscraper came later. The two motifs carry different messages:

The office window that looked out on the factory was identified explicitly or implicitly as the boss's office. . . . These tableaux, with the factory seen from a downward angle, suggested power over a very personal domain. They implied a direct, personal management in which the boss might still know by name the workers over whom he maintained his elevated surveillance.[218]

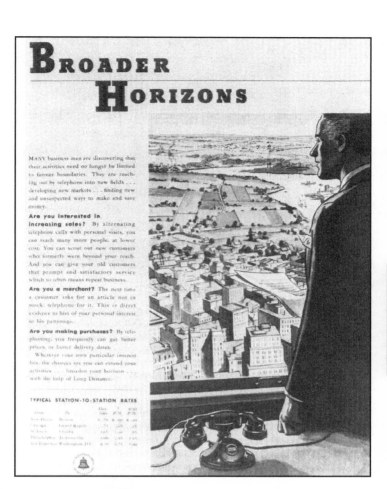

1930s advertisement for AT&T.

This constellation—the power of the CEO over his empire—was replaced by a highly placed but no longer autocratically operating businessman looking toward the horizon, an image with different implications:

> The new business man of the skyscraper office no longer looked upon a scene of production under his control. . . . Instead, his window usually disclosed the tops of other skyscrapers and an occasional airplane. The view offered substitute satisfactions for a loss of individual autonomy in an age of business bureaucratization. . . . Once in a while he might look past the fringes of the city to the

landscape beyond. The horizon was broader than before; the domain more extensive but less under personal control. It suggested less a surveillance of present details than dreams of wider opportunities. In accordance with the enlarged role of planning and scientific research operations, the content and scope of the office view now suggested a window on the future.[219]

The location and transparency of the office no longer served to watch over what one owned, but rather as the source of inspiration and visionary business initiatives. In the skyscrapers of the metropolis, the window of the executive suite became "a window on the future." What powers of persuasion the connotations of the top-floor executive suite possessed for early twentieth-century advertising can be seen from the fact that the presentation of this location was by no means a reflection of actual circumstances. Marchand shows that in the early 1920s, at the height of the factory motif's popularity, hardly any large companies still had their executive headquarters in a rural location next to their production facilities. Management had long since moved to the cities. Moreover, the panoramic views presented in the images of later advertisements were almost always limited by other buildings in the commercial districts of New York or Chicago. The universal view of one's own empire or of the city, however, was too seductive not to be deployed as a gesture of superiority. These fictionalizations illustrated the significance of the new connection between work location and power. The elevator enabled bosses to assume their rightful position. New locutions such as "the upper echelons" attested to the congruence of social and architectural hierarchy. One could imagine a media history of loftiness in which the elevator would play a significant part.

The history of the top-floor executive suite in Germany does not begin until January 3, 1921, the day the compulsory restriction of office buildings to five stories was lifted. Whenever the vertical organization of office buildings was discussed before that date—in a 1911 special edition of the magazine *Bauwelt* dedicated to the office building, for example—it was in the context of a simple observation: "the executive suite [is located] on the second floor."[220] The principle of the *bel étage* still governed the sphere of work as well. With the first multistory buildings of the 1920s—all equipped with elevators—the question of hierarchical order was at last raised anew. The profiles of newly built or vertically expanded office high-rises in architectural magazines of the time are very revealing, since they often included a detailed cross-section of the building as well as information about the function of individual floors. In this context, one question was of primary importance, namely, whether the building was built for a single firm or not. For the assertion of hierarchical ordering in a multistory building was meaningful only if the spaces were occupied for the most part by a single firm. In 1920s Germany, both variations were represented in new multistory office buildings. There were many with office space for rent and a few belonging to single firms. In the latter category—which is the significant one for the present study—the following buildings were the subjects of their own articles in the important architectural magazines: the headquarters of the Klingenberg Power Company (dedicated in 1928, twelve stories),[221] the headquarters of the *Hannoverscher Anzeiger* newspaper (dedicated in 1928, ten stories),[222] the headquarters of Lenz and Company (dedicated in 1928, nine stories, "Berlin's first high-rise"),[223] the tower-like headquarters of the *Stuttgarter Tagblatt* newspaper (dedicated in 1928, seventeen stories),[224] the offices of the *Magdeburger General-Anzeiger* newspaper (dedicated in 1931, with a six-story base topped by an eleven-story tower),[225] the headquarters of Siemens und Halske (the so-called Wernerwerk) in Berlin-Siemensstadt (dedicated in 1931, with a middle section of twelve stories),[226] the headquarters of IG Farben in Frankfurt am Main (dedicated in 1931, nine stories at its highest point),[227] and the headquarters of the Municipal Savings Bank in Breslau (dedicated in 1932, eleven stories).[228]

When we examine the vertical structure of these highest office buildings of the 1920s and 1930s, each built for occupancy by a single firm, it is remarkable to discover that the option of siting the executive suite on the top floors was still hardly taken advantage of. The graphics and blueprints reproduced in the periodicals show that most firms continued to place their executive offices on the second floor (*Hannoverscher Anzeiger*, *Stuttgarter Tagblatt*, IG Farben, Municipal Savings Bank Breslau) and the "very simply furnished"[229] offices on the upper floors were rented out to other businesses (in the case of the Hannover newspaper and the savings bank). A good half a century after the construction of the Equitable Life Building in New York, the concept of the top-floor executive suite had not yet become established in Germany, although isolated headquarters buildings did introduce the new hierarchical order. After the vertical expansion of the Rudolf Mosse publishing concern in Berlin in 1922–1923, for instance, the executive offices were moved to the seventh floor—possibly as the first in Germany.[230] And a newspaper article about the tower-like middle section of the new Siemens Wernerwerk (dubbed "the first factory high-rise in Europe" in Georg Siemens's biography of his famous ancestor[231]) mentions that it contained "the executive offices on the 11th floor."[232] Around 1930, however, such instances were still rare. As in the case of apartment buildings, the turning point for the hierarchical reordering of verticality in multistory office buildings in Germany had to wait until after the Second World War. From the early 1930s on, no more high-rises were built, both because of the depression and, increasingly, because of the fear of aerial attacks. A 1933 report on office buildings in the private sector mentioned the "worldwide crisis" in construction, and noted that "the German Reich has led the way by prohibiting all construction of administrative buildings for a number of years. Provincial and municipal administrations have followed suit."[233]

Not until well into the 1950s did the top-floor executive suite achieve the self-evident status in Germany that it had in New York and Chicago a half century earlier. Between

1957 and 1965, however, such large concerns as BASF,[234] Mercedes,[235] Bayer,[236] and Klöckner-Humboldt-Deutz[237] dedicated their new headquarters, fifteen- to thirty-two-story office towers whose executive suites were all on the upper stories. "After a decade of temporary and interim arrangements," declared the introduction to an illustrated volume about the opening of the BASF building, it was finally decided to construct a twenty-one-story high-rise, the only one of its kind in 1957. "It is easy to see that vertical transport with modern high-speed elevators can be accomplished without difficulty, while there is as yet no practicable means of transportation through long corridors, that is, horizontally. Once this basic question had been answered, the decision in favor of a high-rise had been made."[238] As for the vertical organization of the office spaces, "In addition, we hoped to create work spaces on the higher floors that would be removed from the unavoidable noise of the street and the factory."[239] In 1963, the Bayer company in Leverkusen replaced BASF as the firm with the highest headquarters building in Germany. The executive offices were located on the twenty-ninth floor of the thirty-three-story building; above them were only the kitchens and the dining room.[240] The publication celebrating its opening speaks of the division of vertical space into "normal floors" and "executive floors," a previously unknown terminology brought into being by the establishment of the top-floor executive suite.[241] Recall the multistory pathology of the hygienists; a brief half century later, the top story was once again contrasted to a postulated "normalcy," but now its value was reversed. In the 1960s, during the extensive discussions of the "office landscape" concept and the most efficient way to divide workspaces, the categories "normal floor" and "executive" or "special floor" repeatedly came up. This raised the question of whether the transparency and openness demanded by the advocates of the office landscape should consistently apply to executive work spaces as well. It is interesting that even an explicit defense of the office landscape concept concedes that "for office management and associated functions, a few individual rooms of representative character will be necessary even in open-plan offices."[242] In "office buildings wholly occupied by a single company," these "individual rooms of representative character" should be located on a separate "executive floor." "One can site conference rooms on such a floor and moreover meet the special demands of representing the company."[243] In practical construction terms, for the first office buildings designed according to the principles of the office landscape, this meant that—as in the BP publishing house in Hamburg, designed in 1964—above the four open-plan "normal floors" there was a conventionally designed "executive floor."[244] Thus by the 1960s at the latest, the top-floor executive suite in Germany marked such a clear difference that it could not even be erased by the space-leveling philosophy of the office landscape. In an era that had "internalized" (i.e., forgotten) the technical prerequisites for such a constellation, power and the lofty workplace entered into an apparently natural alliance. It is no accident that a study by advocates of the office landscape concept entitled "Hierarchical Organization of the Office" lists "room location" as the very first of numerous status symbols in an office community. "The executives are located on the top floor,"[245] it declares without further ado. The higher the office buildings rose, the more pronounced this conjunction became. When the Cologne company Klöckner-Humboldt-Deutz published an illustrated volume to celebrate the opening of its sixteen-story publishing house in 1965, it described the executive suite on the fourteenth floor as follows:

> Across from the elevators there is a large hall instead of the individual offices found on normal floors. It offers room for the reception desk and the seating areas required for receiving visitors. In contrast to the design of the other floors, the elevator bank here is free. One can walk all the way around it and from the west side has a magnificent view of Cologne and the factory area.[246]

And in the "Large Conference Room," located one floor above the executive suite, "Through the windows along the side walls, the view stretches from Cologne and the foothills across the Siebengebirge range and the suburbs on the right bank of the Rhine as far as the Bergisches Land region."[247] Panorama, responsibility, grandeur—in the late twentieth century, the elevator made a Petrarch of every CEO.

CONTROLS

THE ELEVATOR OPERATOR AT THE
TURN OF THE CENTURY

In 1909, a few months after uniform regulations for elevators went into effect in Prussia and its provinces, a booklet entitled *Der Fahrstuhlführer* (The elevator operator) was published in Berlin. Since the new regulations required every operator to be examined by the relevant authorities, "it seems to the authors of this modest publication," as they stated in their foreword, "that there is a need for a book from which the more intelligent building superintendant, doorman, servant, etc. . . . can gain enough familiarity with the setup and most important components as well as the operation of his elevator that he will not need an expensive apprenticeship in an operator's school."[1] In addition to information on the various controls and safety features of elevators, the booklet contained the text of the 1908 regulations, and the authors promised success to any halfway talented candidate who studied their text: "Used in the right way, this book will allow him to pass the examination for elevator operator without difficulty. This book is not intended for someone completely lacking in technical know-how; such a person can hardly expect to become a useful operator."[2] Given the existence of official examinations, study guides, and apprenticeships in "operator's schools," it is obvious that the profession of elevator operator at the beginning of the twentieth century depended on a degree of competence and training we can hardly imagine from our contemporary perspective. The job of elevator operator has long since been reduced to a purely ceremonial one. As "liftboy," he exists now only in luxury hotels and department stores, the juvenalization of the title already an indication that his authority has disappeared. The history of the elevator, however, demonstrates how fundamentally different the early operation of the conveyance was from the fully automatic controls today's users take for granted. There is good reason that the very first German "Official Regulations for the Installation and Operation of Elevators," issued in 1893 for Berlin and surroundings, declared the presence of an elevator operator an absolute necessity:

> Passenger elevators and freight elevators that can also carry persons may only be used in conjunction with or under the supervision of special operators. The latter must be at least 18 years old and familiar with the equipment and operation of the elevator, which familiarity must be demonstrated by a certificate of proficiency issued by an expert authority and included in the inspection record. Operators of passenger elevators must in addition enter in the inspection record a written declaration of responsibility for the operation of the elevator.[3]

The regulations of 1893 said nothing about the precise circumstances under which such a "certificate of proficiency" would be issued. The Prussian ordinance of 1908, however, contained "Instructions for Implementation" that referred to the existence of a special "Operator Examination," which was "to be carried out with the greatest stringency" and in the following years resulted in study aids such as the booklet quoted above.[4]

The reason for such conscientious rigor in the process of becoming an elevator operator is to be sought first in the controls of early elevators, both hydraulic and electric, to which the turn-of-the-century regulations referred. The hydraulic elevators of the first years functioned by means of simple cable controls, later operated by hand wheels or cranks. The first electric elevators, which went into service in the mid-1890s, adopted this mechanical principle or were equipped with electric lever controls. Common to all these techniques was a high degree of responsibility for the operator. On the one hand, he had to stop the cab just as it reached the intended landing, on the other, in hydraulic elevators, he also had to regulate the speed by closing or opening a valve between the water line and the piston by means of a control cable or hand wheel. Although an ordinance of 1893 required a governor on the valve allowing a maximum speed of only five feet per second, slower speeds were at the discretion of the operator. The challenges of operating the cable controls in particular were repeatedly discussed in engineering articles and textbooks. This technique was particularly difficult because there was no indication of a neutral mid-position on the cable that ran through the cab, so that the degree of acceleration could not be determined during travel, thus creating a constant danger that inexperienced operators would overshoot the desired landing. And as Ludwig Hintz wrote in his *Handbuch der Aufzugstechnik* (Manual of elevator technology), at the two end points of travel, the overshot "can sometimes be so great that it leads to a reversal of direction, since the starter mechanism for the opposite direction of travel turns on and the cab pauses only a moment at the terminal before it begins to move again in the opposite direction."[5] Lack of skill in operating the cable controls was apt to completely prevent the orderly functioning of the elevator. Beginning in the 1880s, most hydraulic passenger elevators were equipped with cranks or wheels that reduced this difficulty by providing the operator with a fixed reference point, as Hintz describes: "There is a small indicator connected to the crank or hand wheel that shows the neutral position and the settings for full speed in either direction. No matter where the cabin happens to be located, the operator is thereby always able to set the controls at the mid-position and for the desired direction."[6]

Stopping the elevator remained problematic, however, because the operator had to begin to decelerate before he

Illustration of an elevator interior at Lord & Taylor's, Broadway and Twentieth Street, New York City. From *Frank Leslie's Illustrated Newspaper*. Courtesy of the Library of Congress.

was able to see the intended landing. Late braking necessitated laborious corrections at the stop, early braking caused unnecessarily long travel time between floors, and only the most experienced operators were able to combine the highest speed with the greatest precision of stop. The art of the stop was crucial even to the smooth operation of an electric elevator with lever controls. An electric connection between the lever in the cab and the starter mechanism in the cellar ensured that cab movement could be initiated and interrupted without the slightest physical effort on the part of the operator, but since "every large electric motor must overcome starting resistance to be set in operation," the control lever had "several contact studs between the neutral mid-position and the two extreme travel positions" that had to be turned on and off in succession when approaching and halting at a floor.[7] This arrangement made operating even the early electric elevators a complex undertaking:

> The elevator must be operated so that the floor of the cab always comes to a stop even with the landing. In order for this to happen, it is not enough to turn off the operating current at the last moment. For the motor armature, cable drum, cables, and cab have quite a significant mass whose inertia does not simply disappear. For that reason, the current must be turned off a few seconds before the landing is reached.[8]

So many demands were placed on elevator operators in the first decades that, in an early recruiting brochure, the Otis company compared the job to that of a "railroad engineer controlling the movement of his locomotive."[9] Over and above the art of controlling the cab, his task was to ensure the maximum safety of his passengers and, as stated in the 1900 Siemens publication *Instructionen für Fahrstuhlführer* (Instructions for elevator operators), to "close the door to the elevator shaft each time with so much care that, when the cab resumes its travel, the locking bar can properly engage. . . . The operator must make sure the door is properly closed before traveling on."[10]

The story of the most famous elevator operator in German literature vividly illustrates the opportunities this profession offered at the turn of the century and what results the skilled operation of the apparatus could produce. Felix Krull, known to the hotel's patrons by his "stage name," Armand, is one of the last virtuosos of elevator operation. From the beginning, he strives for complete mastery of the electric lever controls of his cab, in contrast to his predecessor Eustache, the quality of whose service depends on the status of his passengers: the less chance of a tip, the higher the step from the floor of the cab to the landing. By contrast, when the hotel director tells Krull to "ride up and down a

Interior view of the Columbian Hotel, Trinidad, Colorado, showing the elevator, workmen, and onlookers, between 1880 and 1885. From Western History/Genealogy Department, Denver Public Library. Courtesy of the Library of Congress.

Cartoon showing elevator crashing through large building. Courtesy of the Library of Congress.

Elevator operator Charles Moore standing in elevator door at Cook County Hospital, Chicago, ca. 1911. Photograph by *Chicago Daily News*, negative DN-0056446. Courtesy of the Chicago History Museum.

Blanche Hildebrand, a woman elevator operator, at Marshall Field's and Company, Chicago, 1918. Photograph by *Chicago Daily News*, negative DN-0070326. Courtesy of the Chicago History Museum.

few times with Eustache or one of the others and see how the mechanism works," Felix replies, "It will be handled with love. . . . I will not rest until I no longer make the smallest step."[11] And the new operator keeps his promise: "I smiled a great deal and said: '*M'sieur et dame*—' and 'Watch your step,' which was quite unnecessary, for it was only on the first day that I was occasionally guilty of a slightly uneven landing; after that I was never again responsible for a step that required a warning."[12] In the course of the novel, we learn how far the chauffeuring artistry of a turn-of-the-century liftboy can get him; in Krull's case, it leads to the lucrative dalliance with Madame Houpflé, an important milestone in his career as a swindler. His initiation to a night of love begins in front of the elevator in the hotel's foyer: "She nodded in satisfaction at seeing me, smiled at my bow which, accompanied by a deferential 'madame,' had some of the quality of an invitation to dance, and let herself be enclosed with me in the bright, suspended room."[13] Felix Krull's mastery—the ride in the elevator as a dance, its elegant operation an element of seduction—is a historic index: not long after the mid-1890s, when this episode takes place, it would cease to be plausible. New control techniques put an end to the elevator operator's need to master the technical apparatus. Whether travel between stories was smooth or jerky, whether the gap at the landing was large or unnoticeable, was no longer in the least dependent on the delicate touch of a human hand.

PUSH-BUTTON CONTROLS AND THE PATH TO SELF-OPERATED ELEVATORS

Not every elevator operator was blessed with the ambition and talent of a Felix Krull. Indeed, by the end of the nineteenth century, the carelessness of the personnel led to increasing demands for self-regulating elevator operation, which also became feasible at a time of improvements in electronic control technology. Above all in New York, which in 1900 still lacked a legally required examination for operators, there was discussion of the need for such an improvement.[14] The topic arose as early as 1891, in the *American Architect and Building News*:

> Another improvement, which is yet to come, will consist, we think, in an automatic stop for the elevator. Nothing is more tedious, clumsy and dangerous than the way in which an inexperienced boy stops and starts an elevator, particularly if he wishes to astonish the passengers by his skill. Often, he purposely fails to stop it entirely at the landing, expecting the passengers to leap in or out. . . . At other times he fails to pull the slipper rope in time, and the elevator stops a foot or two above its proper place. . . . All this dangerous and annoying ineffectiveness might be done away with by an automatic contrivance.[15]

This passage clearly shows the consequences when the skills required to drive a mechanically operated elevator were lacking: carelessness and showing off. In the following years, the apparatus that put an end to the unreliability of all manually operated controls was introduced, first in the United States and France. It consisted of an array of push buttons inside the cab and outside, at the door into the shaft. Their use required no practice or technical know-how whatsoever, and they have remained ubiquitous right up to the present day. The first American building to trust this new device was apparently the Postal Telegraph Building, built in New York City in 1893. Its elevators used a short-lived transitional system: instead of separate buttons for each floor, there was only an Up and a Down button and a dial one had to use to set the intended floor before beginning the ride.[16] The architect Maurice Saglio reported on a similar array in an 1896 article, "City Apartment Houses in Paris." The new buildings he visited in the rue du Luxembourg, for instance, "are served by elevators which seem to me to have reached the last perfection, and I hardly conceive how they could be better." The elevators were intended only for the use of the small number of tenants in the building and therefore were not supposed to need an elevator operator,

> and, as they are to be handled by impractical folks, they are very easily moved and offer complete security. . . . The engineer, M. Pifre,

had the idea of adding electric buttons by which every movement can be arranged. . . . The handling is done by means of two buttons; one bearing the inscription *ascent* and the other *descent*. If you press the button *ascent*, and you let it go immediately, the elevator begins to ascend very slowly. If you lengthen the pressure the speed increases until its maximum is reached. If you wish to go to a certain story, you simply draw a small register bearing the number required, and press the button *ascent*.[17]

We could still call this array a precursor of fully automatic push-button controls, since the speed of travel was still determined by how long the button was held down. But the decisive watershed for the history of the elevator was the complete replacement of cables, cranks, and levers with a control system that "makes possible the use of the elevator for everyone . . . since to set it in motion and especially to stop at a landing, neither know-how nor practice" is required.[18]

In Germany, this new technology was still unknown at the turn of the twentieth century. It was mentioned neither in Philipp Mayer's voluminous entry on elevators in the 1892 *Handbuch der Architektur* (Manual of architecture) nor in the earliest draft of the Prussian elevator regulations of 1900 (the most recent variation mentioned there was electric lever controls).[19] How closely the push button was still identified as a characteristic of American elevator design at this time can be seen from a 1901 electric elevator manual that mentions the innovation of "Otis controls."[20] One can date the appearance of push-button controls in Germany to the year 1903, when the Siemens and Flohr companies in Berlin produced the first elevators with the new technology, already with a separate button for each floor. As a commentator noted in the *Zeitschrift des Vereins deutscher Ingenieure* (Journal of the Association of German Engineers),

Characteristic of these controls is that the elevator is set in motion by contact buttons connected to electromagnetic switches. The buttons can be mounted both inside and outside the cab, at the entry points into the shaft. The elevator's transmission stops on

An example of the early push-button system. From Kerstin Englert and Alfred Englert, *Lifts in Berlin* (Berlin: Jovis, 1998).

> its own at the landing whose contact button initiated its motion. ... Inside the cab, a bank of contact buttons is installed containing only one button per floor, which is used for both ascending and descending travel. ... In addition, at every door into the shaft, a button is installed that serves to call the elevator.[21]

During the next fifteen to twenty years, this configuration became established as the obligatory control principle in passenger elevators and fundamentally transformed the perception of the technical apparatus.

What were the consequences of the push-button system, which an engineering article of 1908 called "the greatest advance in elevator construction in the last eight years"?[22] The advance called into question the need for an elevator operator, for if the passenger needed no special skill, but "only needs an act of volition to make the elevator go where he wants,"[23] no restrictions on who can operate it made sense anymore. In place of mechanical controls, in place of electric levers whose intermediate positions must be turned off

at exactly the right moment when approaching the landing, the push button freed the user from any control activity.
With the tip of one's finger, a circuit was closed, turning on
the motor in the basement, while a toggle switch connected
to the motor's control apparatus saw to it that the current
was interrupted precisely upon arrival at the chosen landing, and the cab stopped exactly at the landing.[24] This new
simplicity of operation had a direct impact on the status of
multistory apartment buildings in Germany. Around 1900,
even well-appointed residential buildings hardly ever had
an elevator because the personnel costs would have been
exceedingly high. With the advent of push-button controls,
they could dispense with these costs, and elevator installation increased. Those first roof-terrace apartments in Berlin
between 1910 and 1913 owed their creation not least to the
new control technology. The elevator's revalorization of the
upper stories thus depended on the push button. The swiftness of the shift can be clearly followed in the elevator codes
of the time—both those already in existence and drafts of
future ones. In 1907, the Berlin code revised a passage unchanged since 1893 stipulating that an elevator must without exception be operated by a certified person. For the first
time, the Berlin building authorities permitted a so-called
self-operated elevator in apartment buildings, thereby creating the legal basis for eliminating the cost of elevator personnel.[25] And finally, the regulations issued in 1908 for the
entire state of Prussia contained, in contrast to earlier edicts
for individual provinces, a fundamentally new categoriza-
tion of those permitted to operate the apparatus. Article 32
("Operators") was now divided into three sections. The first
continued to prescribe an adult operator for "passenger elevators with mechanical controls." The second and third sections relativized this rule: elevators "with electric controls
in the cab" could be operated by assistant operators "who
have reached their fifteenth year." In apartment buildings
(but not in hotels or commercial buildings), installations
"with interior and exterior controls" could "dispense with

the presence of an operator" altogether.[26] The appended "instructions for implementation" of this clause explained that "all cable, lever, and crank controls are to be considered 'mechanical' in contrast to electric push-button controls."[27] In the modifications and additions to the code in the years that followed, we can see the exception gradually becoming the rule. For example, from January 1917 on, the first section of Article 32 began, "Passenger elevators may (with the exceptions noted in Sections II-IV) only be operated by a certified operator."[28] The newly inserted parentheses made it clear that the exceptions now took up more space than the original norm. And in the first elevator code covering the entire German Empire, issued in 1926, the structure of the old article was entirely abandoned. Now the beginning of Article 2 structured the "classification of elevators" in the following way: "1. Elevators with an operator, intended to transport people or freight (operated elevators); 2. Elevators with a capacity of at most six persons without an operator (self-controlled)."[29] Equivalent categories of access replaced the hierarchy of rule and exception.

In the first years after the development of push-button controls, their use remained restricted to elevators in apartment buildings. A circumscribed number of users became familiar with the new mechanism; buildings with a large fluctuation in foot traffic such as hotels and office buildings, however, at first held fast to the combination of elevator operator and mechanical crank or electric lever controls. One can clearly sense the latent mistrust of the new technology from the pages of the construction journals, for instance in a 1907 article entitled "Lever or Push-Button Controls in Passenger Elevators," which stressed the "greater durability and reliability" of the older systems, "since push-button controls are a fairly complicated and sensitive device." Thus the question of which control system is the right one

cannot be answered in favor of the one or the other. In private apartment buildings in which the elevator is sometimes run by the inhabitants (renters) themselves, often at night, and a special operator is not always present, push-button controls have the advantage; on the other hand, in buildings with heavy public foot traffic such as department stores, hotels, etc. in which the elevators are always run by elevator operators, lever controls are usually indicated.[30]

Until after the First World War there was a transitional period in which the authority of the elevator operator persisted, except in apartment buildings. As late as 1917, an instructional booklet was published to help candidates prepare for the elevator operator's examination, essentially the same as those published a decade earlier.[31] By 1920 at the latest, however (and a decade earlier in the United States), the situation had changed. The passage in the elevator code requiring elevators in hotels and public buildings to be attended by certified operators had been removed. And in literary works, the image of the liftboy traces the fading of his creative potential, his demotion to a uniformed lackey. For decades, an elevator operator's job combined operating and maintaining the machine. As one of the instructional booklets stated, he was responsible not just for service in the cab, but also for "inspecting . . . the cables, keeping them well lubricated, and, if they have been severely damaged (snapped wires or torn strands), to replace them as necessary."[32] Now those responsibilities were divided between an unseen mechanic and a visible and usually young liftboy. This division is particularly evident when we compare a figure like Felix Krull with another well-known liftboy from German literature, Karl Rossmann in Kafka's novel *Amerika*, written in 1912–1913. The Hotel Occidental, where Karl takes a job as a liftboy, has more than thirty elevators. Here too, the new boy is broken in by his predecessor (this time named Giacomo instead of Eustache), but the control technology in an American hotel around 1910 leaves no room for differentiated operation or the development of an individual operating style such as Krull's:

> Karl's deepest disappointment was the discovery that a lift-boy had nothing to do with the machinery of the lift but to set it in

motion by simply pressing a button, while all repairs were done exclusively by the mechanics belonging to the hotel; for example, in spite of half a year's service on the lift, Giacomo had never seen with his own eyes either the dynamo in the cellar or the inner mechanism of the lift, although, as he said himself, that would have delighted him.[33]

Karl Rossmann and Felix Krull stand on opposite sides of an epochal divide created by push-button controls. The virtuoso at the end of the nineteenth century who wins the hearts of women with his artful and precise stops has been degraded to simple button pusher. The elevator operator is no longer the lord of his machine, he has become part of it, a constellation whose consequences are played out in the 1920 story "Der Liftboy" by the children's author Anton de Nora: "As soon as someone entered the cab, he doffed his cap and clicked his heels together, as if moved by an *internal mechanism*."[34] We must recall that in 1876, the Otis Company compared the job of an elevator operator with that of a railroad engineer. A quarter century later, the journal *American Architect and Building News* used this same comparison in a discussion of the introduction of an examination for elevator operators. In reply to a remark of the New York superintendent of buildings that an extensive examination was necessary because railroad engineers also had to submit to such a test, the magazine directed attention to the huge difference between the two professions at the beginning of the twentieth century:

> In the latter case practically the whole movement of every part of the machine that creates the movement is under the direct personal control of the engineer and the necessity of caring of it and the ever-changing conditions of the road-bed, grade, traffic, signals, and so on, keep him awake and alert, and consequently the calling has attraction for a high grade of man. But next to passing one's days in the prison cell the most limited career, surely, is that of an elevator-runner.[35]

Thus the history of the elevator cab as a workplace ended in the twentieth century. No longer a place demanding technical know-how, it was at best a slight improvement on a jail cell.

A BRIEF PSYCHOLOGY OF THE PUSH BUTTON

We must not lose sight of the fact that the advent of the push button had much greater impact on the history of the elevator than simply making its operation easier or more economical. Contemporary accounts made clear how fundamentally the perception of the technical apparatus was unsettled by the new control. Especially vivid, for instance, was the description in Arthur Fürst's 1927 manual of popular science *Das Weltreich der Technik* (The empire of technology). Through the "miracle" of push-button control, the elevator seemed to be transformed into an intelligent being: "The elevator in the apartment building, open to use by anyone, no longer seems to be a dead machine, but to possess the ability to think for itself."[36] And Fürst produced a sample of this remarkable ability:

> Let's assume that the elevator cab is located on the fourth floor at the moment. Someone on the third floor pushes the button mounted on the exterior of the elevator shaft. The cab immediately begins to descend and stops at the desired landing. If one pushes the same button when the cab is on the first floor, however, then it ascends, so that it seems to be possessed of an unerring sense of direction.[37]

That the functioning of the control system was perceived as almost magic had to do with a completely new relationship between visibility and invisibility. In the days when elevator operators set the cable in motion by means of a hand wheel or a crank, the technical process could be seen in its context. In the electric elevator with push-button controls, on the other hand, the entire mechanism—electrical connections, control apparatus, motor—vanished behind the scenes. Only the push button remained visible on the surface like some last vestige and seemed to be responsible for the whole spectacle of motion all by itself. The fact that pushing the button completed a complicated circuit and broke it again at the chosen landing remained invisible to the passenger.

One of the most historically important characteristics of the years around 1900 appears to be the increasing removal of technical processes in general into a realm of concealment, and the elevator was one of the most interesting examples of this development. The invention of the push button led in equal measure to new power and new impotence vis-à-vis technical phenomena. Although the machine now obeyed the human without any special effort on his part, the decline of the elevator operator shows that the push button made any particular skill of the human in question obsolete. Automatic controls reduced the volitional component of machine operation to a single initiating motion. One could say that since the late nineteenth century, there has been a rupture in our perception of technical processes. For the push button, as the only visible element of a hidden system of wires, coils, and motors, severs the visible connection between cause and effect. Whatever happens between pressing the button and the desired result—the arrival of the elevator, for instance—has become an abstraction.

Elevator fantasies in literature and film repeatedly focus on exactly this blind spot and take literally Artur Fürst's metaphor of the elevator's "ability to think for itself." The classic 1983 Dutch horror film *De Lift* (a 2001 American remake was entitled *The Shaft*), for example, in which a defective microprocessor causes a cab to become in fact "animate" and kill a series of passengers by moving unexpectedly, is possible only in the historic circumstances created eighty years earlier by the push button. To imagine an apparatus having a "life of its own" becomes possible the moment that real-life control systems hide their operation from view. The same thing goes for less scary versions of the fantasy that belong more to the genre of fairy tale than horror film. In *Der Aufzug* (The elevator), the previously mentioned children's book by Paul Maar and Nikolaus Heidelbach, the little girl Rosa is taken on a trip through the magic landscapes between the stories of her building, but first receives a warning from the dwarf in the elevator: "Push any button! / There's lots to see! / Just not the one / that has a B!"[38] Of course the story ends when Rosa pushes the forbidden button one night and ends the spell. Her returning parents discover her in the basement and carry the sleepwalking child back to her bed. Crucial to the imaginary structure of this story as well is that it is possible only in the age of the push button. What we could call the "fictional impulse" of the story—the idea that an elevator cab could suddenly deliver you to a fairy-tale realm—is tied to the invisibility of the control mechanism. An elevator operated by a hand wheel just wouldn't work as a hermetic wish machine.

When we contemplate the implications of the push button around 1900, one shift becomes especially evident: in the mechanical epoch, an effect such as calling for an elevator was *produced*, not just *activated*. This threshold between producing and activating a movement is especially important in the history of human consciousness. Hans Blumenberg describes this precisely in the essay "Environment and Mechanization under the Aspect of Phenomenology," which posits a theory of the push button using the example of the doorbell:

> There are the old mechanical models: the bell pull or revolving bicycle-style bell. When you operate them, you still have the immediate feeling that you are producing the intended effect in all its specificity; there is an adequate nexus between the act of your hand and the ringing of the bell, that is, when I am confronted by such a device, I not only know what I have to do but also why I have to do it. It's different with an electric bell operated by a push button. The hand's action is related to the effect in a quite unspecific and heteromorphic way—we no longer produce the effect, but only activate it. The apparatus holds the desired effect already completed, so to speak, and ready for us. Indeed, it carefully conceals from us its contingency and the complexity of its production in order to suggest that it is obtainable without effort.[39]

To be sure, there were devices used to activate processes long before the push button: the trigger of a gun, for instance, or the earliest forms of electric telegraphy in the mid-nineteenth century in which an ensemble of visible keys and invisible wires was already present. But only the push button fully developed that constellation whose most important criterion was defined as early as 1876 by the physicist Julius Robert Mayer in his lecture "On Activation," namely, "that there is absolutely no quantitative relationship between cause and effect."[40] In the transitions from crank to lever to push button, the last analogy between activating and activated power disappears, namely, direction. For the direction in which one's fingertip moves is always the same and independent of whether an elevator is supposed to travel up or down. The push button becomes the absolute activation device, and it's a bit surprising that Walter Benjamin makes no specific mention of it in the often-quoted passage from his book on Baudelaire:

> In the mid-nineteenth century, the invention of the match brought forth a number of innovations which have one thing in common: a single abrupt movement of the hand triggers a process of many steps. This development is taking place in many areas. A case in point is the telephone, where the lifting of a receiver has taken the place of the steady movement that used to be required to crank the older models. With regard to countless movements of switching, inserting, pressing, and the like, the "snapping" by the photographer had the greatest consequences. Henceforth a touch of the finger sufficed to fix an event for an unlimited period of time. The camera gave the moment a posthumous shock, as it were.[41]

Benjamin's observation culminates in the invention of the push button, which began showing up in various devices between 1885 and 1895. Besides its function as an elevator control, it is also used as a doorbell, on machine tools, and as a release on fire alarms and camera shutters. The famous advertising slogan of Kodak, which began selling its pocket camera in 1888, thematized the new relationship between user and device: "You press the button, we do the rest."[42]

Already by the end of the nineteenth century, the fingertip was often the only point of contact between humans and their machines. Perhaps, then, it is more than just a historical coincidence that at the same time—in fact, in the same year as one of the first patents for an elevator push button[43]—the fingertip gained importance for quite a different reason: not as a medium of control but of identification. The English polymath Francis Galton published his book *Finger Prints* in 1892, the first systematic study of the use of human prints for the purpose of identification. In remarkable synchronicity, this tiny part of the human anatomy was assigned different functions: the activation of technical processes and the production of unique identification marks. The power and impotence of modern man, his ability to control as well as to be controlled, were both concentrated in his fingertip.

One of the earliest uses of the push button—a little less than a decade before its installation in elevators—was to report fires. It's obvious that modern activation mechanisms would be welcome in fire prevention, for even the most advanced firefighting techniques are unavailing when tardy notification means the firemen arrive at a smoking ruin. But procedures for giving the alarm were long hindered by the problem that they could "only be carried out within earshot of the public in general," as the hefty 1929 *Deutsches Feuerwehrbuch* (German firefighting book) puts it, that is, by sounding a bell or blowing a horn.[44] This often meant that the work of putting out the fire was interfered with by a crowd of onlookers. In the middle of the nineteenth century, the new possibilities opened by telegraphy allowed more discrete communication; aboveground electric lines connecting tire towers to fire department headquarters began to be strung. Then, between 1860 and 1885, there was a proliferation of fire alarm boxes inside buildings and on the street, at first with cranks or pull-down levers, then with push buttons. As the Berlin senior engineer Lucke stressed in the *Deutsches Feuerwehrbuch*, the introduction of electric fire alarm boxes ensured not only more discretion but also a more reliable form of data transfer. The use of the device was so simple that any witness to a fire was able to activate the alarm, "no matter how stupid the person may be who gives the signal."[45] Here Lucke quotes an elderly British colleague and then adds a comment of his own:

> This remark characterizes the purpose of a fire alarm box. Such an apparatus is designed to make it possible for anyone to call the fire department to a particular location by sending a signal to headquarters that identifies the location of the alarm box. The main prerequisite is thus that almost no demands at all are placed on the intelligence of the person giving the alarm, especially since that person will almost always be in an excited state.[46]

That is the good news of the push button: it relieves us of the responsibility of having to produce meaningful information on our own. The fire alarm sent by pushing a button gives the exact location of the fire even if the person who discovered it is not capable of doing so. Someone who is too excited and confused to think and speak clearly can still push a button; when someone is in shock, their fingertip is more reliable than their speech center. At the end of the passage quoted above, Senior Engineer Lucke drew attention to an important distinction. He explained to his readers that the assertion of the English historian of firefighting wasn't really accurate, since he was talking about the older crank-operated fire alarm boxes, whose operation still required a modicum of intelligence from the user, "since if the crank is turned too often, too quickly, or too slowly, it can easily cause errors at headquarters as a result of an unclear signal."[47] The push button alone is equal to any potential deficiency in the user. Whether the button is pressed too quickly, too slowly, or too frequently, the signal that arrives at headquarters is always clear and correct.

The same year the *Deutsches Feuerwehrbuch* was published, an article appeared in the magazine *Der graphische Betrieb* (Graphics business) entitled "Push-Button Controls as a Factor in Operating Efficiency." The text discussed the deployment of the new controls in machine tools in the paper, rubber, and food products industries and described how workers' shorter "manipulation times" result in increased production. It is interesting that in this case too, the decisive advantage of the push button was immediately linked to the latent unreliability of users, and with a racist argument to boot. While in Germany the hefty costs involved would prevent all but the largest machines from being equipped with the new controls, the push button was already in widespread use in American factories for the following reason, according to the author:

> With respect to industrial jobs, we can assume that the intelligence of unskilled workers in America, especially the colored workers, is not on the same level as that of unskilled workers in the cultured states of Europe and therefore, one cannot make great demands on their intelligence. Push-button controls in America are intended to overcome this lack of intelligence among unskilled workers.[48]

Hans Blumenberg's interest, in contrast, was in the alienation of the subject from the technological apparatus in the activation of electric doorbells: "The functional human portion is homogenized and reduced to the ideal minimum of pressure on a button. The technologization makes human actions increasingly unspecific."[49] From the perspective of firemen and economists, however, the advantage of the new controls lay precisely in this leveling. No one needed specialized training to use the button. The push button, one could say, extinguished the genuine authorship of manipulations. While the push button transformed photography, for instance, from an exclusive, time-consuming art form into an instantaneous "snapshot"—an everyday pleasure for the masses—in the case of fire prevention it simply meant greater security. One of the loveliest passages of the *Deutsches Feuerwehrbuch* addressed the frequently advocated use of the telephone to report a fire. Lucke explained his view that the reason this means of communication was not appropriate was precisely that it involved human decisions. He pointed out that a caller could exaggerate, the fire station might be unable to learn the location of the blaze, and in addition, no written record of the conversation would be available. Lucke then recalled an incident when the use of the telephone resulted in a catastrophe:

> It has happened that an entire telephone office [of a fire station] burned to the ground because the last operator, who possessed the admirable courage to call up the fire brigade before leaving her already burning office, could not be persuaded to clearly state where the fire was. In her distress she just kept repeating, "It's burning here in the office," since she must have assumed the fire brigade would know the call was coming from the telephone office.[50]

Such problems are unknown to the push button. Once pushed, it sets in motion a chain of contacts that precludes any misunderstandings. Thus, since the invention of the electric fire alarm box, the business of reporting a fire has been carried out without the unreliable human factor—with one exception, namely, how to distinguish a practice alarm from a real one. For although electric wires and push buttons perform their service so conscientiously, they are not able to differentiate between a serious activation and one meant only to test the system. To clear up that question, communication by telephone was necessary after all. That is why, as Lucke explained, the newest fire alarm boxes were "paired with a telephone installation."

Thus the push button proved its worth wherever the unpredictability of human intelligence could endanger the transmission of data. The withdrawal of the human subject as a responsible creator of information also had a menacing side, however. Pushing a button occurs so quickly and anonymously that from its first appearance, the push button was associated with a sense of unease and fear of random misuse. Not surprisingly, the subject of malicious misuse of electric doorbells, fire alarms, and elevator buttons was mentioned in almost every article about them at the turn of the century. Doorbells were involved mostly in a playful way; an 1896 *Handbuch der Architektur* (Manual of architecture) already declared that they "tempt young people to mischief."[51] The problem was more serious in the case of electric fire alarms, which were misused so often in the first years of their existence that they soon got covered by a protective sheet of thick glass. Since then, the form of fire alarms has been characterized by the curious paradox that the inner threshold of activation is kept as low as possible, but the outer threshold is quite high to protect against misuse. Thus the passerby again needs strength and skill to report a fire, but only to legitimize his action, not for the action itself. What the glass cover seeks to inhibit is the almost magnetic attraction of the push button. Its appearance ignites that general urge to activate things that Julius Robert Mayer was already cognizant of:

> Human nature is such that people like to achieve the greatest effects with the smallest possible means. The pleasure we take in firing a weapon is an eloquent example of this. . . . But even if activating things is an inexhaustible source of permissible joy and harmless pleasure, we must also note that this phenomenon can also lead to the most heinous crimes.[52]

Mayer mentioned assassinations, arson, and tampering with railroad switches and closed with the prognosis, "Well, if our planet were so constituted that it would be possible for someone to blow it up with a bag of dynamite, there would certainly be enough people at any given time willing to sacrifice their own lives in order to blow our beautiful earth into outer space."[53]

What was still an imaginary horror scenario in 1876, the idea of blowing up the whole world with the push of a button, became a much-discussed reality in the second half of the twentieth century in the course of the Cold War. All the dangers of the push button—the irresponsibility of the human subject, the possibility of malicious misuse, the process of information transfer inscrutable to the layman—were united in the myth of the so-called Red Button, which could at any time activate the atomic destruction of the earth. The fear of this ultimate push button, played through in countless novels and films, was the culmination of the entire psychology of its use: the fear of the no longer comprehensible disproportion between cause and effect, the knowledge of its simple, irreversible functioning, and finally, the thought of its indiscriminate use—that a villain might secure access to the Red Button and use it to extort world domination or that, as in a 1980s music video of the English rock group Genesis, a scatter-brained president mixes up the buttons and instead of calling his nurse initiates World War III. With the Red Button, the realization quickly dawned that push buttons eliminated the competence and responsibility entailed in the authorship of an action. The decision to launch missile systems was no longer the result of well-considered negotiations, but rather the matter of a moment, perhaps even the result of a capricious or accidental act. One knows, of course, that such a Red Button never really existed. The mechanism that could set a missile attack from the United States or the Soviet Union (or Russia) in motion is not controlled by push buttons but by a series of electronic decoding systems. According to a description of the so-called nuclear briefcase, a president would have to

> enter a code to approve the process of initiating an attack. The secretary of defense would have to do the same. The third key would be held by the joint chiefs of staff who would have to convert the information received from the president and the secretary of defense into a further number, which would be encrypted and sent to the missiles over special frequencies.[54]

We can already see from the hypotactic sentence structure how much the actuality differs from the myth of the continuously available Red Button. Only a combination of digital codes could allow the worst-case scenario to begin, an activation technology that contradicts the psychology of the push button in all respects: complex rather than simple operation, strictly regulated rather than uncontrolled access, activation as a series of individual, reversible steps rather than a momentary, impulsive act. The fate of the world probably never hung by the thread spun by Cold War hysteria, the thread that the push of a button could snap. The metaphor of the push button, however, by concretizing the fear of nuclear arms, is psychologically consequential.

The crucial point is that push buttons deny us insight into how a technical apparatus functions. As Hans Blumenberg writes,

> Behind every such activator there is a long prehistory of human discoveries, an entire complex of inventive accomplishment; but the activator is so "packaged" that its abstract uniformity removes and conceals all of that from our view—it would be an inferior "product" that allowed us to peer at its innards.[55]

One consequence of this opaqueness, as the Red Button dramatizes, is the fear of overeffectiveness. Push buttons always contain the threat that they could function "too well." However, the opposite threat also exists (and here the elevator comes back into our sights), the persistent possibility that without our knowledge, they may have no effect at all. In his book *Faster: The Acceleration of Just About Everything*, the American theoretician James Gleick reveals a secret about the "door close" buttons present in all recent elevators. This button is supposed to make the doors close immediately, thus saving those precious seconds that tick away between the choice of floor and the beginning of the ride. Gleick quotes the president of the Otis Company to the effect that in elevators in Asia, the "door close" button has long been the most well-worn of all. No button in the elevator seems more important, and yet, as Gleick's research reveals, the wires to this button are often either disconnected or not present at all.[56] The "door close" button enacts a swindle: it gives passengers the feeling that they are getting on faster, but in reality it has no effect at all. In this light, the phenomenology of the push button—Blumenberg's distinction between "producing" and merely "activating," gains a new twist, since it turns out that in the push button, the connection between cause and effect is sometimes not just optically but literally severed. No one can check to see if the control keeps its promise or not, as James Gleick points out:

How often do you press a button and nothing happens? Do you press the already illuminated call button of an elevator a second time even though you suspect that your effort will not result in the elevator arriving sooner? Your suspicion is correct. Computers could tell the elevator to privilege those floors where the call button was used more often, but elevator engineers are not about to provide even more incentives than already exist for people to repeatedly press the button.[57]

Everyday life is saturated with push buttons whose functionality is at least questionable, whether they be the "walk" button at seldom-used pedestrian crosswalks, the buttons on a slot machine, or the "door close" button in an elevator. All these controls suggest to their user that the pressure of a finger can influence the course of events. But the invisibility of the actual mechanism confounds any confirmation of this hypothesis. We cannot say with certainty how many of our daily activations are purely unnecessary doublings of actions that are controlled from somewhere else, defective haptic feedback of the kind Willy Brandt experienced in 1967 when he pushed a button to initiate color TV in Germany. An overeager technician had already sent the image to countless German TV screens seconds before the staged moment of activation.[58] In the end, the effectiveness of this control, as incontrovertible as it seems, is never really ensured. Push buttons can always turn out to be placebos.

INTERIORS

THE STAIRWELL

The multistory apartment buildings that rapidly proliferated in the second half of the nineteenth century created another difficulty besides adding upper floors unsuitable for residences: they contained a number of spaces—corridors, stairwells, and later, elevators—of often indeterminate status. These spaces were part of the building but not of its residential units, and occupied an unstable intermediate position between the private space behind closed apartment doors and the public space outside the building. Revisions of German building codes reveal the increasing attention paid to the stairwell—*das Treppenhaus*—a word increasingly frequent in common parlance beginning in the 1850s.[1] The Berlin building code of 1897, for instance, introduced the previously unknown category "long-term human occupancy" and forbade it in "hallways, staircases, corridors."[2] The amount of time spent in a residential building was legally irrelevant as long as residents were either completely inside or completely outside their separate houses. Only the spaces of multistory dwellings intended purely for transit necessitated the new regulation.

It is no surprise that the new concept of the stairwell as a semi-public space attracted the attention of both building inspectors and public health officials. As the part of the building used not only by all the tenants but also by a wide variety of visitors, it was monitored by health officials almost as closely as basement and attic apartments. In an 1893 conference paper entitled "The Hygiene of Stairways and Stairwells," the Munich physician Josef von Kerschensteiner drew attention to the importance of this question,

> since no part of a building is so often and regularly used, from early morning until late at night, by people of every age, sex, and profession. Children and old grandmothers, messengers, package deliverers and letter carriers, and not least of all doctors, must climb the often towering stairwells in pursuit of their duties. . . . In this regard, the following points should be noted. Hallways provide an image of the building's character; their floors should be tiled and clean. The air in the hallway must be good, and warm in winter to create natural ventilation. . . . The hallway must be well lit day and night.[3]

The increasingly intense public health focus on the stairwell as a heavily trafficked space was closely related to the "increase in knowledge about the natural processes of infection," as the 1894 *Handbuch der Hygiene* (Manual of hygiene) stressed.[4] Pasteur and Koch had researched the conditions for bacterial infections in the early 1880s, and the semi-public spaces of the new large tenements were recognized as a paradigmatic milieu for disease transmission. The danger was particularly acute where the stairwell was exposed to constant touching:

> In our time, when contact infections are universally recognized by bacteriologists and doctors as more prevalent than any other kind, the banister in the stairwell and especially the handrails must receive special attention as a structure particularly well suited to the transmission of infectious diseases. Up to now, a small number of architects have received hygienic training, concede the importance of public health, and have pointed out that the handrail must not be allowed to accumulate dust. But we must demand much more than that from its design: the handrail must be washable, and not just with moist cloths, i.e., with water, but also with disinfectant solutions.[5]

To underscore their demands, the authors adduced a scenario posited in the *Centralblatt für Bacteriologie* (Central newsletter for bacteriology):

> Let us merely assume, for example, a frequently occurring case: on the top floor of a building, a mother whose child has diphtheria and is nearly choking to death uses her finger to remove a coughed-up croup membrane from the child's mouth, or has otherwise touched its mouth. Without taking time to wash her hands, she rushes to the doctor's office and uses the handrail along the stairs. Shortly thereafter, the father of the family living one floor below returns home for lunch, weary from his morning's work. He too uses the handrail. He greets his children as they run to meet him. They take him by the hand and accompany him to the lunch table, where they reach for pieces of bread and transport the diphtheria germs their father's hand had picked up on the railing onto their bread and with it onto the mucosae in their mouth and throat. The transmission can also occur more directly, since one often sees toddlers using the handrails when going up and down the stairs.[6]

Such scenarios show how much the image of the home changed in the age of urbanization. Previously ignored intermediate spaces now frequently came under scrutiny and their dangers were investigated with the aid of the latest advances in medical knowledge. One could say that stairwells and, eventually, elevators as well introduced the element of public contact into the image of apartment buildings, and in the minds of public health advocates at the end of the nineteenth century, contact was synonymous with contamination. That's why manuals of residential hygiene could devote entire chapters to the proper dust-resistant construction of banister handrails. The cleanliness of through traffic had to be assured if the parts of the building meant for common use were not to become sources of collective illness. Paths for infection that, if we are to believe the handbook's authors, "could be even more drastically portrayed,"[7] must be blocked both by the correct use of cleaning agents and a "local police ban" on certain regional habits such as the "beating and brushing of clothes and shoes on the stairwell landings."[8] The latter demand referred precisely to the issue of "long-term human occupancy" of corridors that was regulated for the first time three years later, in 1897, in the Berlin building code. In 1894, however, the stairwell still appeared as a diffuse, judicially unstructured location.

It was typical of the hygienists' thinking that they scrutinized the stairwell not just physiologically, but also morally. For the danger of infection lurking in a building's stairwell could threaten both the immune and the value systems of its residents. Interesting contrasts developed in the debate about communal life in apartment buildings. Proponents of such living argued for its didactic value. James Hobrecht, for example, the initiator of the Berlin development plan of 1862 and—despite his activities in the Public Health Association—one of the greatest champions of apartment houses, provided an eloquent defense of them in *Ueber öffentliche Gesundheitspflege* (On public health). The English tradition of single-family houses, Hobrecht argued, separated the various social classes too radically from each other. While upper-class streets were supplied with all the amenities, only "police officers and sensation-seekers" dared enter working-class neighborhoods.[9] The goal of urban planning must therefore be "diffusion," not "seclusion." Hobrecht portrayed the apartment building, with its clearly structured vertical hierarchy, as a pedagogic establishment of benefit to all its inhabitants, from the *bel étage* to the garret:

> It is a moral education for the well-to-do and wealthy to see and meet other people and come into contact with all levels of poverty and deprivation, while seclusion leads either to hard-heartedness or, in the case of more sensitive natures who happen to encounter poverty (which is never entirely avoidable), to a spurious and nervous humanitarianism.[10]

In the multistory apartment building, on the other hand, the continuous cultivation of the heart developed naturally.

> The children from the basement apartments head off to public school through the same hallways used by the children of privy counselors and merchants on their way to the *gymnasium* that

prepares them for university study. Wilhelm the cobbler from the mansard apartment and old bed-ridden Frau Schulz from the back courtyard whose daughter earns a meager living as a seamstress and charwoman are well known to the residents of the *bel étage*. Here they find a bowl of soup to fortify them when they're ill, there a hand-me-down, and again some help getting their children into a free school, etc. And all this, the result of easy relations among human beings however great their differences in station, is charity that exercises its ennobling influence on the *giver*. . . . The well-to-do, on the other hand, with their cleanliness and social graces—quite apart from the better qualities they obviously possess because of their more scrupulous upbringing—are most definitely a positive social influence on the needy and destitute. Where a working-class English mother lets her child run around unwashed, uncombed, and in rags because she has no incentive to expend effort or time on the child's appearance, the mother from a basement dwelling in an apartment house would not think of doing so, for she knows herself to be observed and subject to the disapproval of the better residents.[11]

Hobrecht's philanthropic attempt to regard the *Mietskaserne*, the "rental barracks," as a moral institution assigned the stairwell a completely different function. What was communicated here was not diphtheria germs, but qualities such as charity and self-respect. The common spaces served as a constant corrective by restraining some from arrogance and others from dissipation. A "natural relationship of give and take" was engendered and, in addition, provided the renters of modest means with several possibilities for additional income: "Here, the daughter of the minor official from the back courtyard can give sewing machine lessons. There, the teacher from the garret apartment can give the schoolboy from the *bel étage* extra tutoring—and can do it without wasting time because of the *short* distance."[12] But these "short distances" between apartments were exactly what made Hobrecht's early encomium such an exception; they more often elicited a flood of vituperation. As we know, most public health advocates rejected the multistory tenement and its stairwell. The potential for contagion, not pedagogy, was their central concern. One of the most prominent of them stated categorically, "The modern style of tenement house creates a widespread individual disposition to infectious diseases."[13] The same could be said for moral infection. It could be observed "that the excessive agglomeration of so many families and men and women of all ages under one roof brings with it many inconveniences, conflicts, and moral dangers that do not usually occur within less crowded buildings."[14] In the nineteenth and early twentieth centuries, the stairwell was a suspect location. One could make a study of the characters in literary works of the time whose existence plays out in these public passageways — Kafka's Odradek, for example, or Melville's Bartleby, who "persists in haunting the building generally, sitting upon the banisters of the stairs by day, and sleeping in the entry by night."[15] They are figures with an identity as unstable as the place they end up in or inhabit from the start.

One last aspect of the discussion of tenement houses is interesting because it shows the hygienists' angle of attack against the stairwell in Germany, namely, the "lavatory question" addressed at tedious length in the public health literature. It is surprising that in the early twentieth century, there were still frequent voices in favor of locating toilets in the stairwells instead of in the meagerly furnished apartments themselves. This argument makes sense only if we assume that hygienic standards for the semi-public spaces of the building were different from those for the private spaces behind apartment doors. As a 1906 essay in the *Zeitschrift für Wohnungswesen* (Journal of residential housing) states, the stairwell in multistory buildings

> assumes a very different character than in a single-family house. While in the latter it is a necessary part of the dwelling, stands in direct communication with its rooms, and often becomes almost a kind of living room in combination with an entrance hall or vestibule, the situation in an apartment building is quite different. Here the stairwell constitutes only an access of sorts — an extension of

the street if you will—to the individual apartments. There is absolutely no reason for the residents of the building to spend any appreciable time in the stairwell.[16]

Part of the dwelling or part of the street, independent room or mere passageway—this was the central question raised by the advent of the stairwell and later the elevator. In Germany, despite early laws against locating toilets outside apartments,[17] the idea took hold that these rooms were to be regarded as external rather than internal. According to the monumental 1902 *Handbuch der Architektur* (Manual of architecture), "Together with the hallways they [stairways in apartment buildings] constitute the continuation of the street and are to be designed accordingly."[18]

If we wish to trace the ambivalent status of semi-public spaces in the early years of the mass tenement, we cannot ignore the emergence of the American apartment house, first in Boston, then primarily in New York. In contrast to the situation in Germany and continental Europe in general, two things particularly stand out. On the one hand, the difference between life in single-family houses and life in apartment houses was perceived as much more drastic in America. On the other hand, the elevator soon played a decisive role in the debates about apartment houses, which is of most interest for the present work. The furious pace of transformation in Manhattan between the erection of the first apartment house in 1869 and the turn of the century, when only an infinitesimal number of single-family houses were still being built,[19] has been described at length by American social and architectural historians.[20] Within only a few years, a "revolution in living"[21] took place that commentators soon reflected upon. It recapitulated the process of mid-nineteenth-century European urbanization as if in time lapse and carried it even further. By 1883, more than 50 percent of the population of Manhattan lived in communal rather than single-family dwellings.[22] An elevator was already installed in the second apartment house ever built, and by the 1880s at the latest had become a standard amenity. American

INTERIORS

architectural critics were surprised to find that the new conveyance was absent from even the most luxurious European apartment buildings. In an 1890 portrait of "one of the largest apartment houses" in Paris, one of them noted the absence of "a luxury which an American would consider indispensable in such a house, but which the Parisian is content to find only in hotels."[23]

One must try to imagine the suddenness of the changes in New York, the utter absence there of the early forms of mass dwellings that existed in large European cities, to understand the skepticism toward the new type of building. Before 1870, the only communal alternatives to single-family houses were "boarding houses" and "tenement houses"—simple hotels for long-term guests and collective accommodations for poor families and newly arrived immigrants. The radical difference between the latter and the new apartment houses was readable from their etymologies, as a contemporary commentator pointed out:

> "Tenement" is derived from the Latin verb "tenere" (to hold), and is the name properly given to a building that is designed to hold or to give shelter to the largest possible number of persons, at the least possible cost to each individual tenant. "Apartment," however, is an anglicized derivation of another Latin verb, "partere" (to divide), and with equal propriety is applied to a dwelling-house, of which the structural and social intent is to separate family from family, and to gratify the desire for privacy that every household naturally feels. . . . Economy, therefore, is the purpose of the tenement—comfort, that of the apartment.[24]

This delimitation of the tenement was typical of the early reception of apartment houses. The latter constituted an intermediate link between the two traditional kinds of dwelling. They emerged to serve a growing class who could not afford a single-family house, but for whom living in a tenement house would have meant an inappropriate decline in status. As an 1878 magazine article put it, an apartment is the perfect dwelling "for a decent, unpretending, small family, 'not in society,' i.e., making no claims to elegance of surrounding, but yet not willing to descend to the tenement-house level."[25] This new intermediate link, however, had elements that tended to draw two spheres closer together that up to then had been completely separate: the carefully closed-off living unit on the one hand and the communal life of numerous families under one roof on the other. Stairwells, hallways, and elevators were the interfaces whose job was to guarantee that this drawing together functioned smoothly, and it is logical that their design received more attention in the traditionless apartment houses of America than in the mass rental buildings of Europe. This was already evident in the event that heralded the birth of the apartment house: in June 1857, Calvert Vaux, one of the architects of Central Park, gave a lecture on multistory European apartment houses at the American Institute of Architects, a date still recalled twelve years later by a leading New York construction industry journal: "Vaux was the first, we believe, to publish a plan showing how several families could be accommodated in one building, and yet kept quite isolated."[26] After describing European rental apartments with their unadorned stairwells, Vaux made clear that American cities could not easily adopt such a design. Up to now, this kind of building was known only "in the inadequate shape of what are known as tenement houses."[27] In the plan of a five-story building with eight apartments that Vaux presented to his audience, the semi-public spaces were therefore laid out differently than in Europe:

It is not at all uncommon in the European buildings on this plan to find the public staircase in the middle of the house, and although ample in dimensions, somewhat restricted in its supply of light and air. Indeed, as a general rule, the public approaches are allowed to be of secondary importance, and the agreeable effect of the rooms themselves, when arrived at, is possibly enhanced thereby; but a different plan must be adopted, if the idea is to be suited to New York needs; the public staircase, which is the unusual feature to which we have to be accustomed, must be made light, airy and elegant; and if possible lighter, airier, and more elegant than any other part of the house.[28]

From the start, this was precisely what distinguished American from European stairwells. Because of its exoticism and bad reputation in tenement houses, more attention was paid to the shared stairwell, "the unusual feature to which we have to be accustomed," in America. The first impression had to be a convincing one if Americans' reluctance to accept the apartment building was to be overcome. In the first apartment house actually built in New York (where it was only logical that Calvert Vaux himself should live), this conception was realized. The four-story building with a total of sixteen apartments was divided by two elegant stairways, so that in each half of the building, as in Vaux's early plan, only two apartments were located on each floor. This arrangement restricted the spaces used in common to a minimum, as we see in a contemporary description of the building: "on arriving on each floor, which represents a separate house, the visitor comes to a private hall door on each landing, without interfering with the privacy of any other family in his passage up and down."[29] The wording of this passage is significant, stressing that the apartments remained "separate houses" each with "a private hall door," that is, they were still single-family houses, merely stacked one above the other, but otherwise no different from the familiar house type. "A family thus situated is quite as private as in the finest residence on 5th Avenue."[30] The semi-public spaces necessary to connect these "separate houses" with the street below had to maintain this status, and it is therefore not surprising that early descriptions of New York apartments regularly emphasized the luxurious decoration of their stairwells. While the lavatory question gradually began to preoccupy the Germans, commentators in America were remarking on interior touches such as the "deep-red Turkey carpet" or the "bronze brackets and chandeliers."[31]

The configuration of residential buildings in New York was changing so quickly during the 1870s that new laws were soon necessary to clarify the situation. In 1878, a legal dispute between two property owners turned on the question of "whether what is called an apartment-house is a tenement-house."[32] In 1872, the plaintiff had purchased a building from the defendant, and one of the terms of the contract was that the latter would not build a tenement house on a neighboring lot. Six years later he began to construct an apartment house there, whereupon his neighbor sued him for breach of contract. American courts had to decide for the first time how to classify the new building type. The existing law, passed in 1867, defined all New York residential buildings with more than three households as tenement houses,[33] but that was clearly inadequate to deal with the new type of building. The court found for the defendant, thereby adding a third category of residential structure in addition to the single-family house and the tenement building. From 1878 on, the apartment house was a recognized legal entity. The judge's opinion acknowledged "the necessity of new terms in common use and in law to discriminate new things."[34] But in the first two or three decades of the apartment house's existence, what exactly constituted this "new thing" remained unclear from both a legal and an architectural point of view.

Just as the apartment house did not show up as an independent, precisely defined category until the voluminous New York Building Act of 1899,[35] the principles of its construction also remained open. The greatest difficulty always seemed to be the delicate balance between closed and freely accessible spaces, the question of "how, in the matter of residence, shall we manage to associate with our fellows just enough but not too much."[36] An examination of the debates about apartment houses in the last quarter of the nineteenth century, with their constant comparisons of New York buildings to their European and especially Parisian counterparts (not surprisingly, apartments were at first called "French flats"), manifests quite evidently the efforts to establish this balance. More sharply than in Europe, the attempt to understand the multistory apartment house as a vertical stack of single-family dwellings and the stairwells as purely interior spaces ran up against the problem of blurred demarcation lines. Where did private space end and public space begin? No one described this critical conundrum more clearly than the architectural team of Hubert, Pirsson and Hoddick, who built some of the most prominent apartment houses of the 1880s. In an 1893 essay, they contrasted the construction principles of French apartment buildings to American practice. The authors set out to demonstrate that the design priorities of most New York apartment houses were false. While the stairwell still received the highest priority in the wake of Calvert Vaux's influential assumptions, the dwelling units themselves were designed to be remarkably permeable. The architects reported the difficulties of a man and his wife who lived in an apartment in one of the most luxurious buildings in Manhattan. The couple complained that the location of the windows in their building and the building it faced allowed too great a view into each other's apartments and that the floors between stories were much too thin to mute the noise from the apartments above and below theirs. Moreover, despite the elegant appointments of the stairwell, it was unclear how one was supposed to behave in them. They expressed their annoyance "that the tenants on the top floor had two somewhat rough and ill-bred boys, who nearly upset our friend's wife one day in their wild rush down the narrow public stairs, and who would not rub their feet on the front door mat, but left prints of their dirty boots all the way up the bright Brussels carpet."[37] The more refined the interior decoration of the semi-public spaces, the more unstable were the codes of behavior expected of their users. The same essay illustrates the ambiguous status of the stairwell by describing some tenants who moved in shortly after the couple mentioned above, "a large family with several men who smoked incessantly, both in their rooms and on the stairs and landings which they used as a regular part of their holding, and where they appeared with a painful disregard as to their toilet." According to the authors, all these gray areas and border violations resulted from the insufficiently clear distinction between private and public spheres in New York apartment houses. As a solution to the problem, they pointed to the structure of spaces in the Parisian buildings on which the New York apartments are modeled. In place of white carpets, their stairwells featured clear relationships: "The stairs and landings are far from being clean or well kept, a rough sweeping once a day being all the attention they receive. . . . In fact, the stairs and landings are regarded as a continuation of the street."[38] All the more impermeable, however, were the apartments themselves; the precisely calculated sequence of rooms as well as the massive floors and walls enabled a high level of privacy.[39] It is significant that in their plea for a purely functional stairwell, Hubert, Pirsson and Hoddick ended up using exactly the same argument Vaux and his followers used to emphasize the need for an imposing one. In both cases, what was called for was an apartment that was simply a single-family house hoisted into the air. New York apartment houses sought to guarantee that by making the public spaces as much like the private ones as possible; the Paris apartment buildings did the same by making the distinction between them as great as possible. "The fact is, that in our sense of the word, the French, except perhaps the very poorest classes, do not live in apartments, *but in small dwelling houses, built one level on the top of another and reached by a narrow ascending street.*"[40]

One of the peculiarities of Hubert, Pirsson and Hoddick's essay was that it was probably the only contribution to the early discussion of the apartment house that analyzed the architectonic difference between Europe and New York in terms of a difference in the history of consciousness. The introductory sentence already announced that it was going to treat the "social aspects" of the apartment house problem, which were related to the difference in class consciousness between the Old World and the New World.[41] The more stringent the social stratification, they claimed, the less problematic the meeting of different tenants in the apartment building:

> In France, the social status of each individual is generally so clearly defined that a freedom of intercourse exists between the various classes of society, utterly unknown in this society. . . . All meet on the common stairs, and the fine lady exchanges cheerful greetings with her poorer neighbors without a thought of presumption on their part or of condescension on her own. With us things are different. All claims to social superiority are bitterly resented by people who regard the elevation of those above them as a mere accident of fortune that a day may reverse, while the favored few strive, through an excessive exclusiveness, to guard their dearly-cherished state of exaltation.

A remarkable thesis: New Yorkers' dislike of public stairwells was an effect of America's unstable social structure. The contingent nature of American social structure must not be repeated in the structure of the apartment house. In complete contrast to the liberality of apartment life in Paris, it was necessary to reinforce the brittle veneer of social identity with rigid spatial separation. Any chance encounter in the stairwell might present a challenge to a family's status, one reason the first New York apartment house in 1869 was already equipped with a rear service stairway,[42] an element present only in the most aristocratic buildings in Paris.[43]

American stairwells were by no means regarded as extensions of the street. Access to them had to be strictly regulated to avoid the harmful influence of inappropriate neighbors or strangers. This is also the reason the first so-called cooperatives were already being set up by the early 1880s, apartment houses purchased or even newly built by a group of future residents. This organized form of living together (which became possible only with a change in the law, since ownership of real property in New York prior to 1880 was possible only as ownership of the land itself)[44] appeared as a logical variant of the "privatization" of apartment houses. On the other hand, a 1907 magazine article entitled "The Radical Evil of Life in Apartment-Houses" showed the disastrous course unregulated rental of apartments could take. It conjured up the terrifying fate of a building housing "a score of families enjoying equal incomes, each of whom has hitherto lived in comfort and contentment in an isolated dwelling."[45] They were driven to ruin by the arrival of a visibly more wealthy family. "Shortly thereafter peace and comfort will vanish from most of the other twenty families, each one of whom, disliking to be outshone, will also try to make a splurge and will sacrifice its children's rights to a 'plush rocker,' a piano, or a too expensive dress."[46] And the author added the laconic prognosis, "That means debt, sooner or later, and debt too often means drink."[47] The place where such a calamitous competition began was the stairwell, and the countermeasures suggested by the article focused on that part of the building. Although the architects of future apartment houses would be powerless against "all the evils of gregarious living," careful planning could prevent excessive encounters among the residents "by segregating each independent home with the most sedulous care to protect its privacy at any point."[48] The article ended by recommending a system of one-way staircases already installed in a few residential buildings in New York. Separating ascending from descending residents at least limited face-to-face encounters and disrupted the downward spiral of social competition, debt, and drink.

THE ASSIMILATION OF THE ELEVATOR CAB

The stairwell's status is crucial because it already raised all the questions that appeared again vis-à-vis the assimilation of the elevator. Both in Europe and the United States, there was a fairly long pause between the advent of multistory residential buildings and the installation of the first elevators. In Paris and Berlin, it was not until almost half a century after Haussmann's and Hobrecht's urban planning that elevators began to be installed in the most expensive apartment buildings. Even in New York, more than a decade went by before the new means of transportation had become a standard feature. The elevator cab intensified the problematic relationship between private and public space, intimacy and anonymity already evident in the stairwell. When every fleeting encounter in the hallway threatens to become a test of the residents' moral integrity and must be avoided by special stairway systems, when hygienists warn of contracting diseases from the shared handrails, how great must have been the challenge to the order of communal life represented by an elevator whose passengers are forced to stand crowded together in a small space? Right up to the turn of the century, there is ample evidence that the initial perception of the unfamiliar machinery in the middle of the building was of something alien. For instance, it caused Chicago's Pacific Hotel, which opened in 1870, to provide a separate "ladies' elevator" for single women and a "gentlemen's elevator" for men and married couples.[49] As late as 1912, in correspondence with the workmen's compensation company where Franz Kafka worked, a Bohemian lodging house owner tried to avoid liability for his electric elevator by claiming that the motor—an essential part of the apparatus—was not located in his building at all but in the municipal power plant. Collective understanding of the "location" and extent of the elevator was so inchoate it allowed a clever businessman to attempt such strategic outsourcing.[50]

Despite the fact that the elevator's vertical breach made building interiors more comprehensible and radically reversed the negative hygienic image of the upper stories, the apparatus was at first eyed with suspicion by public health authorities. It took several decades for the elevator cab to become the self-evident core of residential and commercial buildings. The impediments to this process of assimilation were of several kinds. In the early years, there was a lack of clarity about whether the elevator was primarily a means of transportation or an autonomous room, and this led to a lack of clarity about what behavior was appropriate inside the cab. In William Dean Howells's 1884 one-act play *The Elevator*, one of the very first literary texts set in the apparatus, a lady says to her fellow passengers, "What an amusing thing elevator etiquette is! Why should the gentlemen take their hats off? Why don't you take your hats off in a horse-car?"[51] This question of the correct etiquette illustrates once more the uncertainty we have seen in the debates about the stair-well. What is the function of the semi-public spaces of the building? Should men leave their hats on as they do in other conveyances or take them off as they do in other rooms? In the first decades of its use, the elevator cab was not yet established as a mere vehicle. "We were at a hotel in London where they called it the Ascending Room," responds another passenger in Howells's play.[52] Especially in the United States, an attempt was made to ease entrance into the uncertain sphere of the elevator by sumptuous interior decoration. The cab could not be less elegant than the offices or living rooms to which it brought people. An 1869 Otis Company catalog described the basic features of its cabs: "The car is a sumptuous apartment . . . with skylights, ventilators, and chandeliers supplied with gas through a flexible tube; below richly carpeted, with a large mirror and luxurious so-fas around three sides,"[53] curiosities that some twenty years later still elicited the admiration of a visiting German engineering student: "Characteristic . . . is especially the decoration of the elevators in hotels, theaters and many commercial buildings. With their costly paneling, upholstered seats, ornately framed mirrors, electric lighting, etc. they are like little movable salons."[54] Sumptuous apartments, movable salons—the diction of these descriptions makes clear that in the early years, passenger elevators (unlike the unadorned apparatuses for transporting freight) were not to be seen as a mere conveyance. Their interior decoration, imitating im-movable rooms, was meant to facilitate habituation to the new transportation channel. For the same reason, German elevator cabs at the turn of the century were also sometimes "a highlight of the building, a wonder to behold," as the ju-bilee booklet of the Flohr elevator company in Berlin de-clared.[55] In the years after 1900, however, expensive interior decoration soon disappeared, not least in view of the significantly shorter travel times of electric elevators. Plush seats and chandeliers were removed, to be replaced by interior design that was more and more functional and focused on the greatest possible efficiency. From the twentieth century on, the cab was nothing but a transit space.

Another impediment in the course of early elevator history was the impossibility of continuous operation. Strange as it sounds today, in 1870 the Equitable Life Building briefly considered running its two elevators according to a fixed schedule.[56] The first generation of American elevators, driven by steam, was fundamentally dependent on external power generation that closed down at night.[57] We take it for granted that elevators are continuously at our disposal, but that did not become an established fact until the arrival of hydraulic and electric technology and continuously accessible sources of water and electricity. In the mid-1870s, for instance, the Osborne was New York's most modern apartment house, and among its amenities was a "steam elevator, running from 7 A.M. to 12 P.M."[58] In these years, a mere seven-hour interruption was a token of the highest possible service, as an 1882 *New York Times* reportage also documented: "in most cases . . . the time during which the elevators are run is not sufficient to accommodate the tenants of the immense buildings. Placards are displayed in some of the hallways setting forth the fact that the elevators will be in active operation only between the hours of 8:30 in the morning and 5 in the evening."[59] The piece quotes a lawyer with an office on the tenth floor of a commercial building on the drastic consequences of this sort of regulation:

> I was detained in court one day until nightfall, and when I returned to the tall building in which my office was situated and discovered that I must walk up nine flights of iron stairs I felt like fighting. However, it was absolutely necessary for me to go to my office, and I walked. When I reached my office I was more dead than alive. Upon recovering consciousness, I saw, to my horror, that I required some copying ink and the bottle was empty. There was nothing for me

to do but travel down those stairs to Nassau Street and purchase some ink. I procured the ink, and after I had returned to my office reeled like an intoxicated man, and I thoroughly believed that I was about to die.[60]

Thus in the early years of the elevator's existence, the fact that operation was shut down during the night (a practice forbidden by the New York Fire Department in 1899[61]) suggests that it was still perceived as an apparatus extrinsic to the building. It is obvious that this interruption of operation had to do with the structure of the energy supply and thus with concrete technical limitations. But we cannot overlook the more basic and abstract mistrust of a machine not yet perceived as completely reliable. This mistrust was much clearer in Germany, where it was still observable well into the twentieth century, the age of electric push-button controls and optimized safety devices. One piece of evidence is the "key regulation" still in force in the nationwide elevator code of 1926. It prescribed that in residential buildings, keys for the locked cab could be distributed only to residents over fourteen years of age. Independent access to the cab was unavailable to children and visitors.[62] Thus the implantation of an elevator into a building met with resistance and rejection, a reaction that led to a series of important changes to the New York legal code in 1885. Up to that year, the vertical extension of buildings was completely unregulated, but now a maximum height of eighty feet was established for residential buildings.[63] The reason for this measure was different from that for similar restrictions being introduced in European cities. The development of the upper stories and the construction of buildings of eleven to sixteen floors had long since occurred in New York. The so-called Daly Law, named after State Senator James Daly (1843–1892), was not intended to categorically forbid apartments on the upper floors, but rather to slow down all too rapid growth. One of the critical points in this regard was the elevator. According to Elizabeth Hawes, the proponents of the law "were worried that disease might thrive in long communal halls and crowded elevators. Before its passage, advocates of the Daly bill had focused their attack exclusively on apartment buildings, painting them as unwieldy and unhealthy structures, calling physicians to present evidence that their tenants were more liable to symbiotic and contagious diseases than ordinary households."[64] We're familiar with the connection made between the threat of infectious disease and the stairwell. With the elevator, however, this problem became acute in the early 1880s and led to consequences in the building codes. As a magazine article about the hygiene of apartment houses so vividly described it, "Enter a close, overheated hall; get into an elevator, whose glaring gas jets make one fancy he is in a Russian bath, and which ascends with this rickety, jarring creak—so common in elevators—at each floor feeling an increasing sense of suffocation till you reach your destination."[65] In 1885, the New York authorities attempted to reduce the health risk of such an encounter, by limiting building height on the one hand and on the other by issuing an ensemble of specific elevator regulations, the first of their kind. One of them had to do with the maximum carrying capacity of the cab: "Every passenger-elevator shall have the weight it can carry displayed prominently on a metal plate in raised letters."[66] Ever since, the familiar sign next to the push-button controls lists the maximum weight and number of passengers.

When one traces the elevator's progress from alien intruder to core of the building, one must also look more closely at the changes in its operating technology that have already been touched upon at the beginning of this study. The increasing integration of the new means of transportation and passengers' decreasing hesitancy to make use of it were both closely connected to the rationalization of its function. The development of elevator construction between 1870 and 1900—the transition from the (directly or indirectly powered) hydraulic to the electric elevator—is the story of a continuous effort to situate the installation more and more efficiently, so that it occupied less and less space.

The biggest disadvantage of the direct-drive hydraulic machines was that the piston under water pressure that drove the cab upwards had to of course be sunk into the ground to a distance equal to the height of the building above ground. This made it impossible not only to retrofit a building with the vehicle, but also to install it in new buildings built on rocky ground—New York City, for example. As a consequence, New York was the location of "only a single" direct-hydraulic elevator in its entire history.[67] Such difficulties led to the construction of modified water-pressure systems in which pulleys transmitted the motion of the piston to that of the cab. Although the constituent parts of these so-called indirect-hydraulic elevators (the drive-piston, pulley drums, pressure pumps, water tanks, and water lines) still occupied an enormous amount of space, they could now be installed on any sort of ground since their considerably shorter pistons could be housed in an area beneath or next to the cab, and either horizontally or vertically. Within a short period at the end of the 1870s, this operating system replaced the expensive steam elevators with their high energy demands and dominated American elevator construction into the 1890s. In Germany, it constituted a frequent alternative to the predominant direct-hydraulic elevator.[68] The replacement of water pressure with electric power, which took place in the years around 1900, must also be seen mainly as a greater rationalization of the functionality and siting of the machinery within the building. An essay to accompany Werner von Siemens's first presentation of an electric elevator at the Mannheim Industrial Exhibition of 1880 emphasized the fact that the then current hydraulic elevators were "often barely feasible" because of their space requirements.[69] Once the safety and acceleration problems of the earliest electric machines were solved by the early 1890s, the most important arguments for their introduction were their inexpensive operation and ease of installation in existing buildings. The Otis Company advertised its new generation of elevators with the consideration that such an installation was no longer a complicated matter; the vehicle was "well suited to many places where it has heretofore been impracticable to use such an apparatus."[70] This turning point in the history of technology—the increased ease of installation of the electric devices—was particularly important for the final cultural assimilation of the elevator at the turn of the century. Before the 1890s, elevators were cumbersome apparatuses that took up a lot of space; now the ensemble of motor, control apparatus, and cable drum (whose dimensions required no more than an "area of modest size"[71]) could fit into a small machine room in the basement or attic. In contrast to the exposed functionality of the direct-hydraulic elevator with its piston running right through the middle of the building, the electric elevator seemed to almost be a vehicle without an engine, consisting of nothing but a cab inside a shaft. This technical change, together with a complete muffling of the considerable noise made by early elevators retrofitted into stairwells, set in motion a change in perception after 1900, a change one could call the elevator's "naturalization." Thanks to the invisibility of its technology, the electric-drive elevator was seamlessly integrated into the building. As a German advertising brochure put it, "Not a sound betrays to the uninitiated the presence of machinery; the cab glides up and down in almost ghostly quiet."[72]

Such was the situation by the early twentieth century. Twenty or thirty years earlier, however (to return once again to the irritations of the first elevator passengers), there was no question of a completely smooth ride. Yet one must understand their distrust and fear as the almost inevitable by-products of any new technical apparatus. Wolfgang Schivelbusch has traced such difficulties of assimilation in his classic work on the history of railroad travel. That comparable symptoms would be found in elevator passengers a quarter century later was already suggested by the name given to the first models: the "vertical railway." Like its name, its catalog of health risks was modeled on those of its horizontal predecessor. Schivelbusch devotes an entire chapter to

Elevator machinery in basement of Telegram Building, 227 Walnut Street, Harrisburg, PA. Courtesy of the Library of Congress.

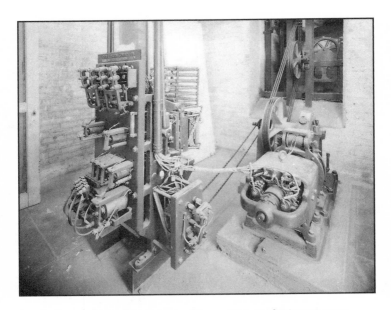

Detail of controls, electric motor, and lower sheaves of Otis passenger elevator added in 1921, basement of Woodrow Wilson House, 2340 South S Street, Northwest, Washington, DC. The original equipment, shown here, operated on direct current from the Massachusetts Avenue trolley line, abandoned in 1961. Courtesy of the Library of Congress.

Detail of Otis motor, Woodrow Wilson House, 2340 South S Street, Northwest, Washington, DC. Courtesy of the Library of Congress.

the "pathology" of the railroad and mentions an 1857 study of the train's influence on the physical condition of firemen and engineers. The study identified the constant shaking of their bodies from the vibration of the cars as a problem: "In order to ameliorate the jolts and to react to the engine's motions with greater ease, these people spend almost all their time standing on the front part of their feet, raising their heels up from the floor."[73] Despite this therapeutic stance, however, some of the personnel as well as a large number of passengers suffered disturbances of their nervous systems. In the early history of elevator travel, very similar diagnoses and therapies were discussed. In 1890, *Scientific American* introduced a syndrome it christened "elevator sickness":

> The elevator in modern big buildings has only one drawback, the sickness it causes when the car is suddenly stopped. To people of a delicate constitution this sickness is often such a serious matter that to them the elevator is a dangerous blessing. . . . The stoppage of the elevator car brings a dizziness to the head and sometimes a nausea to the stomach. The internal organs want to rise in the throat.[74]

The reason for this excessive stress was not constant vibration, as in a train, but abrupt stopping, especially when traveling downward. The braking maneuver was such "that all parts of the body are not stopped at the same moment of time. The feet being next to the car floor stop with the car, while other portions of the body continue moving."[75] As a countermeasure, the article recommended a very precise positioning of the body, just like the railroad hygienists three decades earlier: "If the body as a whole can be arrested at the same time with the feet, there will be no sickness. This can be done by placing the head and the shoulders against the car frame."[76] Imagine medically knowledgeable New Yorkers descending in an elevator around 1890 and all pressing up against the cab walls as they reach the ground floor! But it is all too easy to make fun of this scenario from the enlightened standpoint of today. Only an inadequate understanding of history can regard such long-forgotten fears and contortions as merely ludicrous and uninformed. On the contrary, a hundred years later, we must seek to understand why a series of medical diagnoses and preventive measures had existential significance in their day, although their unreality elicits patronizing smiles only a few decades later. Beyond improvements in the technical comfort of the machine, Wolfgang Schivelbusch explains this process with reference to Freud's theory of a shield against stimuli. Continuing exposure to a previously unknown impulse such as the speed of a railway car gradually desensitizes the "skin layer of consciousness." While the first generation of passengers still used to traveling by coach experienced this stress on their consciousness so powerfully that it caused nervous irritation, the next generation had already become accustomed to it. Apropos the spread of reading material for train travelers in the second half of the nineteenth century, Schivelbusch writes,

> The train passenger of the later nineteenth century who sat reading his book thus had a thicker layer of that skin than the earlier traveler, who could not even think about reading, because the journey was, for him, a space-time adventure that engaged his entire sensorium.[77]

The cultural assimilation of the elevator ride occurred in a comparable but accelerated fashion. After only a few years, all traces of "elevator sickness" and suggestions for its prevention had vanished because, to use Schivelbusch's phrase, the "inorganic protective layer due to civilization" has been initiated.[78]

Freud's metaphoric conception of unlocalized changes in perception and consciousness provides a vivid model for human assimilation of technical apparatuses. But Freud's model does not address a relationship of importance for the historian of technology, namely, the relationship of individual experience to the discursive rules of historical processes. The contortions of early elevator passengers raise the question, how seriously can one take these complaints from our contemporary point of view? How "real" were they? There is no doubt of the factuality of those passengers' subjective suffering. The drastic consequences of nervous overload were still evident in a 1930 German article about modern elevators in New York: "The unpleasant feeling of nausea one has when a German elevator slows and stops disappears in the new American models."[79] With just as much justification, however, one can point to a quasi-fictional component of these complaints, a recurring phantom pain during the early years of new technological advances, a pain whose intensity seems incomprehensible only a few decades later. What is it that evolves in this brief interim? Is it in fact an ability we can only ascribe to the individual, as Schivelbusch says with Freud, a stabilization of the perceptual apparatus, the consciousness, the imaginary cortex? Or must we ignore human bodily sensations in general as a historical source and describe our ancestors' discomfort as something of a simulation enforced by the rules of discourse? There is a confusing dual structure in the relationship of the individual to history. Even the sensory certainties of suffering follow a predictable order of physical reactions, so that the undeniable reality of their dizziness, queasiness, or nausea can be regarded with equal plausibility as the hysterical symptoms of a transitional period—a hypochondria of the epoch and not of individual people. The basic question is how much credence we should grant individual "experience" in historiography. It is Foucault's main question in his discourse analysis and in the course of a few methodological shifts, and he answered it with varying degrees of rigor. In his only explicitly theoretical historical work, *The Archaeology of Knowledge* (1969), any interest in a historical signifier is eliminated. It is only a question of showing the distribution of historical assertions: "What, in short, we wish to do is to dispense with 'things.' . . . To define these objects without reference to the *ground*, the *foundation of things*, but by relating them to the body of rules that enable them to form as objects of a discourse."[80] We can gauge how justified this method is when we apply it to the physical feelings of early elevator passengers. For if even a feeling such as pain—at first glance the most reliable "foundation of things," a stable reality behind the mutable web of language—proves to be a product of a certain historical constellation, then historiography appears in fact to be possible only as something secondary, as a reconstruction of discourse practices and not of events, emotions, or facts. Where then is man to be found in the humanistic sciences, if his most substantial utterances can be understood as transient background noise during his adaptation to technological devices? And this background noise is not merely characteristic of a naïve early stage of "industrialized consciousness."[81] Our present-day statements are by no means more firmly grounded. It is easy to identify similar constellations at the beginning of the twenty-first century.[82] Historiography must constantly reflect upon the interaction between subjective feeling and discursive order. In this process, the followers of Foucault as well as others have played the worn-out card of "social construction" once too often and with too much confidence. It is more fruitful to think further about the relationship between experience and discourse in light of an interesting formulation of Joachim Radkau's. In his study of the history of neurasthenia, he tries to get at how a particular historical situation "unleashes experience."[83] In the early years of technological conveyances (or information sources), one repeatedly encounters this factor of the "unleashing" of pathological syndromes such as "elevator sickness." Four years after its first mention in *Scientific American*, the *Washington Post* quoted a Chicago physician to the effect that "Cases of elevator sickness are on the increase. It is now becoming well defined. Its effects are found in an increased number of cases of brain fever and disordered nervous system."[84] This confident announcement of his findings was apparently the last mention of the disease in American publications.

URBANIZATION AND SPATIAL FEAR: THE CAB
AND CLAUSTROPHOBIA

While elevator sickness and its therapies disappeared after less than a decade, another syndrome appeared shortly before it and gained a permanent place in the classification of neurotic symptoms, namely, claustrophobia. The history of psychiatry records a remarkable ensemble of symptoms that appeared almost simultaneously between about 1870 and 1880: phobias of varying intensity and all related to spatial threats. At the height of the urbanization process in Europe and the United States, one finds lines of connection between the history of architecture and the history of medicine, and we can ask whether the massive changes occurring in late nineteenth-century cities are related to previously unknown nervous disorders. In 1872 the Berlin psychiatrist Carl Otto Westphal published an essay in the *Archiv für Psychiatrie und Nervenkrankheiten* (Archive of psychiatry and nervous diseases) that began with the acknowledgement, "For several years, patients have repeatedly come to me with the curious complaint that it is impossible for them to walk across open squares or through certain streets."[85] Westphal presented three decades-long case studies and coined a name for his patients' symptoms ("for it seemed desirable to have one"): agoraphobia.[86] The new syndrome, according to Westphal, was different from other mental illnesses "especially as the occurrence of the pathological affects (fear, etc.) is essentially attached to certain external circumstances and disappears immediately when they are removed."[87] The concrete catalysts of the neurotic disturbance were not yet precisely categorized in this foundational description of *Platzangst* ("spatial fear," the German word that encompasses both agoraphobia and claustrophobia), and so the two kinds of unease engendered by especially large and especially small spaces were repeatedly confounded in case histories. Of one of the patients, for instance, Westphal wrote, "It was for the most part impossible for him to take long walks (e.g., to the Tiergarten park), also trips in rented carriages, omnibuses, droshkies, etc. Further, he had to avoid traveling by train, while the use of his own carriage presented no difficulties."[88] Thus in Westphal's article, the concept "agoraphobia" still included various kinds of fear of spaces.

Eight years later, a text of equal importance for the history of psychiatry stressed the necessity of a more precise separation and a name of its own for agoraphobia's "complementary illness." The Frenchman Benjamin Ball, in a lecture entitled "De la claustrophobie," spoke of a neurosis "tout opposé"[89] to Westphal's observations and described two cases—all that he had seen so far[90]—in which the patient's symptoms were triggered only by enclosed spaces: a younger man no longer able to spend the night in his bedroom because he thought the walls were closing in on him, and a woman attacked by feelings of trepidation while climbing the stairs of a tower and ever since unable to be in small rooms. Ball was the first to introduce this explicit illness into the psychiatric literature. His essay ended with three axiomatic conclusions in which he identified a new variation of the nervous condition, a "fear of enclosed spaces," which was to be understood as "a real psychosis, not a simple sensory problem" and in the future should be classified under the name "claustrophobie."[91] Thus by about 1880, European psychiatry had already described two varieties of spatially determined phobia, at a time when public discussion of nervous illnesses increased dramatically with the publication of the New York physician George Miller Beard's *Neurasthenia* of 1880.

The physiologically unlocalized condition of permanent overstimulation and exhaustion was one of the most discussed pathological phenomena of the late nineteenth century, "the signature of our cultural epoch."[92] It is unusual that this syndrome, which has recently been very thoroughly researched,[93] can be traced back to a single author. *Neurasthenia* immediately became a best seller and was translated into German only a few months after its appearance.[94] A decade later, the editor of the *Handbuch der Neurasthenie* (Manual of neurasthenia) summarized Beard's contribution: "Thanks to Beard's book, the illness became known to the entire educated world, and the enormous increase of cases of neurasthenia in recent years comes not only from various conditions of our time, but also from the fact that the fortunately invented word with its no less fortunate explanation is easily understood everywhere."[95] Beard's central concern—repeated in numerous variations both in *Neurasthenia* and in the more cultural-historically oriented *American Nervousness* of a year later—was to interpret the general enervation of the epoch as an illness of civilization. Sentences such as "The chief and primary cause of this development and very rapid increase of nervousness is *modern civilization*"[96] and "Civilization is the one constant factor without which there can be little or no nervousness"[97] recurred regularly in these two foundational documents of the discussion of neurasthenia. In their large-scale studies, Anson Rabinbach and Joachim Radkau have worked out the cultural-anthropological and political implications of this syndrome in detail. In the context of the present chapter, one strand of symptoms from the many variants of neurasthenia is especially important: a group of illnesses that Beard, following the diagnoses of Westphal and "my friend Professor Ball,"[98] called "topophobias." With this designation, he attempted to classify complaints that include agoraphobia, claustrophobia, and more specific spatial fears of individual patients such as fear of churches or bridges. For instance, as Müller wrote in his 1893 manual of neurasthenia, "This fear of open places or squares is, however, only one phase of a great variety of spatial fears. . . . To be precise, the genus spatial fear should be named topophobia, of which agoraphobia is only one species, a particular kind of spatial fear."[99] As a component of neurasthenic complaints, the spatial fears attracted increasing attention in the 1880s, especially since the topophobias proved to be representative of the entire syndrome, "a certain indicator for the understanding of nervous conditions," as Müller put it.[100]

It is revealing that the earliest descriptions of the spatial phobias all observed the causes of the condition from a similar perspective. We have already mentioned Beard's vehement criticism of American civilization and its metropolises, but German physicians also suggested that their patients' symptoms could have something to do with the architecture of big cities. It is no surprise that one of the first textbooks of psychiatry to mention agoraphobia as a new category of neurotic disturbance included this observation: "This curious anomaly was first observed among the population of large cities (Vienna, Berlin, Munich)."[101] A patient of Carl Otto Westphal explained to him that

> a large open space out in nature is easier to cross than one of equal size that is surrounded by buildings, "because nature is on the whole refreshing and has a positive effect on him." Large boulevards, especially when they run across flat open ground (he mentions, e.g., the Tempelhof Chaussée) make him extremely uncomfortable.[102]

Thus agoraphobia was part of the "pathology of the city"[103] that came increasingly into view at the end of the nineteenth century, the subject of a recent book by the architectural historian Anthony Vidler. "If agoraphobia was by definition an essentially spatial disease," writes Vidler, "many psychologists insisted that it was equally an urban disease."[104] Referring to Westphal's texts, the French physician Edouard Gélineau even speaks of a "malaria urbana."[105] In some European metropolises, the connection between architectural changes to the city and pathological symptoms in its inhabitants was explicitly mentioned. Vidler mentions the Austrian architect Camillo Sitte, who related Westphal's diagnoses to the fundamental reshaping of Ringstrasse in Vienna in the 1860s and 1870s, with its creation of boulevards and wide squares in the tradition of Haussmann. Sitte wrote in his 1889 book *Der Städtebau nach seinen künstlerischen Grundsätzen* (City planning according to artistic principles),

> Recently a new nervous condition called "agoraphobia" has been identified. Numerous people are supposed to suffer from it, i.e., they always feel a certain fear, an unease, when they must cross a large, empty square. . . . Agoraphobia is the newest, most modern illness. Quite natural, for in the little old squares one feels very comfortable. . . . On our gigantic modern squares with their yawning emptiness and oppressive boredom, even the inhabitants of cozy old towns are susceptible to the fashionable illness called agoraphobia.[106]

Nervous illnesses manifested as an appropriate reaction to the monumentality of modern urban architecture. Vidler mentions one sufferer who made this connection especially vivid, a patient by the name of Vincent who wrote as both an agoraphobe and an architectural critic in a short 1919 essay in the *American Journal of Psychology*. Vincent described what triggered his phobia:

> However the architecture of the building has much to do with the sort of sensation produced. Ugly architecture greatly intensifies the fear. In this connection I would remark that I have come to wonder if there is real art in many of the so-called improvements in some of our cities, for, judging from the effect they produce on me, they constitute bad art.[107]

The agoraphobe became the most reliable seismograph for the quality of modern architecture; aesthetic sensibility was translated directly into neurotic disturbance.

If the symptoms of agoraphobia, first recorded around 1870, seemed to be connected to the reshaping of big cities and the replacement of jumbled old town centers with boulevards and open squares, the same could be said for the simultaneous appearance of fear of explicitly enclosed spaces. At least as striking as the intimidating expanses of the new city centers in the last third of the nineteenth century was the increasing compression of social life in the metropolises. Infrastructure such as public transportation created a crisis of spatial experience in the opposite sense as well. At one point in his essay on Baudelaire, Walter Benjamin quotes Georg Simmel's well-known statement,

"Before buses, railroads, and streetcars became fully established in the nineteenth century, people had never been put into the position of having to stare at each other without exchanging a word for minutes or even hours on end."[108] Precisely such an alliance between the history of modern transportation and the destabilization of ingrained forms of perception and communication is of interest for the history of claustrophobia, especially because from a certain point on, these means of transportation—and the elevator above all—became the paradigmatic locations where this phobia could be observed. An excerpt from a recent standard work demonstrates how self-evidently the elevator is associated with the condition. The symptoms of claustrophobia can be traced back "to small, enclosed spaces: elevators, but also being closed in a bus, train . . . or sitting immobile in a barber's or dentist's chair."[109] The sentence identifies the elevator as the prime example of the category "small, enclosed space," while all other critical locations are reduced to the status of less severe variations by the phrase "but also." Thus in professional psychiatric discourse, the topography of this neurosis has long since been decided (in 1966, a journal article entitled "Claustrophobia and Depression" had already termed the former the "classic elevator phobia"[110]). An analysis of the historic conditions of claustrophobia, however, needs to feel its way back to the point where this long-standing diagnosis first began to be established. The question is, if the elevator cab is regarded as an undisputed synonym for a threatening "claustrum"—the enclosed room—then what part does its appearance play in the spread of the neurosis?

In the history of psychiatry, the infrequent studies devoted explicitly to claustrophobia are remarkable in their repeated concentration from the beginning on case histories involving the same locations. Modern means of transportation are the focus as triggers for the phobia: in addition to the elevator, the earliest studies mentioned the subway[111] and railroad cars.[112] Claustrophobia was so intimately associated with the realm of public transportation that a large empirical study from 1949 came to the conclusion that as a rule, claustrophobes should avoid using "trains, elevators, subways, airplanes or ships."[113] According to the neurologists' observations, it was precisely at the intersection of mobility and restricted space that the syndrome threatened to arise. If one then goes on to ask why it was the elevator among all other means of transportation that was the most important trigger, one must recall a certain intensification of the spatial situation in the cab. Certainly the incomparably confined space of this location disconcerted passengers and led authors of early architecture manuals to recommend that elevators "be sufficiently large and so equipped as to take account of the comfort of the passengers so as not to engender a very understandable sense of unease in non-experts during their sojourn in it, however brief. Such a sense even today prevents many persons from using the elevator."[114] But there was also the danger of some technical malfunction trapping one in the tiny space for an unforeseeable length of time. Paul Virilio once remarked that every new means of transportation produces a previously unknown type of accident: the "shipwreck," the train "derailment," the airplane "crash."[115] The elevator, whose danger of falling was soon eliminated, produced at the end of the nineteenth century the new accident type "getting stuck." Sensitive catch mechanisms that are activated by as little as an overstretched cable as well as malfunctions of the electric motor halt the elevator's travel between floors and dramatically extend one's transient presence in the cab. The very first literary texts in which the elevator plays a central role already provided information about the phobic implications of such an accident. In 1875, four years before the article in which Benjamin Ball coined the term claustrophobia, *Harper's Weekly* published a story entitled "In an Elevator." Two guests at a dinner party in a distinguished New York apartment house get stuck for several hours in the elevator cab on their way to the fourth floor. And when they exit the cab after a slow and inconsequential drop back down to the ground floor, they are physically unharmed but emphatically swear "that we should never venture again into an elevator."[116] Less than a decade later, William Dean Howells dramatized a very similar situation in his one-act play *The Elevator*. In this piece, not two but six people get stuck in an elevator between the fifth and sixth floors. Once the malfunction is repaired and the cab is brought back down to the fifth floor, the liftboy is about to set the elevator in motion again when there arises, as the stage direction says, "a joint cry from the elevator." The victims in this text, too, intend to avoid the elevator after their ordeal. "Thank you! We'll *walk* up this time."[117]

The unease in the confined and opaque cab of the elevator, widespread in the first decades of its history, was only intensified by the latent danger of getting stuck. One could say that the new type of accident for its part also produced a new syndrome, that long-lasting "elevator sickness" called claustrophobia that depended on the specific malfunction of a particular conveyance just as "railway spine" and traumatic neurosis depended on the train crash.[118] Thus the genesis of spatial phobia is inseparable from the genesis of urban architecture, a fact also obvious from the historical reception of agoraphobia. Against this background, it is interesting that psychiatric and psychoanalytic research on claustrophobia completely ignores the historical context of the neurosis. In the most cited studies from the first half of the twentieth century (those of Oberndorf, Bagby,[119] Miller,[120] Eisler, Terhune, and above all Bertram Lewin, whose 1935 article was regarded as standard for thirty years[121]), one finds detailed discussions of the supposed basic psychic cause of the illness (the fetus's fear of being driven out of the womb), but no consideration of the "materiality" of spatial fear—of possible architectonic circumstances, for instance. Thus the professional discussion of claustrophobia in the early twentieth century clearly continued the complete ahistoricity of psychoanalysis for which Freud, in his eagerness to establish a science of the psyche, provided the model.[122] The suspicion that the fear of enclosed spaces noticeable in the last third of the nineteenth century could have had something to do with the increasing density of urban life was at the most tacitly acknowledged in the remarkable continuity of a certain form of therapy, namely, removal to the country. This treatment already had a place in the foundational works on claustrophobia. Thus in *Neurasthenia*, George Miller Beard mentions a patient, a student at an urban university, who "was compelled to give up his studies and become a farmer."[123] Benjamin Ball, on the other hand, at the end of his essay criticized the recommendation of the Bologna psychiatrist Raggi that leaving the city was already sufficient to allow the neurosis to subside. Ball adduced the massive nature of the syndrome and maintained that it required additional pharmacological treatment.[124] The stubborn persistence of this alliance between spatial fear and the stresses of city life in research on claustrophobia was nicely illustrated by a remarkable passage in a 1973 essay entitled "Indecision and Claustrophobia." With reference to the widespread alternative lifestyles of this era, the well-known American neurologist Raymond Gehl wrote,

> I have been struck by the frequency of the appearance of claustrophobic symptomatology in my patients and have wondered . . . whether the increasing complexity of life, with congestion, pollution and crowding of all types, including the complexities of political, economic and social life, has given some cultural sanction to this particular neurotic solution. . . . Incidentally the youth of our society, whom I tend to think of as the "claustrophobic generation," are in large numbers seeking freedom from the pressures of modern life in the cities and suburbs and relief from the feeling of their parents on their backs by taking to the open road and the rural open country.[125]

A century after the first victims of agoraphobia and claustrophobia showed up in a metropolitan and urban context, the hippies and dropouts of the early 1970s appeared to be the direct inheritors of that persistent "malaria urbana."

THE POLITICS OF THE ELEVATOR

THE DOUBLED SHAFT: PRIVATE AND SERVICE ELEVATORS

Around the turn of the century, with the number of elevators on the increase, there were various schemes to defuse its threat as a location of fortuitous public encounters. At stake was the establishment of orderly traffic patterns in multi-story buildings that would help avoid unwanted encounters in a small space. Two kinds of elevators received special attention. Both stringently restricted access to a building's apartments: the service elevator on the one hand, and the private elevator on the other. That the latter made its first appearance in New York and remained virtually unknown in European apartment houses was a logical result of the greater American skepticism toward communal living. An elevator that carries one directly from the entrance hall to one's own apartment avoids the danger of running into other tenants. Built in 1884, the Dakota—a ten-story castle-like edifice on the still largely unbuilt west side of Central Park—established the apartment as a luxurious place to live.[126] It has four passenger elevators so that on average only two apartments per floor—and sometimes only one—are served by each. According to a chronicler of the building,

> Because there were so many passenger elevators, public hallways on each floor were unnecessary: where two apartments had to be reached from the elevator, a small foyer would give access to both, and in many cases at the Dakota, the elevator gave onto only one apartment on a floor. In that case, the elevator could open directly into a tenant's private foyer, with no public hall at all.[127]

The Dakota initiated the history of the private elevator, the installation of a vertical passage that made movement in a multistory residential building completely independent of public spaces. This transportation option was so essential to the development of the image of New York because it prepared the way for the final phase of the transformation of Manhattan in the first two decades of the twentieth century: the willingness of the most wealthy class to sell their remaining mansions on Fifth Avenue, together with their building lots, and move into the apartment houses rising in the same location. Elizabeth Hawes describes this "last stage of transition" in the architectural history of the city, when the divorced wives of great industrialists like William K. Vanderbilt II or Edward Hutton agreed to the demolition of their mansions only on condition that it would not affect the exclusivity of access to their new upper-story apartments.[128] So around 1920, a series of residential buildings of unheard-of size were erected on both the east and the west side of Central Park with multistory apartments of over twenty rooms, supplied with "separate entrances and individual elevators."[129] According to a newspaper article from 1926, some mansions were reconstructed in their original form within the apartment building on their original site:

> The mansions gone? No: they have simply moved—moved into the apartment houses. . . . The most striking example of the saving and reconstruction of a mansion took place a few years ago, when a well-known Fifth Avenue house at the corner of Ninety-second street was torn down and rebuilt on the twelfth floor of the building that was erected on its former site.[130]

The article names the prerequisite for such a substitution: "One of the unique features of this super-apartment is that it retains the privacy it has always had. Its entrance lobby and elevators are not shared by others."[131] Elizabeth Hawes mentions a similar story—the conversion of Betty Hutton's fifty-four-room mansion into the largest New York apartment building ever—and gives the particulars of its entrance: "To ensure her autonomy, they cut a private porte cochere into the side of the building, which gave entrance to a private elevator that ascended directly to a three-story suite that filled its crown."[132] We must recall the discussions of stairwells and elevators in American construction journals, the continuing lack of clarity about where the public sphere ended and the private sphere began. For decades, the main problem in integrating the elevator into the residential building was its oscillation between interior and exterior space. The private elevator for the very wealthy put an end to such unacceptable mixing by extending interior space right out to the entrance threshold, just as in the single-family houses of the past, also putting an end to the latent dangers of social and hygienic contamination conjured up again and again in the early days of the elevator. The private elevator allowed one something like one's own address even in a sixteen-story building. This was literally true in the case of Mrs. William Vanderbilt II: her apartment with its separate entrance and private elevator also had its own house number.[133] If, as Bernhard Siegert says, identity is "a question of deliverability,"[134] the private elevator ensures that its exclusivity is not diminished.

At about the same time as the private elevator, a sort of negative model was also developed in the apartment houses of New York. The service elevators that led from separate building entrances to the kitchens and laundries of the apartments also created exclusive access, but in a negative sense. They prevented encounters between the residents or their guests and the servants, and were an attempt to preserve the system of main stairway and back stairway characteristic of multistory apartment buildings in the United States, and to a lesser extent in Europe, before the advent of the elevator. The service elevator also appeared for the first time in the Dakota as well as contemporary buildings such as the Central Park Apartments and the Berkshire. As Elizabeth Cromley notes, "Big budgets enabled Hardenbergh [the Dakota's architect] to separate service stairs and elevators from those for tenants and their guests, placing the service circulation in the centers of the four sides of the Dakota's courtyard and accessible only from a service level one floor beneath the open-air courtyard. Thus servants were kept apart from tenants' stairs and elevators."[135]

Unlike private elevators, there was some thought about installing service elevators in German apartment buildings. In the luxurious pre–World War I Berlin apartments that can be considered the avant-garde of a new vertical hierarchy, it was apparently one of the basic amenities. A column entitled "Hochherrschaftlich" (Lordly style) that ran in the first months of the construction journal *Bauwelt*, founded in 1910, regularly reported on ten- or twelve-room apartments "in the elegant old neighborhoods of western Berlin" that had all been built "within the last year."[136] A common feature of all these buildings was a service elevator, such as the one in a "modern residential palace" on the Lützowufer: "The front stairs are executed in oak and the stairwell also contains a modern elevator. A separate elevator is installed next to the back stairway for the domestic servants."[137] One of the first *Bauwelt* columns under this rubric explained why people around 1910 considered installing a service elevator. The problem was that the upper stories of baronial Berlin apartment buildings were still difficult to rent despite their elevators. The reason was that the servants, "for whom the elevator in the front of the building is taboo," refused work on the upper floors.[138] The article played on the increasing shortage of domestic servants at the beginning of the twentieth century: "Because the market is good for domestics, but bad for the wealthy tenants, those considering renting an apartment on the upper floors are still not willing to pay the same rents as for the second floor, for higher up they suffer the disadvantage of the shortage of servants."[139] An elevator for the servants was regarded as a concession to the increased difficulty of work on the upper floors. How rarely this project was carried out even in the most baronial buildings, however, was suggested by the final sentence of the *Bauwelt* column. In the face of the high installation costs, "it is not impossible that the elevator for domestic servants will become more frequently installed in distinguished buildings."[140]

We need to take a close look at those episodic, quickly fading efforts to double the shaft, so to speak, and establish distinctions in transportation. In Germany, there was no trace of private elevators, and separate elevators for domestic servants appeared for only a short time and in a very few special cases. Obviously the character of the vehicle was not very well suited to upholding class differences. We must recall the organization of access to multistory residential buildings before the elevator, the system of front and rear stairways, as described in the 1902 *Handbuch der Architektur* (Manual of architecture): "In well-furnished rental apartment buildings, there are auxiliary stairways for the use of domestics. They must therefore be located near the service areas and easily accessible from the courtyard."[141] Already in "mid-priced apartment buildings," the entry continued, "in addition to the main stairway, an auxiliary stairway for domestic servants is desirable or necessary and in many places, regarded as quite indispensable."[142] In turn-of-the-century Berlin, a sign at the entrance to the main stairway in many buildings announced that it was "For Residents Only." "Servants and purveyors must use the auxiliary stair."[143] What caused the leveling of access in the decades after 1910? No apartment building erected after the Second World War (and probably none in the 1920s either) possessed more than one stairwell or one elevator. Without a doubt, the widely studied disappearance of the servant class played a decisive role.[144] With the elimination of full-time domestic servants in multistory buildings, the need for separate traffic routes also faded away. Thus we can understand the separation of access routes deemed necessary for seventy-five years in the retrospective light of the well-documented and far-reaching changes in the structure of employment after 1900.

But one could also shift perspective for a moment and ask which purely architectural factors played a role in such a speedy transformation. Could it not be the case that the swath cut by the elevator shaft in and of itself created the structural conditions for an increasing unification of access routes? It is revealing that the very first commentaries on the installation of elevators in residential buildings stressed this effect. Thus the *New York Times* declared in 1870, "The elevator, to be sure, is, not to be paradoxical, a great leveler."[145] The elevator not only collapsed the strict vertical hierarchy of nineteenth-century apartment houses. The conveyance's egalitarian function was also a result of its concentration of traffic, replacing winding stairways with its direct channel. If we seek to understand why a concept like the service elevator did not last, we must also consider the consequences of the shaft itself, in addition to all the sociohistorical reasons. As far as their construction is concerned, it would not have been a problem to equip the baronial Berlin apartments of 1910 with a second elevator in the rear. That plans to do so were not realized—that the principle of separate access routes was not carried forward from the era of the stairwell into that of the elevator—suggests a change in the image of the building and its inner structure in the twentieth century. To a certain extent, the elevator democratized access. Among the most obvious expressions of this process were the regulations, initiated soon after the conveyance established itself, that posited the average weight of its passengers. The earliest version of the elevator code for Prussia and its provinces, which took effect in 1908, already declared, "On each entry door into the elevator shaft and in the interior of the cab a sign shall be posted with the clearly legible words 'Passenger Elevator' as well as the permissible carrying capacity, including the operator, in kilograms. The weight per passenger is assumed to be 75 kg."[146] This value, obligatory in every German elevator to this day, expresses the leveling power of the conveyance.[147] One could call it the elevator's political potential. The combination of shaft and cabin both thwarted the class divisions of horizontal transportation systems and promoted an egalitarian image of man. Literally and figuratively, every passenger in the elevator had equal weight.

THE LIMITS OF PRESTIGE: VERTICAL TRANSPORT
AND THE WANING OF MONARCHY

If it is true that the elevator not only transports people but also promotes a particular image of them, if its installation is one of many interventions in the organization of buildings and thus also of societies, then the following passage from the memoirs of Hedda Adlon, widow of the hotel owner Lorenz Adlon, is especially revealing. It depicts an incident from the 1913 wedding festivities for Princess Viktoria Louise, Kaiser Wilhelm II's only daughter. Eight hundred guests were to be housed in the Hotel Adlon on the Pariser Platz near the Brandenburg Gate. A few days before the event, the hotel's planning was put to the test:

> Suddenly we were told that the Kaiser's brother-in-law Duke Ernst Günther zu Schleswig-Holstein and the duchess could not stay in a suite on the fourth floor, as had originally been planned, although it was the duke's express wish to stay on that floor and no other. . . . Now that had to be changed. The Court Steward's Office had given instructions that the duke and duchess were to be accommodated in an apartment on the second floor. The reason given was that the tsar of Russia could not ride the elevator!
>
> The tsar had announced that he would come to the Hotel Adlon to pay a courtesy call on the duke the day before the wedding, and we were told that under no circumstances could the tsar be expected to climb the stairs to the fourth floor.
>
> Russian court protocol governed every step the tsar took and nowhere did it mention an elevator. Thus there were no instructions for how the tsar and his retinue were to behave in such a situation. Should he enter the cab first? Was he permitted to keep his hat on? Who should operate the elevator's crank? and God knows what else.
>
> The protocol had survived unchanged from the days of Catherine the Great. Catherine, of course, had never ridden an elevator for the simple reason that there weren't any back then, and that's why the protocol contained not one word about this means of vertical transportation. . . . At any rate, an apartment on the second floor was prepared for Duke Ernst Günther zu Schleswig-Holstein.[148]

The elevator collided with the traditionally prescribed movements of the sovereign, and Tsar Nicholas II was not the only ruler of the time who had reservations about the new conveyance. On the contrary, a fear of the elevator was conspicuous among European monarchs at the turn of the century.

It was known that Kaiser Franz Joseph I of Austria would not visit his longtime mistress, the actress Katharina Schratt, in her upper-story apartment in Vienna because he had "an aversion to elevators."[149] And the publication celebrating the 150th anniversary of the Otis Company relates how long it took for Queen Victoria to overcome her hesitation to install an elevator in Balmoral Castle.[150]

What is the explanation for these monarchs' shared uneasiness about the new apparatus? Consider two characteristics of the elevator: first, its previously mentioned leveling tendency. A few years after the incident in the Hotel Adlon, the German Standards Committee carried forward the work of the first elevator codes by establishing compulsory standard dimensions for shafts and cabs—"in order to facilitate the economical manufacture of elevator parts"—as well as maximum carrying capacities.[151] The elevator quickly developed into a completely standardized entity for the use of a group of statistically normed passengers and thus represented a fundamental contradiction to the spatial privileging of a monarch. But it was not just a question of the image of the elevator passenger and the conflict between the democratic principle of the conveyance and the distinctiveness of the monarchy. The second and possibly decisive reason for the monarchs' aversion had to do with the spatial positioning of the elevator, the incompatibility of the enclosed, opaque shaft with the stage-managing of their public appearances. Why was it impossible for Nicholas II to ride the elevator when he visited the Hotel Adlon? Why would the use of the vehicle be such a violation of court protocol? It was only a pretext to say that the protocol had remained unchanged since the eighteenth century and did not mention the elevator: the tsar had no problem riding in an automobile in Berlin, for example. No, we must ask to what extent the appearance of the elevator was a threat to the way the rulers presented themselves by manipulating space and how they were seen. As a historian of court culture puts it, "The foremost consideration in all court ceremonials is the practical one of who steps forward and takes precedence. The priority of rank at each level, as well as the deference to be paid to that priority, must be visible and ascertainable at every moment."[152] The greatest possible open space and the greatest possible visibility of relationships are the prerequisites for public appearances of the ruler, who must always take center stage. The elevator shaft confounds these arrangements; it is the dark place in a completely open room and interrupts the continuum of visibility. The aura of the monarch—the effect of successful staging—was at risk in the elevator, both because of the opacity of the shaft and because of the lack of distance between him and the other passengers. The inability of the court steward to decide "how the Tsar and his retinue were to behave in such a situation—should he enter the cab first? Was he permitted to keep his hat on? Who should operate the elevator's crank?"—was due less to the absence of rules than to the intuition that entering the elevator would be a violation of protocol. In the narrow, enclosed cab it would be impossible to maintain any kind of aura as it was famously defined by Walter Benjamin: the "unique phenomenon of a distance, however close it may be."[153]

How much the ceremonial exploitation of space is unsettled by the elevator can be gauged by the fact that for centuries, vertical movement has represented a sensitive problem for public displays of power. The history of courtly culture demonstrates that the main staircase of a castle or palace played a central role in receptions and other state functions from the Renaissance to the twentieth century. The earliest evidence of a decidedly political function for the stairway comes from sixteenth-century Venice, in the context of state ceremonies on the Scala dei Giganti, the Staircase of the Giants in the Doge's Palace, where the limitations on horizontality imposed by the crowded city necessitated the staging of official events along a vertical axis: "Since there was not much room to stage a colorful, ceremonial scene in a foreground hemmed in by the canals, there was a need for some background, an arrangement of groups in a steeply rising prospect."[154] The Staircase of the Giants, which continued into the interior of the palace, became the "platform for the loftiest ceremonies of state," as the architectural historian Josef Bayer wrote at the end of the nineteenth century:

> Standing on this platform, the newly chosen Doge would place on his head the princely *beretta*, the symbol of his rule, before the crowd of inhabitants. Here the most distinguished of the Signoria would assemble around the head of state when some special occasion required him to appear with his retinue on San Marco Square or board the ceremonial gondola.[155]

The political function of the staircase was still restricted to the exterior of the building in the sixteenth century. Not until the Baroque era was "the prestige expressed in the Renaissance by the flight of stairs in front of the building . . . moved entirely indoors."[156] The paradigmatic example of such an interior staircase is surely the famous Grand Escalier des Ambassadeurs in Versailles, built in the 1670s for Louis XIV. The central role played by this staircase in courtly protocol—during the arrival of foreign emissaries or the return of the king himself—remained the model for reception protocols right into the nineteenth century. Especially the critical moment of the first meeting of host and visitor usually took place on a palace's main staircase, with the hierarchy of relationships expressed by how many steps the one was to ascend or descend toward the other. In the seventeenth- and early eighteenth-century manuals of etiquette,[157] the rulebooks for the life at court, there are a number of descriptions of such occasions that show that "in European court protocol . . . the order of society also finds symbolic expression in the stairwell."[158] The most influential of these handbooks was Julius Bernhard von Rohr's 1729 *Einleitung zur Ceremoniel-Wissenschaft der grossen Herren* (Introduction to the science of the ceremonials of great persons), which included these instructions in the chapter "On Visits and Personal Audiences":

If the host has not ridden or been driven out to meet his guest out-side the princely residence, then he will meet him in the palace, either at his carriage or on a staircase, or in a particular room, according to the difference in station or to the prerogatives of one before the other. A distinction is often made concerning how far and how many steps the rulers themselves or their princes and other relatives, or their ministers should take to receive the visitors and lead them to their rooms.[159]

The richly decorated Grand Escalier with its lowest central flight rising to meet the two side wings was carefully calculated to serve the function of a "state space," down to its decorative elements running along the steps.[160] The various busts, stucco work, and paintings had symbolic significance. A visitor climbing the steps passed four battle scenes representing the latest conquests of Louis and his brother. Eight stucco sculptures on the ceiling showed the most important military and political events in the king's career. A partially glassed-in ceiling and illusionistic frescos "that seem to open toward the sky like a gallery" created the feeling of great space.[161] The Grand Escalier was designed explicitly as an instrument of power. Every state visitor to Versailles was to be impressed and intimidated by the greatness of his host. The splendor of the staircase suggested that one found oneself "at the political and cultural center of the world,"[162] an impression underscored by allegorical frescos representing the four continents. On the other hand, these decorations were to also stimulate the king's own image of himself when he returned from a victory in battle, a concern that obviously was the first impulse for the construction of this ceremonial flight of stairs.

We can conclude the following from the appearance of the Grand Escalier: for centuries, interior spaces designed to demonstrate the authority of absolute or monarchical states were oriented along a vertical axis. In state receptions, the staircase was the stage upon which a passage was played out. The continuity of the practice is clearly evident. Johannes Paulmann's study of meetings between monarchs from the *ancien régime* to the First World War demonstrates how closely nineteenth-century court protocol, although never officially recorded, adhered to seventeenth-century patterns.[163] The infrequent mention of these questions in unpublished correspondence between the courts shows that the ceremonial reception of a visiting ruler hardly changed at all. The first, carefully modulated contact of the visitor with the monarch and the royal household still always took place on the main staircase unless the host had ventured outside the palace to meet the arriving guest. In an 1821 document from the court in Vienna on the occasion of an impending visit from George V, the sequence of movements on and around the stairway was precisely choreographed. Once the arrival of the two monarchs together at the palace was announced,

> the royal household of His Majesty the King will meet them at their carriage and then precede them. Their Royal Highnesses the Princes will receive His Majesty [crossed out: "on the steps of the staircase"] at the foot of the staircase and their Royal Highnesses the Princesses will meet His Majesty in the middle of the Grotto-Hall (there being no other anteroom on the garden side of the palace).[164]

Johannes Paulmann, who unearthed this document, emphasizes that "up to the First World War, this ceremonial is typically the final act of an arrival, with minor variations depending on location and circumstance."[165] The deployment of people along the vertical axis enacted an orderly hierarchy for the benefit of the visitor. Each member of the royal household was assigned a specific static or dynamic position: the highest court officials lined up below and along the sides, the princes greeted their father and the visiting monarch on the steps, the princesses received the arrivals on the second floor. Monarchical political ceremonial was always coupled with the principles of rigid distribution and complete visibility of movements in space, which made the problematic nature of the elevator immediately apparent. Although as a technological substitute for the stairway it accelerated the mere act of climbing up or down, the displacement of the vertical passage into a shaft eliminated all possibility of ceremony.

It may be purely historical accident that the triumph of the elevator and the fall of monarchies temporally coincided, but if we take seriously the proposition that "social order always corresponds to architectonic order," we can draw some connecting lines.[166] The end of a method of rule whose image depended on maintaining precise positions and distances corresponded to the end of a method of building whose interior vertical structure was the prerequisite for such positioning. Every building constructed around the core of an elevator shaft, on the other hand, contributed to the disappearance of the monarchical ordering of space. Perhaps this rupture in political and architectural history around the turn of the century can be illustrated by comparing two building types similar in their size and public orientation: on the one hand the monarch's palace, and on the other the grand hotel. The former traditionally got along without a passenger elevator, while the latter was one of the first places where it was installed, beginning in the 1870s. In his essay "The End of the Ceremonial," Gotthardt Frühsorge shows the extent to which the luxury hotel replaced the royal court as the focal point of the metropolis, the location of advanced etiquette. He even identifies the hotel owner as a "successor to the lord steward or major-domo, the director of a large household."[167] The fundamental difference between court and hotel was that in the latter, the formal ordering of space around a central point had dissolved. The distribution of people no longer followed a ceremonial, but was now left to their free circulation. We must recall the building where the collision of courtly protocol and modern transport occurred in 1913. It was the grand Hotel Adlon, and perhaps in this unimportant incident, the multifarious connections between architecture and politics become visible: from the grand staircase to the elevator, from the court to the hotel, from the monarchy to the republic. Future studies of political systems should not leave the elevator out of consideration.

Barely fifty years later, another incident involving a hotel elevator and a state visit occurred that is like a complementary story in the post-monarchical era. Nikita Khrushchev was supposed to give a talk to two thousand American businessmen in the Waldorf-Astoria Hotel. On the way down from his tower suite, he and some Secret Service agents got stuck in an elevator for half an hour. When the cab finally descended to the third floor, KGB and CIA agents were waiting with drawn revolvers.

> The door opened, and everyone in the elevator was so pale, not knowing whether it had been done externally or what had happened. . . . The Russians and Khrushchev probably thought it was an attempt to assassinate him. Of course there were many apologies made, but it was a mechanical problem. The elevator had gotten stuck! And then he went into the ballroom . . . and everybody looked as if the war was going to begin.[168]

In this episode from a time without courtly protocol or any exact prescription for the distance between bodies, the latent danger in this means of transportation for heads of state—a danger the turn-of-the-century monarchs sensed intuitively—became reality. The total opacity of the channel through which the cab moves engenders jittery nerves, especially when it gets stuck, and almost caused a real political crisis at the height of the Cold War. In the Waldorf-Astoria, Khrushchev would not even have had the option of dispensing with the elevator as did his tsarist predecessor; by the late 1950s, stairways in New York luxury hotels were nothing but emergency exits. Once again, the intertwining of political and transportation systems became visible. In a country without any monarchical tradition, the elevator shaft had already replaced the main staircase as the principle of vertical organization by the late nineteenth century. Elaborately choreographed political appearances were no longer planned in the democratic age. But the darkened space around a head of state contains a diplomatic risk, as the Khrushchev incident demonstrated.

If, as we have said, the significance of the ceremony lies in the visible identification of any person's status at any given moment, then the problematic nature of the elevator was manifestly on display in the "elevator etiquette" of federal offices in Washington to which *Harper's Weekly* devoted an article in 1910. "Elevator-conductors everywhere have their troubles, but these are nothing compared with the trials of the elevator-conductors in the Federal departments at Washington,"[169] the article began, and went on to describe the complex system of privileges in the buildings of the State, War, and Navy Departments that placed almost inordinate demands on the skill of the operators. An officer's rank determined his prerogatives in the elevator. If a cabinet secretary was waiting for the cab, for example, an assistant signaled his rank by pressing the button three times, causing the elevator to interrupt its travel immediately and return, pick him up, and bring him to the desired landing. Other passengers already in the elevator had to simply wait to be taken to their own destinations, according to their position in the hierarchy. Superficially, everything functioned according to the traditional principle of protocol—at stake was the preservation of a rigid ranking—but the article recounted the breakdown of that principle on the morning of a state funeral, when numerous high-ranking officers were in the War Department.

> A major . . . was on the lift, and was being shot up to the third floor, when the sharp ringing of the three bells announced the appearance on the ground floor of the Secretary of War. Down shot the elevator. The big Secretary and the little major saluted, and before the salutation was over two bells rang, meaning that an officer of high rank wished to ride.
>
> In this case the Secretary of War was, of course, the main proposition, and, accordingly, was ushered out at the second floor first. Then up flew the elevator to the fourth floor to answer the two bells, to take on a brigadier-general who desired to descend to the street

floor. The major found it necessary to do a little more saluting. The elevator proceeded to the ground floor, and the brigadier-general departed, and the major, who had now been carried by the floor of his destination twice, breathed a sigh of relief and thought his turn had come. But not so. Just at that moment two bells rang on the second floor, and this time there got aboard the chief of staff, with another officer, and down they went, major and all.[170]

Whether the major left the cab still in possession of all his faculties is not recorded. This story exemplifies how the elevator frustrates the preservation of ceremonial order. The conveyance resists the elaboration of distinctions, and only the express elevators of the largest office buildings, reserved for the personnel of the executive suite, allow a relatively untroubled observance of privilege. Its structural constraints, however, make the elevator's politics by nature egalitarian.

THE ELEVATOR IN LITERATURE, FILM, AND ADVERTISING

SITE OF CONTINGENCY: THE ELEVATOR AS ORGANIZER OF CITY NARRATIVES

As we have seen, in the first decades after the passenger elevator's arrival, its potential as the scene of crises was soon recognized. Elevator encounters between complete strangers in a space even more constricted than the railway compartment provoked discussions among architects, physicians, and psychologists of the apparatus's status and risks. If we seek to understand why the elevator is still such a popular location in novels, films, TV series, and advertisements with urban settings, we need to keep in mind the latent threat embodied in this unobservable intersection of individual lives. What is it about the cab that makes it such a significant element in the spatial structure of city narratives and thus in the poetics of modernism?[171] An initial answer to this question emerges against the backdrop of the canonical works of modernist experience and aesthetics, works continuously referred to in academic analyses of literary portrayals of the big city.[172] In Poe's *Man of the Crowd*,

Baudelaire's *Painter of Modern Life*, Georg Simmel's *Die Großstadt und das Geistesleben* (The metropolis and intellectual life), and Walter Benjamin's Baudelaire studies, the most salient characteristic of urban life is the increasing contingency and multiplicity of its encounters. Baudelaire's declaration, "By 'modernity' I mean the ephemeral, the fugitive, the contingent"[173] is widely recognized as the "incontrovertible definition of the modernist aesthetic."[174] The elevator cab—in the days of Poe and Baudelaire just beginning to be installed in the grand hotels, by the time of Simmel and Benjamin a permanent part of urban architecture—is the contingent locale par excellence. Here the greatest possible anonymity is conjoined with the greatest possible intimacy of contact. The utter randomness of encounters there, reinforced by the absence of class differences and schedules, collides with the complete enclosure that inevitably produces proximity and togetherness. The writings of Georg Simmel in particular returned again and again to the self-discipline demanded of city dwellers at the turn of the century in order to get used to the proximity of strangers. Urban traffic with its multiplicity of fleeting encounters required a kind of sensory shield—protective measures nowhere more urgently needed than in an elevator. Even before the conveyance had become firmly established in European metropolises, literary works were already drawing attention to the oppressive atmosphere of the cab, as in a 1906 prose miniature by the Viennese feuilletonist Peter Altenberg:

> It is dreadful to ride up together with a stranger. You feel the duty to strike up a conversation and worry obsessively from floor to floor about what to say. There's the same embarrassed tension in the air as at high school final exams. At last you blurt out "Farewell" in the tone you would use if you'd just made a friend for life.[175]

The elevator's status as the paradigmatic site of precarious public encounters is clear from its frequent use as an example in the most important sociological theories about public interactions. In his essay "The Territories of the Self," for example, Erving Goffman attempted to classify individual spatial needs in interpersonal relations. At the end of a discussion of "personal space"—that sphere "within which an entering other causes the individual to feel encroached upon"—he observed, "All of this may be seen in miniature in elevator behavior."[176] The elevator cab proved to be a kind of laboratory for the ethnology of urban life, where the structuring of space between two human guinea pigs and the rules of maintaining their distance from each other could be observed under ideal conditions. In a long footnote, Goffman went on to quote a colleague's empirical study of behavior in elevators that revealed the consistent spatial distribution of bodies in an elevator: the "first entrant takes up the corner near the controls or one of the rear corners; the next entrant is likely to take up the corner diagonally across from the taken one. The third and fourth passengers take up the remaining corners, the fifth the middle of the rear wall, the sixth the center of the car."[177] The passengers' predictable sociogram, their reflexive maintenance of the greatest possible distance from each other, was based on the fact that the anaesthetizing of attention was even more difficult to maintain in an elevator than in the means of horizontal transportation often mentioned by Simmel. Neither windows nor reading material offered the possibility of avoiding interaction. How persistently the apparatus challenges the maintenance of Goffman's "territories of the self" can be measured by how relatively ineffective the strategies for avoidance of contact are even today, after a hundred years of elevator use. Thus it is no surprise that literary and sociological observations of the atmosphere in the cab have hardly changed in the course of the twentieth century. In a prose sketch entitled "In an Elevator" and written thirty years after Peter Altenberg, Christian Bock described the encounter of two neighbors in an elevator:

> It so happens that two of you are standing close together in the ascending elevator and you suddenly feel embarrassed in each other's presence. Sort of like you had some cooked macaroni in your pocket and don't want the other guy to find out. But it's already

seeping through to your skin and you still have a long, long way to go to the fifth floor.

What's the point of staring at the other guy's tie? Should you examine the elevator walls on which there's nothing to examine? And if you're forced to look your fellow human being in the face—what can you say? It's just stupid to suddenly say what a beautiful day it is. He already knows that; he was just out there. And so I do what others have done before me and blurt out the senseless question, "Oh, you're going to the fifth floor too?" (When you've known for years that you both live on the fifth floor.)[178]

Bock's text anticipated the sociologic theory of "personal space" and proxemics by a quarter century when he concluded, "We feel overcrowded on our scant two square meters of elevator floor, because our condition in life is usually predicated on a distance of at least three meters from the next person."[179] A recent study of the "minimizing of presence" in elevators by the Cologne sociologist Stefan Hirschauer reaffirmed the continuity of this feeling of crowding and anxiety right up to the present day. His empirical observations of elevator passengers confirmed the findings of Goffman as well as the impressions of Altenberg and Bock. Hirschauer set out to show that preserving one's separateness and avoiding contact with other passengers was a complex social achievement. Precisely maintained physical positions and "corridors of vision" ensured the systematic avoidance of communication.[180] "Space 'speaks' for proxemics," as Umberto Eco once wrote apropos Hall and Goffman's theory of adequate distance relationships.[181] In the elevator cab, this "speaking" is a dense murmur that every passenger tries to ignore.

In order to identify the specific function of the elevator in big-city stories, we must compare their narrative method with the way they configure the locations of their action. Beginning in the last third of the nineteenth century, a similar dynamic of dispersal became apparent in both urban life and urban novels: as social life in the metropolis became more heterogeneous, novels employed more simultaneous narrative strands. We must keep this connection in mind between a development in social history and its reflection in narrative technique; the diffusion of individual biography in the wake of urbanization that Georg Simmel so often wrote about—the proliferating and unstable locations and relationships—was recapitulated in the transition from the organic "novel of education" to the panoramic novel of contemporary life. By the late nineteenth century, the development of an individual life no longer stood so firmly in the narrative foreground, but rather (as Karl Gutzkow put it in his early poetics of the "social novel") the portrayal of a "*Nebeneinander,*" a simultaneous "being together," an oscillation between various figures and plot strands.[182] While most scholars seldom mention the influence of urbanization on narrative theory, in his 1978 study of English and American novels, Gerhard Hoffmann writes that the "increase in the number of plotlines" and the "strengthening ... of plot simultaneity versus pure chronology" are some of the most conspicuous shifts in the poetics of nineteenth-century novels and go hand in hand with the increasing complexity of their spatial organization.[183] Thus heterogeneity and contingency are characteristic not only of the structure of perception and communication within the expanding cities, but also of the plot structures of big-city fiction. A decade before Hoffmann, Volker Klotz's study of the "narrated city" formulated the thesis that in the novel, "the city comes into its own as an object of literature."[184]

With these considerations as background, what literary role does the elevator play? We must examine the recurring tasks assigned to it in both literature and film. In stories set primarily in hotels, offices, or apartment buildings and as a result of this topography involving multiple contingent encounters, the elevator cab often serves as a kind of hinge. The cab, combining freedom of access while stopped and hermetically sealed impenetrability while in motion, acts as a decisive intersection of biographies and plotlines. In the midst of the general fleetingness of personal exchanges, it introduces a brief moment of intimacy invisible from without. As a dramaturgic device, it makes almost inevitable what private, service, and express elevators were meant to forestall. Especially fiction and films set in hotels exemplify the fundamental significance of the elevator for plot structure. As a location of chance encounters with momentous consequences, it sets the story in motion or integrates a simultaneous plot strand.

An elevator scene stands at the very inception of Vladimir Nabokov's literary career. At the beginning of his first novel, *Mary*, written in 1925–1926, two Russian exiles get stuck together for twenty minutes in the elevator of a Berlin boarding house: the longtime resident Lev Ganin and the newly arrived Aleksey Alfyorov. Their chance meeting initiates a fateful connection, for shortly afterward Ganin recognizes in a photograph of Alfyorov's wife the love of his youth, left behind in Russia and now on her way to join her husband in Berlin. This discovery plunges Ganin into a frenzy of memories, and causes "the entire kaleidoscope of his life to shift."[185] Only at the last minute does he abandon his plan to beat his fellow resident to the train station and start a new life with Mary. The opening scene in the elevator initiates the story and prepares for the revelation of the hidden connection between the two strangers. The curiously emphatic words uttered by Alfyorov in the cab—"Don't you think there's something symbolic in our meeting like this, Lev Glebovich? When we were on terra firma we didn't know each other. Then we happen to come home at the same time and get into this contraption together"—don't reveal their full significance until much later.[186] In point of fact, one could very well call their meeting in the stuck elevator symbolic, since it is already a compressed image of what will be played out in the rest of the short novel: the random connection of two biographies. As the garrulous Alfyorov says in the cab, "We stepped in without a word, still not knowing each other, glided up in silence and then suddenly—stop."[187]

An elevator lurches to a stop and a novel begins. In the same year that Nabokov's *Mary* appeared, the Berlin writer Paul Fechter published the best seller *Der Ruck im Fahrstuhl* (The lurch in the elevator), a novel that follows the same narrative pattern. Instead of a hotel or boarding house, the story is set in an upper-class apartment building during the economic crisis of the 1920s and narrates the downfall of the well-to-do Jordan family, who live on the fashionable second floor. Little by little, they are forced to go to work for the ambitious radio store owner Alwin Hempel and also surrender their apartment to him. In the first chapter, entitled "The Symbol" (like an echo of "something symbolic" in Alfyorov and Ganin's meeting), Amélie Jordan and her two daughters Toni and Eva get stuck in the elevator. Hempel, who just then happens to be returning home to his sublet lodgings on an upper floor, is able to rescue them with the help of the janitor. This incident, the eponymous "lurch in the elevator," is referred to again and again in the course of the long-winded novel. The apparatus that lurches to a halt on a September evening in 1923 becomes the symbol for the historical dynamics of the country's economic troubles and the characters' lack of social orientation. An impoverished businessman, for instance, asks Toni Jordan's architect friend Gieseler,

"You've never experienced a lurch?"

"What kind of lurch do you mean?" asked Gieseler.

Traugott Lehmann looked at him. "What kind of lurch? Why—the kind that pulls you up by the roots and tosses you somewhere or other."[188]

There are similar exchanges at various points in the novel, always focused on the metaphor of the "lurch."[189] When Alwin Hempel at last takes over the reception rooms in the Jordans' twelve-room apartment, hires Eva Jordan as his private secretary, and suggests to the rest of the family that from now on they enter the rooms they still occupy in the rear of the apartment via the servants' stairway, Eva muses on the course of events:

"I have the feeling that in such moments, our life got suddenly jarred the same way that"—she gave a little laugh—"the elevator did when Toni tore open the doors and we got stuck and you came and got us out."

She looked at him pensively. "How remarkable it is; you helped us out on that occasion and got the elevator going again, and now it's almost the same. . . . If you hadn't come and rented the apartment and hired me—I don't know how we would be surviving today. We were just as stuck as the elevator."[190]

Fechter's novel is just one—unusually emphatic—example of the elevator's use as an important narrative pivot point in many urban stories. Although seldom or never again deployed as such an unrelenting metaphor, this device can be discovered in literature and film to the present day. One could call the dramaturgic use of the elevator a response to the difficulty of narrating the twentieth-century metropolis, an answer to the question of how and where both relationships can begin and narrative structures can be built in the anonymous web of passersby. Of course there are other public places where strangers are brought together in a small space and chance encounters are transformed into fateful fellowships. Think of the train compartment and its narrative potential for such novels as Patricia Highsmith's *Strangers on a Train* or Agatha Christie's *Murder on the Orient Express*. But the elevator's specific advantages are the everyday frequency of its use and the incomparable speed with which it can reorder a group of people. In the elevator, fluctuation and hermetic isolation coexist in a unique relationship. Precisely its self-evident daily use and its herding together of strangers in a multistory building make it such a popular location in big-city stories. It would be impossible to list all the Hollywood films set in hotels, offices, and apartment buildings in which the elevator is a determining plot factor. (In Sofia Coppola's 2003 *Lost in Translation*, to cite a recent example, the encounters of the two main characters are staged in and around the elevator, from their first eye contact in the crowded cab to their farewell in front of the bank of elevators in the hotel lobby.)

To analyze the cab's narrative function, however, we must return to its ability to bring together a fortuitous collection of people and their parallel plotlines. There is no other text that uses this double ability as transparently as does Arthur Hailey's best seller *Hotel* (1965). One of the most successful hotel novels of the twentieth century, it was later made into a movie and expanded into a television series. The novel is set in the neglected grand Hotel St. Gregory in New Orleans, and Hailey narrates more than a half dozen parallel stories of various guests and employees. For 540 of the novel's 580 pages, the characters have no direct contact with each other. The hotel magnate O'Keefe arrives with his girlfriend, Dodo, intending to buy the St. Gregory. The crooked bell captain, Herbie Chandler, embezzles money from the hotel and brings it to the brink of financial ruin. The Duke and Duchess of Croydon have killed a woman and her daughter in a hit-and-run accident and solicit the help of the hotel detective to smuggle their damaged car out of town. The hotel thief "Keycase" Milne accidentally finds the wallet containing the payoff money for the detective. All these plotlines are narrated in separate chapters until the moment when four of the protagonists—Dodo, Chandler, the Duke of Croydon, and Keycase—get into the same elevator cab, which malfunctions and plunges to the ground. Here the cab's narrative function is different than in the novels of Nabokov and Fechter. Instead of serving as the starting point that enables the story to be told, it ties the separate plotlines together at the end. It is revealing for the novel's structure, however, that the final catastrophe is foreshadowed by repeated mention of the dangerously neglected elevator number four, one of twenty in the 1,600-room hotel. In the very first chapter, the cab starts to move only after a long hesitation ("It's the connections I think, either here or up top. . . . Had quite a bit of trouble lately," says the lift boy[191]), and in the course of the novel the ramshackle elevators are often mentioned as a sign of the St. Gregory's general state of neglect. When the chief engineer tells Peter McDermott, the newly promoted assistant general manager, about the elevator's problems and says the apparatus will eventually reach a "death point," McDermott heeds the warning. "Peter was still thinking about the chief's words when he entered his own office. What was the death point, he wondered, for an entire hotel?"[192] The larger history of the neglected hotel is reflected in the smaller history of the elevator; again, the apparatus serves a symbolic function in the context of the narrative.

At the end of the novel, things come to a head in several regards. O'Keefe's takeover of the hotel is as good as decided; McDermott (with his colleague Christine Francis the last bastion of conscientiousness in the St. Gregory) is about to prove Chandler's embezzlement; and the irregularities in the operation of the elevators can no longer be ignored: "Now, today, number four was starting and stopping jerkily at every floor."[193] The composition of the story and its rhetoric of steadily increasing suspense culminate in the final catastrophe in the elevator. There are two reasons for this focus: in terms of narratology, the cab inside the building is the most appropriate place to bring the parallel life stories together; in terms of dramaturgy, the elevator's fall represents the collapse of the St. Gregory as a whole, but also its rebirth. The four passengers gathered randomly there are all in the midst of a crisis: Dodo has been abandoned by her lover, O'Keefe; Croydon has decided to turn himself in to the police; Chandler is about to be fired; and Keycase needs to make a quick getaway after his surprise coup. Thus it is the representatives of the old St. Gregory cosmos who come together in elevator four. And since things have taken a turn for the better just before the accident (a guest has unexpectedly purchased the hotel and named Peter McDermott manager), the elevator's fall at the end of the novel appears to be an eerie purification, a final shock before the completely new beginning. McDermott's first official act on the very evening of the crash is the rehabilitation of the elevators:

"On Monday, a team of consultants would fly from New York to begin planning for replacement of all passenger elevator machinery with new. It would be the first major expenditure of the Albert Wells-Dempster-McDermott regime."[194] The "death point" of both the elevator and the hotel itself has been overcome.

SITE OF TRANSFORMATION

In addition to the cab's narrative utility as an intersection of various plot strands, its creation of a space completely sealed off from view (during its travel) also comes in handy in big-city stories. There is no other public space where one can feel so securely and completely alone, if only for a few moments. It is this aspect of brief but absolute seclusion that allows the elevator to play such a decisive dramaturgical role. A much-beloved cliché in films and television series set in office buildings is the image of two colleagues who board the elevator on an upper story and emerge several floors below with red faces and disordered clothes. But lovers aren't the only ones who exploit the invisibility of the cab interior. Single passengers also profit from what Nicholson Baker in his novel *The Mezzanine* calls

> a unique moment of true privacy—truer, in fact, than the privacy you get in the stall of a corporate bathroom because you can speak loudly and sing and not be overheard. L. told me once that sometimes when she found herself alone in an elevator she would pull her skirt over her head. I know that in solo elevator rides I have pretended to walk like a windup toy into the walls; I have pretended to rip a latex disguise off of my face, making cries of agony; I have pointed at an imaginary person and said, "Hey pal, I'll slap that goiter of yours right off, now I said *watch it*!" The indicator light and slowdown give you enough warning to adjust your glasses and reassume a hieroglyphic expression before other passengers get on.[195]

The elevator cab produces a seclusion that tempts people to do outrageous things ("Something happens to men in elevators. Must be the change of altitude—the blood rushes to their head, or something—boy, I could tell you stories," complains the lift girl Fran in Billy Wilder's film *The Apartment*[196]). But if the ride is prolonged it can also have dire consequences and even lead to the gibbet. That at least is the message of what is probably the most famous elevator story of them all. Julien, the protagonist of Louis Malle's thriller 1957 *Elevator to the Gallows* (based on the novel by Noël Calef), gets stuck in the office elevator for a weekend after murdering his boss and disguising it to look like a suicide. Meanwhile, a young couple steals his sports car and commits another murder with his pistol. In the novel, Julien is convicted not for his actual crime, but for the second murder, with which he had nothing to do.[197] For the time between Saturday afternoon (when the elevator is turned off by the building's superintendent) and Monday morning, there are no witnesses to his whereabouts. He is stuck in a vertical non-place while the plot runs its course on the horizontal: the boulevards of Paris and the roads of the surrounding countryside.[198] Not even the confession that he has killed someone else at the time in question can help him, for the judge does not believe his story. "It was suddenly clear to him that he had an irrefutable but fatal alibi: the elevator."[199] Calef's novel refers insistently to the blind spot in the topography of buildings (as well as criminal cases): the modern, completely enclosed cab. Julien seems to sense its ominous nature immediately after killing his boss, for as he descends in the elevator with the superintendent (shortly before he makes the mistake of rushing back into the elevator to retrieve a forgotten and damning piece of evidence), he says, "I think these elevators installed in the wall are odious. . . . It's like being stuck down a well. I liked the old elevators much better. You could see the floors passing, the steps. . . . In here, its stifling."[200] The progress of the story confirms Julien's prophecy. Whatever happens in the elevator, whether during a brief trip from one floor to another or in the long hours after getting stalled, is unknowable from without and can never be verified (in a forensic reconstruction, for instance).

Thus one could say that in the era of the wide-open executive suite, the elevator cab to some extent took over the role played by the attic in the late nineteenth century—a thankless role indeed. As the technological apparatus freed the upper regions from their dubious stigma, it became stigmatized itself.

In *Elevator to the Gallows*, Julien falls victim to the elevator's hermetic isolation. If you consider the uses the elevator is put to in Hollywood films of recent decades, however, this malevolent role is the exception rather than the rule. It is much more usual for the cab to act as an accomplice. Its invisibility offers the carrier of some secret a reliable opportunity to let his guard down for a brief interval, even in the midst of the bustle of an office building or hotel. The same is true for clandestine lovers who must meet in the elevator and for individuals whose public identity is based on a falsehood. If we look at the topography of films in which the focus is on someone leading a double life, we find that elevators often play a prominent role. Costume-changing transvestites, swindlers, and superheroes who lead a normal life until it's time to don a spandex costume and save the world all need somewhere to change undisturbed. In the big city, this refuge of transformation is often the elevator. Superman regularly uses elevator cabs in the office towers of Metropolis to shed his identity as Clark Kent. In Billy Wilder's *Some Like It Hot*, Tony Curtis and Jack Lemmon escape the Mafia killers in a Florida hotel thanks only to their costume changes in the elevator.[201] Having escaped their pursuers disguised as members of an all-girl band, they exit the elevator in the next scene as a wheelchair-bound invalid and a bellhop, but the latter's high heels give them away. Shortly thereafter they rush up the stairs in bellhop uniforms and leave the elevator and the hotel dressed as women again, unrecognized by the mafiosi waiting to waylay them in the lobby.

But no film integrates the elevator into a double life so consistently as *The Secret of My Success*, in which Michael

J. Fox plays the ambitious young graduate Brantley Foster, who comes to New York seeking his fortune as an executive but ends up with a job as a mailroom clerk in his uncle's company.[202] He exploits this position to read internal company memos and become more knowledgeable about the firm's structural weaknesses and personnel problems than many of the managers themselves. When he discovers a vacant office in the huge but poorly managed enterprise, Foster begins posing as a new executive named Carlton Whitfield. With his creative ideas about how to avoid a hostile takeover, Whitfield soon gains respect and influence within the company. His greatest challenge, however, is how to manage his double existence between the mailroom and the executive suite. When he needs to transform himself back into the mail clerk Brantley Foster after his first appearance as Carlton Whitfield, his secretary comes upon him changing clothes in his office. At this point in the story, the elevator makes its appearance and from then on proves to be the actual "secret" of Brantley's "success." Not only is it the most direct route between the floors of the skyscraper, but the cab with its stop button is the only place in the entire building where Brantley can safely change his clothes without being observed. The unreliability of elevator number three, which gets temporarily stalled several times a day, becomes a leitmotif. Its cab is also the keeper of another of Brantley's secrets: it is the catalyst of and favorite location for his love affair with Christy, his coworker from the executive suite and the mistress of the company president when the movie begins. By the end, she and Brantley take over the business.

Stories like *The Secret of My Success* clearly illustrate the strategic function of the elevator shaft. It is the darkest location in the midst of the brightly lit public space. The topographical structure of the film is a result of the change in the interior structure of buildings already well under way by the end of the nineteenth century with the improvement of sanitary and heating systems as well as the introduction of the elevator. Ever since, buildings contain an invisible system of pipes and shafts, "widely ramified arteries throughout every floor of the building, of which the outside observer is totally unaware," as one commentator wrote in 1910.[203] The elevator shaft stands in the center of these arteries and becomes, especially in the midst of an office building's public spaces, a privileged place of secret messages and private acts.

In the same vein as the film and literary connections, there is an interesting phenomenon that was one of the germs from which the present study grew: the marked frequency of the elevator as a setting for commercials. In recent years, at least eighteen to twenty spots shot in elevators have appeared on German television alone, including ads for Campari, Volkswagen, Head and Shoulders, Burger King, and Nescafé. Why does the elevator seem to meet the particular aesthetic and dramaturgic requirements of this genre so well? Obviously, its hermetic privacy and opportunity for unobserved transformations offer ideal conditions for a convincing presentation of a product's effectiveness.

Even more obvious, however, is the temporal congruence between the length of a commercial and an elevator ride. This gives the ads' content a kind of Aristotelian unity of structure: the length of the narrated plot corresponds to the length of the characters' presence in the cab. An ad for glasses from the Fielmann Company, for example, begins with two colleagues entering the office elevator. Their conversation reaches its promotional climax when the one with the elegant glasses tells the other how reasonably priced they were, whereupon the cab door opens and their ride (and the ad) is over. It is hard to imagine another narrative setting with foreordained limitations so perfectly fitting the time constraints of the commercial spot. The beginning and end of the elevator ride seem almost natural limits for the presentation, even more effective because the doors of modern elevators open and close like the curtains of a theater.[204] Accompanied by an acoustic signal, their opening means the story is about to begin. Several ads use this dramatic moment to good effect; ads for Eclipse Flash chewing gum and Spee Gel laundry detergent begin at the precise moment a high-pitched gong signals the opening of the cab door. The background music either begins with the sound of the gong, as in these two ads, or comes to an abrupt halt at the end of the ride, as in a German Burger King commercial in which Cindy Crawford boards a shopping center elevator already occupied by two clueless guys. The matching time constraints of the location and the ad can even form part of the ad's pitch. A commercial for Jet Set nail polish, for instance, exploits the brief length of the ride to underline how easy it is to use the product. A businesswoman enters the cab on the fourth underground level of an airport and begins to apply the polish. By the time she's reached the ground floor, her nails are dry. "One application is all it takes; our ultra-quick formula dries in a minute," promises the voice-over, a promise convincingly underscored by the scene of the action.

The compression of time corresponds to the compression of space in the enclosed cab, a repeated theme especially in ads that feature the fantasy of an unexpected erotic encounter. The fantasy of wish fulfillment is that a tiny impulse is all it takes to transform two strangers into a pair of lovers for the duration of the trip, and this is precisely the take-off point for products purporting to make their users more attractive. They will provide the catalyst for fulfilling the fantasy. In a spot for Axe deodorant, a mousy fellow enters an elevator in which the fragrance of the previous passenger still hangs in the air. A beautiful woman enters behind him—a woman clearly unattainable for him under normal circumstances. But the seductive power of the lingering fragrance in the confined space is such that she pushes the stop button. Cut to the woman exiting the cab with an embarrassed look while smoothing down the hem of her dress. A similar commercial for Rama margarine shows a woman returning to her apartment after buying food for breakfast. She gets stuck in the elevator with a man. She has a bag of croissants and he has a tub of Rama. Since it's an ad for a respectable German margarine, they content themselves with sitting on the floor and sharing breakfast, but even margarine acquires aphrodisiac powers in the elevator cab, and when the machine starts running again, the woman clandestinely presses the stop button (which, at least in commercials, seems to have no other function). If most commercials use more or less explicit sexual connotations to stress their products' ability to increase the attractiveness of their purchasers, there can hardly be another setting where that effectiveness is so directly put to the test. The presence of the right deodorant, margarine, beverage (in the Campari ad), or ice cream (in a Langnese ad) awakens an irresistible desire in whoever is present, and the sealed cab provides the perfect setting for its immediate gratification.

Quite apart from all erotic attraction between passengers, there is still another reason its spatial characteristics make the elevator such an appropriate setting for these commercials. Its cramped space ensures uniquely intense visual and olfactory impressions. The kind of products that favor elevators for their commercials show that ad agencies are well aware of this characteristic: deodorants, laundry detergents, chewing gum, sheer hosiery, and two kinds of dandruff shampoo—all products that ameliorate defects and produce effects perceptible only at close quarters. After riding together in a crowded elevator, a female coworker lets the businessman in a Head and Shoulders spot know that he has dandruff. In a commercial for a German clothing manufacturer, the head of the firm surprises a job applicant arriving late for an interview as she changes her stockings in the elevator. He's so dazzled by their sheerness that he hires her on the spot. As the mama's boy in a laundry detergent ad enters the elevator, he sees that a neighbor's basket of laundry is so dirty it's going to need extra-powerful Spee Gel. Last but not least, the Axe deodorant man is the beneficiary of the olfactory intensity of the nearly airtight cab. The elevator is the ideal vehicle in which to advertise body care products because there is no other public place where people are more susceptible to sensory impressions. Nowhere else are body odor, halitosis, and dandruff so noticeable; nowhere else is the need for the right cosmetics and stockings so obvious. The combination of these two factors—the possibility of an erotic encounter and the intensification of sensory stimuli—makes the elevator the ideal setting for commercials. In the cab's hermetic isolation, the passengers become perfect guinea pigs in the ad agency's laboratory.

THE MOMENT OF TRUTH: THE STALLED CAB AS SECULAR CONFESSIONAL

In novels, films, and commercials, elevators get stuck with a frequency that bears no relation to official statistics. As Nabokov's *Mary* and Fechter's *Der Ruck im Fahrstuhl* show, elevators tend to appear in big-city stories precisely, and only, at the moment they stop working. Although malfunctions have been infrequent exceptions since the development of safety mechanisms in the early twentieth century, they seem to be the rule in fictional narratives. The reason for this statistically indefensible preference is undoubtedly that, while one can (with difficulty) ignore uncomfortable physical proximity for the length of a normal ride, it becomes oppressively unavoidable in the case of a malfunction. We stand motionless for the few seconds of a usual ride, our gaze fixed on the illuminated floor numbers or our own fingernails. Our bodies and eyes immediately begin to move again if the cab comes to an unexpected stop. We breach the defensive walls we have erected around ourselves upon entering. From one moment to the next, a collection of individuals studiously ignoring each other becomes a group thrown together by fate, a "closed society" par excellence.

Thus it is no surprise that the very first literary works to use the elevator as a setting have a stalled cab at the center of their action. In 1875, an anonymous author published a short text entitled "In an Elevator." As far as we know, it was the first elevator story ever written, and it appeared at a time when the spread of the apparatus in hotels, apartment

INTERIORS

houses, and office buildings had only just begun. The story tells how a man and woman from New York high society came to fall in love. At her wedding reception in an apartment hotel, the bride, Estella Blodgett, tells a friend how she became better acquainted with the young professor who is about to become her husband. They had met a year earlier and knew each other slightly, but she hadn't liked him very much. "I used to be dreadfully afraid of him. . . . He isn't a society man at all, and doesn't know how to get on with young ladies." Her opinion changes dramatically, however, when they meet in an elevator on their way to a dinner party and get stuck between floors. In the cramped cab, the awkward professor turns out to be an entertaining conversationalist. "All his scholarly stiffness melted away; he was easy, merry, friendly, and oh, so kind!" says Estella, and even after several hours together, they still have things to talk about: "Poetry, science, religion, gossip." Since they miss out on the entire dinner, their hosts pass them sandwiches through the wire lattice enclosing the cab. As a final sign of his gallantry, the professor divides the snacks with the point of his umbrella. By now, Estella's earlier dislike has been transformed into unexpected intimacy: "I found myself talking to him about all sorts of trifles, which the day before I should as soon have thought of confiding to the observatory." After an inconsequential drop to the ground floor, they finally exit the cab not as distant acquaintances, but as lovers. "So then and there your romance began?" asks Estella's friend at the end of the reception, which, sentimentally enough, is being held in the same apartment where the dinner party took place a year earlier. "Then and there," Estella replies.[205]

In 1894, nine years after this little story appeared in *Harper's Weekly*, William Dean Howells published the previously mentioned one-act play *The Elevator*. This text also first appeared in *Harper's*, and it is possible that Howells was familiar with the 1875 work, for the spatial structure and dynamics of his play follow a very similar pattern. Again, the occasion is an elegant dinner party—this time a Christmas dinner for ten guests in a Boston apartment house—and an unreliable elevator is the central location where six people, including the lift boy, encounter each other. They are the spouses, aunts, sons, and daughters of guests already in the apartment awaiting their arrival. They are all a bit late and get stuck together in the cab just short of the landing where they want to get out. Half the dinner guests are in the elegant salon, the other half crowded into the elevator; Howells constructs a spatial and behavioral dichotomy. The scenes of the first half of the play take place in the apartment, those of the second in the elevator, and Howells's main theme is the bourgeoisie's control of their emotions. In the salon of the host, Mr. Roberts, the growing anxiety about where the other guests are must be suppressed. Right at the beginning, Mrs. Roberts is upset because her elderly and often unpunctual aunt is late. When the doorbell rings and her husband ushers someone else into the apartment, she heaves a "suppressed sigh" noticed by Dr. Lawton, another guest. A moment later, he comments on her perfect composure as she welcomes the new arrival: "Now let me see how a lady transmutes a frown of vengeance into a smile of society welcome," and she answers him in an aside behind her fan, "Didn't I do it beautifully?"[206] As the evening progresses, however, the hostess's social façade begins to develop cracks as she worries about the missing guests. Under the pretext of having the food served, she leaves the room, whispering to her husband, "If I don't go somewhere and have a cry, I shall break down here before everybody."[207] Those present in the apartment try with all their might to keep up a good face; this is no longer the case for those stuck in the elevator. The mishap disrupts all etiquette in the cab. Mr. Miller and Mrs. Curwen, whose spouses are waiting for them in the apartment, begin to flirt with each other. An especially strong attraction forms between Dr. Lawton's daughter and a young man by the name of Mr. Bemis, whose father is already in the apartment. The girl is close to fainting and Bemis takes her hand:

YOUNG MR. BEMIS, *caressing the hand which he holds:* Don't be
  frightened.

MISS LAWTON: Don't leave me.

YOUNG MR. BEMIS: No, no; I won't. Keep fast hold of my hand.

MISS LAWTON: Oh, yes, I will! I'm ashamed to cry.

YOUNG MR. BEMIS, *fervently:* Oh, you needn't be! It is perfectly
  natural you should.[208]

As in the anonymous 1875 story, the stuck elevator gives
rise to a love affair. For when the passengers' cries for help
are finally heard in the unenclosed shaft and the lift boy
gets the machine moving again, Bemis keeps the promise
he made in the halted cab. As the rescued passengers enter
the apartment at last, he detains his new acquaintance for
a moment:

YOUNG MR. BEMIS, *timidly:* Miss Lawton, in the elevator you
  asked me not to leave you. Did you—ah—mean—I MUST ask
  you; it may be my only chance; if you meant—never?

MISS LAWTON, *dropping her head:* I—I—don't—know.

YOUNG MR. BEMIS: But if I WISHED never to leave you, should you
  send me away?

MISS LAWTON, *with a shy, sly upward glance at him:* Not in the
  elevator!

YOUNG MR. BEMIS: Oh![209]

Although Howells's play doesn't end with a wedding, he
leaves us in no doubt that this elevator mishap, too, has
started a love affair.

These early literary documents clearly demonstrate that
the elevator was used as a counter-location to the official
spaces of bourgeois life. It is no accident that in both texts,
the elevator mishap is set against a social event. The lack of
formality in the stalled cab is in stark contrast to the formal
dinner party with its disciplined gestures and conventional
conversations. In the elevator, public masks are lowered.
Just as the passenger alone in the cab can divest himself of
social restraint or a false identity for one unobserved moment, Howells and his anonymous predecessor show that
true selves can also be revealed between couples or among

INTERIORS

the members of a group. In the stalled elevator we find out who we "really" are. This has become the recurring narrative function of the cab in literature and film. Recent films regularly employ the elevator as the place where the truth is revealed, a continuity that owes much to the fact that conveyance in a restricted space remains an irritation, a short-term, exceptional circumstance.

This is precisely the context of what is perhaps the only feature film to take place almost exclusively in an elevator, Carl Schenkel's 1984 *Abwärts* (Downward).[210] On a Friday evening, four people get stuck in the elevator of an office building: Jörg and Marion, colleagues in an advertising agency and obviously also longtime friends in private life; Gössmann, an unassuming white-collar worker carrying a briefcase; and Pit, a young man who probably also works for one of the many companies with offices in the building. Their initial amusement at the mishap soon gives way to real concern. Jörg and Pit climb out into the shaft but can't figure out what to do, and the situation begins to get out of hand. The two get into an altercation during which Pit loses his balance and falls down the shaft, thereby precipitating the crucial passage of the film. When Jörg climbs back into the cab through the ceiling hatch, Marion and Gössmann accuse him of murdering Pit. They begin to fight, and in the struggle, Gössmann's briefcase (which he's been clutching the whole time) falls to the floor and out spill bundles of bills—more than a half million Deutschmarks. Like the clasps of the briefcase, the protective mechanisms the characters have been sheltering behind also give way. The surprising discovery of the briefcase's contents is a kind of signal that they can no longer have any secrets from each other. At the same time, the lights go out and the three of them sit in the dark, only reinforcing the atmosphere of confession that now prevails. Gössmann, the unassuming elderly employee absconding with the week's cash receipts, thought this would be his final trip in the elevator. Now he begins to tell the story of his life, a long string of humiliations. He joined the firm as an unskilled worker right after the war, and has been exploited by his boss ever since. "He always threatens to kick me out into the street, and what would I do then at my age?" He's been planning his revenge for a long time, and decided to break into the safe on this evening because an information technology consultant was in the office that afternoon talking about the accounting methods of the future, and Gössmann realized that his job is about to disappear. No sooner has he finished his confession, with its bitter insight into his own expendability, than Marion pipes up and says to Jörg,

"You've got to admit the same thing about yourself."

"What?"

"That nobody expects anything from you anymore. You're empty, burned out. You can't get anything started on your own."

At first, she tells him that their boss, Mr. Meiers, doesn't think much of him, but then she immediately segues into their personal relationship:

"You pushed me away, too, back then. You tried to keep me under your thumb at work and then play the big shot in bed. I couldn't defend myself, but now I know better. You take the credit for projects other people have developed, ideas I thought up and realized, but that's all over now. Meiers knows all about you, he told me so. Your days are numbered, you're all washed up. . . . He offered me your job and I accepted."

In the darkened cab, in the uncertainty of their situation, the lies they live with are stripped away one by one. The consequences come sooner than expected, for shortly after Marion's last words, the power is restored and phone contact with the doorman's desk is reestablished. Even Pit, whom they thought dead, has managed to drag himself, badly injured, back up onto the cab's roof. But the confessions have been made, the biographies irreversibly damaged, and so it is only consistent that the mishap ends fatally for Jörg after all, even though they are all safe. He is killed trying to retrieve the money from the cab as it plunges to the bottom of the shaft.

INTERIORS

The role of the elevator in both *Abwärts* and the story "In an Elevator," when Estella ends up telling the professor "all sorts of trifles" about herself, is reminiscent of another confined, dark space: the confessional. Simmen and Drepper have pointed out the similarities in design, especially in the case of the 1913 Woolworth Building. The tallest building in the world from 1913 to 1930, it was labeled the Cathedral of Commerce during its opening ceremonies. From its outward appearance to details of its interior design, such as the elaborate filigree of the elevator cabs, it awakens associations with Gothic churches. "The classicist skyscraper of the first epoch varies the idea of a sanctuary on its ground floor with elevator doors that look like the paneling of a confessional," write Simmen and Drepper, but without mentioning the functional similarity that emerges from the stalled elevator's role in literature and film as a secular confessional.[211]

How can this persistent reference be explained? It would appear that sealed-off boxes engender a particular inducement to confession. Obviously, there must be a certain connection between the enclosedness of the space and the truthfulness of the utterance. To explain this connection, we must examine the history of the confessional and ask why the institutionalized location of confession in Christian culture became more and more enclosed over the course of many centuries. An annual confession, as the prerequisite for taking Communion, was made mandatory by the Fourth Lateran Council of 1215. At first, churches set up a simple armchair where the priest sat and heard the confession of the penitent kneeling before him. The two confessional stories in Boccaccio's *Decameron* (written between 1348 and 1353) conform to this pattern.[212] In visual representations, too, one can see the practice of completely open confession well into the sixteenth century.[213] This image of confession did not change until the Council of Trent in 1551, whose decrees regarding the sacrament of penance were a response to the Reformation. Since the traditional absolution, performed by the priest laying his hands on the penitent, was

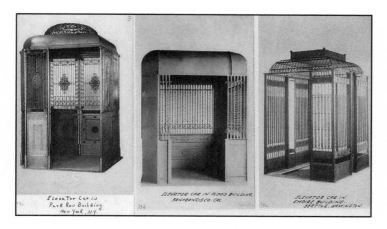

Early elevator cars often looked like confessionals. *Left*, elevator car in Park Row building, New York City; *center*, elevator car in Flood Building, San Francisco; *right*, elevator car in Empire Building, Seattle, Washington. From *Hecla Iron Works from 1876 to 1908* photo gallery, New York Public Library. Courtesy of the Science, Industry, and Business Library of the New York Public Library, and the Astor, Lenox, and Tilden Foundations.

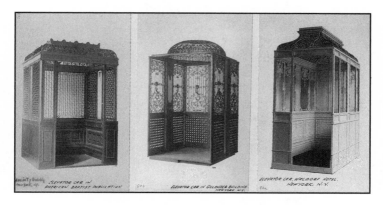

Left, elevator car in American Baptist Publication Society building, New York City; *center*, elevator car in Gillender Building, New York City; *right,* elevator car in Waldorf-Astoria Hotel, New York City. From *Hecla Iron Works from 1876 to 1908* photo gallery, New York Public Library. Courtesy of the Science, Industry, and Business Library of the New York Public Library, and the Astor, Lenox, and Tilden Foundations.

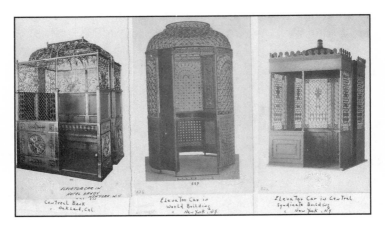

Left: elevator car in Hotel Savoy, New York City; *center*: elevator car in World Building, New York City; *right*: elevator car in Central Syndicate Building, New York City. From *Hecla Iron Works from 1876 to 1908* photo gallery, New York Public Library. Courtesy of the Science, Industry, and Business Library of the New York Public Library, and the Astor, Lenox, and Tilden Foundations.

Loeser Building, Brooklyn, NY. From *Hecla Iron Works from 1876 to 1908* photo gallery, New York Public Library. Courtesy of the Science, Industry, and Business Library of the New York Public Library, and the Astor, Lenox, and Tilden Foundations.

now replaced by the priest simply making the sign of the cross, thus obviating the need for physical contact, "it is possible to realize the pastoral wish often expressed in synods and councils for a clearer separation between father confessor and penitent."[214] In his commentary on the council's decrees, written in the 1560s, Saint Charles Borromeo, archbishop of Milan, was the first to give a precise description of the new confessional:

> The entire box should be made from boards—of walnut or other wood—and enclosed on every side, including from behind and above. Only the front should stay open—and completely open. However, except in highly frequented churches, a door with metal or wooden rods about four inches apart should be installed so that when the confessor is absent, lay persons, vagabonds, and reprobates are not able to idly sit or sleep here in disregard of the confessional's purpose.[215]

The officially prescribed form of the closed confessional was finally published in 1614 in the liturgical manual *Rituale Romanum*. In the course of the seventeenth century, it became established not just in Italy, but in France, Germany, and overseas missions as well, and by the nineteenth century was "the only approved place for the sacrament of penance."[216] In the intervening centuries, the design of the confessional was subject only to minor variations. The two-part confessional described by Borromeo was gradually replaced by a three-part one in the seventeenth century, with a central compartment for the priest and two side compartments for the kneeling penitents. In addition, beginning in the eighteenth century, the front side of the confessional was closed by a solid door, making its insulation even more complete.

Neither in the decrees of the Council of Trent nor in Borromeo's description is there any discussion of the sixteenth-century Church's motives for enclosing the location of the sacrament of penance. What is the explanation for this change? One could say that the insulated confessional is the materialization of a fundamental change in the act of

INTERIORS

penance in early modernity, a change from the mere enumeration of one's violations to the examination of one's conscience, so that the penitent confesses not just his misdeeds, but also his hidden desires and intentions. The request for reconciliation was no longer directed to the entire congregation in a public ceremony, but only to the priest as the representative of God, and this concentration on a single recipient of the confession is matched by the concentrated space of the confessional.[217] Inside the confessional, probably for the first time in the history of the West, the language of confessing took shape. As Foucault repeatedly stresses, it is a language that is synonymous with the formation of modern individuality. Precisely because the admission of sin became an intimate conversation with God, however, all potential disturbances had to be rigorously excluded. For multiple reasons, the early modern Catholic Church was in discussion about the formal conditions of the confession, and it was no accident that the end of public confessions before the priest's chair coincided with the prohibition of the practice—widespread in the Middle Ages—of confessing by letter or messenger. In his 1828 "historical-critical" study of confession, Heinrich Klee wrote of the debates about the permissibility of this practice:

> The scholastics argued for and against the validity of confessions and absolutions made via letter and messenger. Some believed it was sufficient that the priest know the condition of the penitent and for that, a letter or message was enough. Others said that each sacrament had its particular element and in the case of penance, that was the oral confession and must remain so. There is something vital about an oral self-accusation, something that proceeds from within and strongly affects the penitent (like any heroic method), something that symbolizes the struggle to free oneself from sin and that is completely lost in the written confession of someone physically absent. Later [at councils from the fourteenth to the seventeenth century] this method of confession and absolution was prohibited.[218]

This indissoluble intertwining of space, presence, and veracity is characteristic of the early modern debates about confession. The enclosure of the location and the obligatory presence of the penitent were two results of the same concern: to concentrate, as much as possible, the conversation between the sinner and God's representative. The sincerity of the confession and the spirit of absolution could not be allowed to dissipate in the porous channels of epistolary correspondence or the open spaces of a church. The insistence on personal presence and enclosed space continues to be maintained today in the face of calls for confession by telephone or via the Internet.[219] A 1980 theological encyclopedia, for example, states that "Confession also has *external requirements* that must be observed: a space closed to visual and aural observation and to disturbance by third parties or by telephone, so configured that it promotes concentration rather than distraction."[220] With complete ease, this passage passes from a physical description to an anthropological declaration; the closure to observation helps the penitent concentrate and prevents his being distracted. This coupling of spatial configuration to an image of the human subject has resulted in an official location for Christian confession unchanged for more than half a millennium.

We must always have the genesis of the confessional in mind whenever an elevator gets stalled or turned off in a Hollywood movie. It is almost inevitable that an atmosphere of confession will develop in the elevator cab, and the moment of truth will not be far behind. The following is an undoubtedly incomplete list of recent films in which precisely this happens.

In *My Best Friend's Wedding* (1997), a young bride meets her future husband's longtime (female) best friend during preparations for the wedding. At first, they exchange pleasantries and try not to embarrass each other, but when they find themselves alone together in a department store elevator, the bride presses the stop button and confesses her worries.

In *Vanilla Sky* (2001), the boundaries between reality and dream are completely wiped out after David Aames, the inheritor of a publishing company, is badly injured in a car crash. The complex solution of the puzzle comes in a fifteen-minute conversation in an elevator at the end of the film.

In *Shallow Hal* (2001), the hero, Hal Larson, constantly pursues beautiful women without success until he gets stuck in an elevator with a famous televangelist (making the religious association explicit). Hal asks the preacher for help, and after cautioning Hal against such superficial values, the televangelist hypnotizes him so that from now on, he will judge women only by their inner beauty. This is the turning point in Hal's life and the beginning of comedic complications, for upon exiting the elevator, grossly overweight but affectionate women look like supermodels to him. In the end, his conversion in the elevator is so convincing that even after the preacher unhypnotizes him, he marries a woman who never would have interested him in the past.

The most extensive use of an elevator as a secular confessional, however, is in *You've Got Mail* (1998), a remake of Ernst Lubitsch's film *The Shop around the Corner*. Joe Fox, owner of a bookstore chain, and Kathleen Kelly, who runs an independent bookstore, have long since fallen for each other via an anonymous e-mail correspondence, although they're face-to-face combatants as she struggles against being taken over by his company. When Joe arrives late for their first rendezvous as e-mail correspondents and catches sight of Kathleen, he realizes who he's been exchanging e-mails with and can hardly believe his luck; he's been interested in her since their first adversarial encounter, but hasn't had the courage to tell her how he feels, partly because he's not ready to separate from his wealthy but hysterical wife. The second half of the film shows Joe's inner turmoil about whether to tell Kathleen the truth or simply forget her. The decisive moment arrives when Joe and his wife return from shopping and get stuck in the elevator on the way to their luxury apartment. In the cab are a half dozen residents of the building, and when they've been stopped for a few minutes and nothing is happening, they begin to get restless. Finally they sit down in a circle and begin to tell each other what they will do differently once they're freed from this dire situation. On the one hand, the scene points to an ancient cultural model—the birth of narrative from the avoidance of mortal danger—prefigured in two foundational texts of narrative art: *The Thousand and One Nights* and *The Decameron*. On the other hand, the ritual in the elevator is extremely reminiscent of a confession, for one after another, the passengers ask to be forgiven earlier transgressions and promise to lead better lives if they are rescued. Joe keeps recalling Kathleen's face while the others are speaking, but his wife paws through her purse looking for breath mints and chatters away in a loud voice. When it's finally her turn, she has nothing to say but, "If I ever get out of here, I'm having my eyes lasered." At that moment, Joe finally decides to leave her and reveal his identity to Kathleen. By the time the confessions are at an end and the fire department gets the elevator doors open, he's made up his mind to change his life. The following scene shows Joe and his dog Brinkley in their transitional residence on his houseboat as he comments in voice-over, "I came home tonight and got into the elevator to go to my apartment. An hour later, I got out of the elevator and Brinkley and I moved out. Suddenly everything had become clear."[221]

In the stalled elevator, the entire truth of an existence is revealed, even if it's the pure narcissism of an Upper East Side Manhattanite who even in the face of death can think only of maximizing her physical appearance. Just as contemporary Catholic theology regards confession as a "celebration of return,"[222] the elevator marks a similar turning point in the dramaturgy of these films. The confession in the cab clears the way for either reconciliation or renunciation. It remains to be asked why this moment of decision in stories from the big city is so often staged in blocked elevators and not in spaces of comparable size such as train compartments or private rooms in restaurants. The intensity of the atmosphere seems to be bound up with the tension between movement and stagnation. When something that normally fluctuates rapidly slows down or stops, it causes a disturbance in relationships. Georg Simmel repeatedly described the extent to which the functioning of modern urban life is tied to the mode of circulation, especially the circulation of money. In *Philosophie des Geldes* (The philosophy of money), he wrote,

The modern, sensitive, nervous person would be brought to complete despair by the physical proximity of such an enormous number of people as share contemporary urban culture, with its commercial, technical, and social intercourse, were it not that the objectification of that circulation's character brings with it an inner boundary and cushion. Monetized relationships, be they obvious or disguised in a thousand forms, establish an invisible, functional distance between individuals. That distance constitutes an inner, compensatory shield against the overwhelming proximity and friction of our cultural life.[223]

Simmel's reference to the circulation of money and its result—the necessary distancing from our fellow city dwellers—is important in this context. We recall a particular detail from stories of elevator catastrophes such as *Hotel* and *Abwärts*: those briefcases of stolen money that one of the passengers (Keycase the hotel thief or Gössmann the office worker) is smuggling out of the building. These stories involve a double tie-up in traffic: the hitch in the circulation of people is also a hitch in the circulation of money. And this is precisely the reason the stalled elevator is such a perfect location for the dramatic climax of conflicts: beyond the atmosphere of the confessional, it produces that excessive proximity that Simmel says can be kept in check only by fluent, trouble-free circulation. With incomparable swiftness, paralyzed elevators make urban operating temperatures rise, and such a seemingly incidental motif as smuggled money—yearning to quickly get back into circulation—dramatizes that rise in temperature, if we follow Simmel, better than anything else. In this way, every elevator malfunction frustrates the cooling function of the circulatory paradigm described most recently by Helmut Lethen in his study of the anthropology of the interwar years in Germany:

> Traffic transforms morality into objectivity and enforces functionally correct behavior. Participation in traffic is a provisional affair (which embeds one, with the illusion of freedom, in the prescribed streams). No place where an individual can put down roots. . . . One's points of rest are provisional: waiting rooms, lobbies, train compartments, subway stations, *lifts*, surface rail platforms, terminals, depots, open-plan offices.[224]

The "unease" that Lethen says arises "when the traffic flow is suddenly interrupted or backed up for a long time"[225] is intensified in the elevator, where fiction and film can portray it more sharply than in any other means of transportation. The crises that unfold in the cab are one sign among many that the elevator is a paradigmatic site of modernity.

INTERIORS

NOTES

NOTES TO THE INTRODUCTION

1 Goodwin, *Otis*, 8.
2 Shultz and Simmons, *Offices,* 42.
3 Greville, *Memoirs*, 391–92.
4 "Editor's Easy Chair," *Harper's New Monthly Magazine*, June 1853, 131.
5 Simmen and Drepper, *Fahrstuhl*, 9.
6 Goodwin, *Otis*, 13.
7 Otis Elevator Company, *First Hundred Years*, 3.
8 Otis, *E. G. Otis*, n.p.
9 Goodwin, *Otis*, 8.
10 "The Balloon Ascension," *New York Times*, June 10, 1854, 4.
11 "Crystal Palace Notes," *Scientific American*, June 10, 1854, 309.
12 "Machinery at the Crystal Palace," *New York Daily Tribune*, May 30, 1854, 6.
13 A detailed description of its operation is provided by Kennedy, "Vertical Railway," 892.
14 According to the official company history by Goodwin, *Otis*, 17.
15 "Otis Tufts, the Inventor," *New York Times*, November 8, 1869, 3.
16 "Notes on Elevators I," *American Architect and Building News*, no. 232 (1880): 245.
17 Kennedy, "Vertical Railway," 888.
18 Ibid., 890.
19 Ibid., 889.
20 "The Rise of Elevators," *American Architect and Building News*, no. 1460 (1903): 96.
21 Simmen and Drepper, *Fahrstuhl*, 14.
22 Gavois, *Going Up*, 83.
23 Gray, *Ascending Rooms*, 204.
24 Otis, *E. G. Otis*, n.p.

25 For example, Victor H. Bernstein, "Elevators for a Hoist," *New York Times*, November 25, 1934, 5: "It was only eighty years ago that the elevator really has its beginning in New York City, in a dramatic moment."

26 For example, in 1870, a cable-drawn elevator patented by Tufts was installed in the New York Equitable Life Building, the first office building to have one. See Hugh McAtamney and Company, *Master Builders*, 13.

27 Otis Elevator Company, *Otis Bulletin*, 1. Thus the history of the elevator confirms what David Gugerli and Daniel Speich write about retroactively composed beginnings in their *Topographien der Nation*: "Once success has been achieved, it provides the confidence necessary to translate the 'original' complexities of every actual beginning into the discursive clarity of an initial spark pregnant with promise for the future" (99).

28 Goodwin, *Otis*, 8.

29 Aristotle, *Poetics*, chaps. 7–13.

30 See Fleck, *Entstehung*.

31 Ibid., 101.

32 Riehl, *Naturgeschichte*, 142–96 (the chapters "Das ganze Haus" and "Die Familie und die bürgerliche Baukunst").

33 Ibid., 185.

34 Ibid., 165.

35 Bachelard, *Poetics*, 26.

36 Gray, *Ascending Rooms*, 62: "Almost without exception, new hotels after 1860 in New York City and elsewhere incorporated at least one elevator into their design."

37 Equitable Life Assurance, *Hyde*, 119.

38 Schmitz, "Hydraulische Aufzüge." The article concluded, "It should also be noted that for about a year now, Pfaff's furniture warehouse in the Französische Strasse has an elevator operating according to the system described above."

39 "Amerikanische Personen-Aufzüge in Berliner Häusern," *Deutsche Bauzeitung*, February 5, 1887, 61–64.

40 Indirectly driven hydraulic elevators were in wide use between the 1870s and the 1890s. In these, the cab is not placed directly on the drive piston. Hydraulic power is transferred via block and tackle, and the cab is suspended on a cable. This variant of the hydraulic technique was needed especially in cities and regions where bedrock made it difficult to sink the piston completely below ground level.

41 Koolhaas, *Delirious New York*, 139.

42 Robinson, "Tall Office Buildings," 185. See also Schuyler, "Evolution," 421: "It is certain that the earliest and the most indispensable of the factors which have enabled the construction of these mighty monsters was the 'passenger elevator.'"

43 Mujica, *History,* 21.

44 Steffens, "Modern Business Building," 41–42.

45 Ibid., 47.

46 On the development of steel frame construction in Chicago and shortly thereafter in New York, see Rappold, *Bau,* 27; Mujica, *History,* 21–28; Giedion, *Space,* 188–206; Webster, "Skyscraper"; Shultz and Simmons, *Offices,* 18–41; and Balzer, *Hochhaus,* 86–91.

47 Steffens, "Modern Business Building," 50: "There are engineers who can lay the foundations for fifty stories."

48 Mujica, *History,* 21.

49 On the speed of hydraulic elevators, see Gutermuth, "Mitteilungen" and "Neuere Konstruktionen." On electric elevators, see Bohny, "Amerikanische Hochbauten," 365.

50 Mujica, *History,* 21 (emphasis in original).

51 Palme, "Woolworth-Gebäude," 253.

52 Canguilhem, "Gegenstand der Wissenschaftsgeschichte," 22.

53 Giedion, *Mechanization,* 20.

54 Koolhaas, *Delirious New York,* 27.

55 Petersen, *Elisha Graves Otis,* 12.

56 Otis, *E. G. Otis,* n.p.

57 Reuleaux, *Gutachten,* 11.

58 See the extensive discussion in Simmen and Drepper, *Fahrstuhl,* 99–107.

59 Mülder-Bach, "Poetik," 199.

60 On the development of transport techniques in mining, see Schönberg, "Technische Entwicklung"; Heilfurth, *Bergbau;* and Suhling, *Aufschließen.*

61 Most precisely described by Heinrich Lottner, "Die Fahrkunst auf der Steinkohlegrube Gewalt," *Zeitschrift für das Berg-, Hütten- und Salinenwesen,* vol. 1, pt. B (1854): 120–44.

62 Quoted by Bornhardt, *Albert,* 16.

63 Reprinted and annotated in Verein für die bergbaulichen Interessen, *Entwicklung,* 272–73.

64 Bergpolizei-Verordnung, "Die Befahrung der Schächte mittels Seile betreffend," *Zeitschrift für das Berg-, Hütten- und Salinenwesen,* vol. 18, pt. A (1870): 69.

65 A good example are the more than one hundred questions covered in the July 1867 catalog of the Royal Main Mine Office in Breslau. The condition of the shaft, the transporting machinery, the cables, and so on must be conveyed to the authorities down to the last detail. See "Bekanntmachung des Königl. Oberbergamtes zu Breslau vom 29. Juli 1883, betreffend die Anträge auf Ertheilung der Erlaubniss zur Seilfahrt auf Bergwerken," *Zeitschrift für das Berg-, Hütten- und Salinenwesen,* vol. 31, pt. A (1883): 74–77.

66 See Hand, "Bergmännische Lebens- und Arbeitsweise."

67 Hintz, *Handbuch*, 2.

68 Goodwin, *Otis*, 8.

69 Heinrich Lottner, *Leitfaden zur Bergbaukunde*, ed. Albert Serlo, 2nd ed. (Berlin, 1873), 112.

70 See Malmedie, "Fangevorrichtungen," esp. 355 and 365.

71 Ibid., 353.

72 Verein für die bergbaulichen Interessen, *Entwicklung*, 332.

73 Selbach, "Kritik," 13.

74 See Hude and Hennicke, "Central-Hotel," 188. The speed of elevators in the high-rises of New York and Chicago at this time was five to six and a half feet per second. See Gutermuth, "Mitteilungen," 774.

75 Selbach, "Kritik," 59.

76 See "Deutsche Allgemeine Ausstellung für Unfallverhütung: Aufzüge der Berlin-Anhaltinischen Maschinenbau-Aktiengesellschaft zu Berlin-Moabit," *Zeitschrift des Vereins deutscher Ingenieure*, 1889, 631.

77 See "The Immensity of Elevator Travel," *American Architect and Building News*, no. 1188 (1898): 1–2; and Allen E. Beals, "The Elevator as an Enhancer of Land Value," *Real Estate Record and Builders' Guide*, August 12, 1911, 208–10.

78 Flohr Maschinenfabrik, *Personen- und Lastenaufzüge*, 43.

79 In high-rise buildings in large American cities, on the other hand, there were numerous fatal cab accidents into the early twentieth century, as one can read in the pages of the *American Architect and Building News*.

80 The accident is described in great detail in "Elevator Accident," *American Architect and Building News* 3, no. 117 (1878): 104.

81 As they are described in a popular German children's book: Maar and Heidelbach, *Aufzug*, n.p.

82 Flohr Maschinenfabrik, *Personen- und Lastenaufzüge*, 16.

83 Hintz, *Handbuch*, 3.

84 Ibid., 86.

85 Flohr, "Neuere Aufzugsanlagen," 275.

86 Urban, *Unfallverhütung*, 1.

87 Ibid., 8.

NOTES TO CHAPTER 1

1 Robinson, "Tall Office Buildings," 194.

2 Sullivan, "Tall Office Building," 203.

3 Wiener, *Warenhaus*, 325.

4 Schuyler, "Sky-Scraper," 232.

5 The dumbwaiters that began to show up in royal and imperial residences at the end of the eighteenth century exploited precisely this linearity to prevent the attempted poisonings

that often occurred when food was delivered via convoluted stairways. The direct, vertical duct between kitchen and dining room was impossible to tap into.

6 Wiener, *Warenhaus*, 326.

7 Gray, *Ascending Rooms*, 75.

8 Quoted in ibid., 78.

9 "Polizei-Verordnung" (1893), 258.

10 Ibid.

11 Mayer, "Aufzüge," 171.

12 The most drastic examples are supplied in a forensic study by Moritz Ganzoni, *Die Ursachen und die Verhütung der Liftunfälle mit Berücksichtigung des vorliegenden Entwurfes von Vorschriften über Bau und Betrieb von Aufzügen* (Zurich, 1917), 22–26, in a chapter entitled "Causes of Accidents in Inappropriately Constructed Elevator Shaft Enclosures."

13 Flohr Maschinenfabrik, *Personen- und Lastenaufzüge*, 43.

14 Ibid., 60.

15 Gray, *Ascending Rooms*, 67, on the 1870 Equitable Building.

16 There is an exact description in Young, *Art and Enterprise*, 55–56.

17 Blanke, "Cliff-Dwellers," 358.

18 Mann, *Vulkan*, 309.

19 Ibid., 312.

20 Reuleaux, *Gutachten*, 8–9.

21 Mayer, "Aufzüge," 170–71.

22 Hintz, *Handbuch*, 157.

23 K. Dümmler, "Treppenhäuser und Fahrstühle," *Zentralblatt der Bauverwaltung*, December 28, 1907, 687–88.

24 Bachelard, *Poetics*, 25–26 (emphasis in original).

25 Mayer, "Aufzüge," 163 (emphasis added).

26 Ibid., 181.

27 Drews, "Moderne Aufzüge," 659.

28 Fechter, *Ruck*, 49 and again, in almost the same words, 329.

29 Freud and Breuer, *Studien*, 120.

30 On the development of push-button controls, see chapter 3.

31 Siemens-Schuckwertwerke, *Technisches Heft No. 8: Steuerungen für Aufzüge unter besonderer Berücksichtigung der Druckknopfsteuerung*, 4th ed. (Berlin, n.d., circa 1910), 31.

32 Freytag, *Soll und Haben*, 43. Although an 1858 English translation is available online (http://www.gutenberg.org/files/19754/19754-h/19754-h.htm), a comparison with the German original shows that the anonymous translator simply left many things out. The entire passage quoted above, for instance, is translated thus: "The house itself was an irregular and ancient building, with wings, court-yards, out-houses, short stairs, mysterious passages, and deep recesses." See also

Fritz, *Menschen in Büroarbeitsräumen*, 69–79, who lists "some contemporary descriptions of the convoluted space relationships in old merchant establishments" (75) as examples of how hard it was to keep track of whether workers were present or absent.

33 Architekten-Verein zu Berlin, eds., *Berlin und seine Bauten*, 2 vols. (Berlin, 1877), 444.

34 Ibid., 451.

35 Albert Gut, *Das Berliner Wohnhaus: Beiträge zu seiner Geschichte und seiner Entwicklung in der Zeit der landesfürstlichen Bautätigkeit (17. und 18. Jahrhundert)* (Berlin, 1917), 154.

36 Wischermann, "Mythen," 348–49.

37 Ibid., 349.

38 See Engels, "Zur Wohnungsfrage," 260–63; Giedion, *Space*, 641–79; Benjamin, *Arcades*, 120–49; and Sennett, *Flesh and Stone*, 329–32.

39 Speich, *Helvetische Meliorationen*, 317.

40 Ibid.

41 Ibid. The regulation of the upper Rhine by Johann Gottfried Tulla prompted similar conclusions; see Heinrich Cassione and Karl Spiess, *Johann Gottfried Tulla, Der Begründer der Wasser- und Straßenbauverwaltung in Baden: Sein Leben und Wirken* (Karlsruhe, 1928), 7: "Without Tulla's life's work, the Rhine valley would be an inaccessible, fever-ridden swamp, avoided by human inhabitants. Thanks to him, the Rhine is the beneficent receiving stream of the entire upper Rhine watershed and, due to the further work of Honsell, the main traffic artery of the countries surrounding its upper reaches."

42 Foucault, *Discipline and Punish*, 143.

43 See Giedion, *Space*, 644.

44 Theodor Mundt, *Paris und Louis Napoléon: Neue Skizzen aus dem französischen Kaiserreich*, vol. 1 (Berlin, 1858), 210–11.

45 Foucault, *Discipline and Punish*, 143.

46 See Benjamin, "Paris," 72–73.

47 Foucault, *Discipline and Punish*, 141.

48 See David Jordan, *Die Neuerschaffung von Paris: Baron Haussmann und seine Stadt* (Frankfurt am Main: Fischer Verlag, 1996), 280.

49 Quoted by Benjamin, *Arcades*, 186.

50 See J. M. Chapman and Brian Chapman, *The Life and Times of Baron Haussmann: Paris in the Second Empire* (London: Weidenfeld and Nicholson, 1957), 181. See also Giedion, *Raum*, 444: "The transformation of Paris   . occurred during the feverish middle years of the age of the railroad."

51 See Roskothen, *Verkehr*, 180.

52 See, for example, Wasserfuhr, "Gesundheitsschädlichkeiten."

53 On the topography of Kafka's *Trial*, see chapter 2.

54 Foucault, *Discipline and Punish*, 143.

55 P. Jenisch, *Haustelegraphie: Eine gemeinverständliche Anleitung zum Bau von elektrischen Haus-Telegraphen-, Telephon- und Blitzableiter-Anlagen* (Berlin, 1897), 69 (emphasis in original). The earliest pneumatic and electric doorbell installations on residential dwellings appeared in Germany at the end of the 1860s, but were restricted to luxurious single-family homes; see Goldschmidt, "Elektrische Haustelegraphen," *Deutsche Bauzeitung*, 1867, 94–96. Prior to Jenisch's publication, manuals and pamphlets for electricians contain no indication that the principle of the doorbell was also known in multistory buildings in the form of a bank of doorbells. An 1893 publication similar to Jenisch's states, "It's quite rare today to find a building without an electric house telegraph," but probably refers only to single-family houses. J. Sack, *Die Haustelegraphie und Haustelephonie: Eine kurzgefasste praktische Anleitung zur Herstellung von Haustelegraphen- und Haustelephon-Anlagen*, 2nd ed. (Berlin, 1893), 2. If we accept the passage in Jenisch as evidence that the first banks of doorbells were installed in the late 1890s, it becomes clear from a 1910 manual how quickly this innovation proliferated after the turn of the century: "In the vast majority of buildings in a modern city, a doorbell is installed for each apartment. Its purpose is to let the inhabitant know that someone is waiting to be admitted at the entrance door." Otto Canter, *Die Haus- und Hotel-Telegraphie und -Telephonie*, 3rd ed., revised by Paul Riemenschneider (Vienna and Leipzig, 1920), 51. We can thus date the widespread introduction of the bank of doorbells to the years between 1895 and 1910.

56 Simmel, *Soziologie*, 711.

57 Foucault, *Discipline and Punish*, 191.

58 Benjamin, *Arcades*, 126.

59 Michel Serres and Nayla Farouki, eds., *Thesaurus der exakten Wissenschaften* (Thesaurus of the Exact Sciences; in French original, *Le trésor: Dictionnaire des sciences*) (Frankfurt am Main: Zweitausendeins, 2001), 37. See also John Haugeland, "Analog und analog," in *Analog/Digital—Opposition oder Kontinuum? Zur Theorie und Geschichte einer Unterscheidung*, ed. Jens Schröter and Alexander Böhnke (Bielefeld: Transcript Verlag, 2004), 42, on the analog principle: "Changes occur gradually or continuously without any 'gaps.' Detents or stops are excluded." Unlike the digital principle, "every (relevant) position or shape is permitted—there is no such thing as shapelessness."

60 Thus Friedrich Kittler describes the digital principle in "Geschichte der Kommunikationsmedien," in *Raum und Verfahren*,

ed. Jörg Huber and Alois Müller (Basel: Stoemfeld/Roter, 1993), 185.

61 See Calef, *Fahrstuhl*; and Louis Malle's film.

62 Generlich et al., *Fahrstuhlführer*, 14.

63 Koolhaas, *Delirious New York*, 85.

64 Ibid. (emphasis in original).

65 Zola, *L'Assommoir*.

66 Ibid.

67 The title *Pot Luck* is a play on this basic constellation of the novel.

68 Zola, *Pot Luck*, 5.

69 Maar and Heidelbach, *Aufzug*, n.p.

70 Ibid.

NOTES TO CHAPTER 2

1 Roth, *Hotel Savoy*, 12–14.

2 Ibid., 20.

3 Ibid., 28.

4 Ibid., 43.

5 Ruttenbaum, *Mansions*, 106–8.

6 See Lis Künzli, ed., *Hotels: Ein literarischer Führer* (Frankfurt am Main: Eichborn, 1996), 51.

7 Roth, *Hotel Savoy*, 33–34.

8 See Mann, *Confessions*, 4, where Krull says he was born "a few years after the glorious founding of the German Empire." After successfully dodging the draft, he must be eighteen or nineteen years old when he reaches Paris. So the hotel episodes take place around the mid-1890s.

9 Ibid., 129.

10 Ibid., 142.

11 Morehouse, *Waldorf-Astoria*.

12 Ibid., 137.

13 Ibid., 144.

14 Morehouse quotes an employee of the Waldorf-Astoria: "We feel, at times, like this is a private UN where many things are discussed and many problems arranged" (141).

15 See ibid., 187.

16 See ibid., 180.

17 See Moritz Hoffmann, *Geschichte des deutschen Hotels: Vom Mittelalter bis zur Gegenwart* (Heidelberg: Hüthig Verlag, 1961), 208: "The years from 1871 to 1914 were the period of greatest growth in touristic travel and thus also in the hotel industry."

18 Karl Baedeker, *London und Umgebungen*, 12th ed. (Leipzig, 1896), 8.

19 Karl Baedeker, *Nordost-Deutschland (von der Elbe und der*

Westgrenze Sachsens an) nebst Dänemark, 24th ed. (Leipzig, 1892), 30.

20 Karl Baedeker, *Berlin und Umgebungen*, 9th ed. (Leipzig, 1896), 4.

21 See Karl Baedeker, *Belgien und Holland nebst dem Grossher-zogthum Luxemburg*, 19th ed. (Leipzig, 1891); and Baedeker, *Österreich-Ungarn*, 25th ed. (Leipzig, 1898), passim.

22 Karl Baedeker, *Nordamerika: Die Vereinigten Staaten nebst ei-nem Ausflug nach Mexiko* (Leipzig, 1893), xxvi.

23 Karl Baedeker, *Paris: Nebst einigen Routen durch das nördliche Frankreich*, 15th ed. (Leipzig, 1900), 2.

24 Karl Baedeker, *Oberitalien: Mit Ravenna, Florenz und Livorno*, 18th ed. (Leipzig, 1911), 430.

25 Karl Baedeker, *Deutschland in einem Bande*, 4th ed. (Leipzig, 1925), xvi. Almost identical sentences are also in *Paris und Umgebung*, 20th ed. (Leipzig, 1931) and *Österreich*, 30th ed. (Leipzig, 1926).

26 Karl Baedeker, *Südbayern, Tirol und Salzburg, Steiermark, Kärn-ten, Krain, Istrien und Württemberg*, 10th ed. (Coblenz, 1862), xiii.

27 Karl Baedeker, *Die Schweiz nebst den angrenzenden Theilen von Ober-Italien, Savoyen und Tirol*, 20th ed. (Leipzig, 1883), xvii.

28 Karl Baedeker, *Mittel- und Norddeutschland, westlich bis zum Rhein*, 20th ed. (Leipzig, 1883), 2.

29 See Karl Baedeker, *Paris und seine Umgebungen*, 11th ed. (Leipzig, 1885), 3 (exactly the same list in the editions of 1888 and 1896).

30 Baedeker, *Paris,* 15th ed., 4.

31 Bachelard, *Poetics*, 17.

32 Ibid.

33 See Siegfried Wichmann, *Carl Spitzweg: Kunst, Kosten und Kon-flikte* (Frankfurt am Main: Propyläen, 1991), 18, who calls the work "probably the most popular German painting of the 19th century."

34 Hans-Joachim Raupp, "Carl Spitzweg: Der arme Poet," *Wallraf-Richartz-Jahrbuch: Westdeutsches Jahrbuch für Kunstgeschichte*, vol. 46 (1985): 256.

35 Ibid., 262. Raupp mentions a number of pictures that deal with the motif of the garret poet, e.g., J. W. M. Turner's *Garreteer's Petition to His Muse* (1809), Tommaso Minardi's *Self Portrait in the Garret* (after 1813), and Honoré Daumier's *Poet in the Garret* (1842). See also Becker, *Urbanität*, 107, who adds the follow-ing to Raupp's list: Kaspar Braun's *Garret Room of a Poor Poet* (1832) and N. Widemann's *Artist's Garret* (1836).

36 Tieck, *Überfluss*, 244.

37 Ibid., 194.

38 Detlef Kremer, "Fenster," in *Das Denken der Sprache und die*

Performanz des Literarischen um 1800, ed. Stefan Jaeger and Stefan Willet (Würzburg: Königshausen and Neumann, 2000), 216.

39 Tieck, *Überfluss*, 195.

40 Ibid., 217.

41 Hoffmann, "Corner Window," 378.

42 Tieck, *Überfluss*, 234.

43 Ibid., 247.

44 Wischermann, "Mythen," 352.

45 Friedrich Wasmann, *Ein deutsches Künstlerleben von ihm selbst geschildert*, as quoted in Adelheid von Saldern, "Im Hause, zu Hause: Wohnen im Spannungsfeld von Gegebenheiten und Aneignungen," in *Geschichte des Wohnens*, vol. 3, *1800–1918, Das bürgerliche Zeitalter*, ed. Jürgen Reulecke (Stuttgart: Deutscher Verlags-Anstalt, 1997), 153.

46 See Wischermann, "Mythen," 363.

47 Eberstadt, *Handbuch*, 84.

48 See, for example, A. Schneer, *Über die Zustände der arbeitenden Klassen in Breslau mit Benutzung der amtlichen Quellen des königlichen Polizei-Präsidii und des Magistrats* (Berlin, 1845) as well as various contributions to the *Zeitschrift für practische Baukunst* (Magazine of practical construction), founded in 1841 and the first publication to report regularly on the living conditions in tenement houses.

49 Beginning in the 1860s, this term became established among the critics. See Geist and Kürvers, *Berliner Mietshaus*, 220. In 1900, the city planner Joseph Stübben proposed calling buildings of more than four stories and twelve apartments *Mietskasernen* (see Zimmermann, *Von der Wohnungsfrage*, 11).

50 Foucault, *History*, 140, 137.

51 See Philipp Sarasin, *Reizbare Maschinen: Eine Geschichte des Körpers, 1765–1914* (Frankfurt am Main: Suhrkamp, 2001), esp. 95–172, which analyzes, with different emphasis, the hygiene movement that had already begun in the early nineteenth century in France.

52 Zimmermann, *Von der Wohnungsfrage*, 93.

53 Thus the founding of the Lower Rhine Association for Public Health in 1869 was a direct result of the Cologne cholera epidemic of 1866. See Beate Witzler, *Großstadt und Hygiene: Kommunale Gesundheitspolitik in der Epoche der Urbanisierung* (Stuttgart: Steiner, 1995), 12.

54 Quoted in Hobrecht, *Gesundheitspflege*, 6.

55 Ibid., 10.

56 Ibid., 12.

57 Well documented in Geist and Kürvers, *Berliner Mietshaus*, 142–69.

58 See, for example, Hermann Wasserfuhr, "Zur Organisation der Sterblichkeitsstatistik," *Deutsche Vierteljahrsschrift für öffentliche Gesundheitspflege*, no. 2 (1872): 185–99; and Robert Volz, "Zur Einführung einer Mortalitätsstatistik," ibid., 200–209.

59 Hermann Schwabe, "Einfluss der verschiedenen Wohnungen auf die Gesundheit ihrer Bewohner, soweit er sich statistisch nachweisen lässt," *Deutsche Vierteljahrsschrift für öffentliche Gesundheitspflege*, no. 1 (1875): 73.

60 See the extensive statistics covering eighteen cities in Eberstadt, *Handbuch*, 200; also the data for Berlin in Geist and Kürvers, *Berliner Mietshaus*, 468–69; for Zurich, see also Helmuth Wolff, "Die Stockwerklage und der Wohnungsmarkt," *Zeitschrift für Wohnungswesen*, no. 16 (1907): 213–16.

61 Here, for example, in W. Strassmann, "Anforderungen der öffentlichen Gesundheitspflege an die Baupolizei in Bezug auf neue Stadttheile, Strassen und Häuser," *Deutsche Vierteljahrsschrift für öffentliche Gesundheitspflege*, no. 1 (1875): 54.

62 Hermann Wasserfuhr, "Über die Sterblichkeit der Neugeborenen und Säuglinge in Deutschland," *Deutsche Vierteljahrsschrift für öffentliche Gesundheitspflege*, no. 4 (1869): 533.

63 Rudolf Virchow, *Reinigung und Entwässerung Berlins: General-Bericht über die Arbeiten der städtischen gemischten Deputation für die Untersuchung der auf die Kanalisation und Abfuhr bezüglichen Fragen* (Berlin, 1873), 67.

64 Ibid.

65 Wasserfuhr, "Gesundheitsschädlichkeiten," 194.

66 Flügge, *Großstadtwohnungen*, 103.

67 Statutory health insurance was introduced in Germany in 1883.

68 See a reproduction of the questionnaire in Geist and Kürvers, *Berliner Mietshaus*, 461.

69 See Gesine Asmus, ed., *Hinterhof, Keller und Mansarde—Einblicke in Berliner Wohnungselend, 1901–1920* (Reinbek bei Hamburg: Rowohlt, 1982).

70 See *Bauordnung für die k. Haupt- und Residenzstadt München vom 3. April 1879* (Munich, 1879), § 35.

71 See *Bauordnung Wien*, § 42.

72 See *Neue Bau-Ordnung Prag*, § 73.

73 See Willert, *Zusammenstellung*, 130.

74 See Berger, *Bauordnungen*, 107.

75 *Neue Bau-Ordnung Prag*, 280.

76 Ibid., 279.

77 Berger, *Bauordnungen*, 111–12.

78 Willert, *Zusammenstellung*, 105.

79 Ibid., 129.

80 *Bauordnung Wien*, § 51 (cf. *Neue Bau-Ordnung Prag*, § 76: "The installation of attic apartments in the city is prohibited").

81 *Neue Bau-Ordnung Prag*, § 104.
82 See Max Sommerbrodt, "Über Sterblichkeit und Todtgeburten in abnorm hoch gelegenen Wohnungen," *Deutsche Vierteljahrsschrift für öffentliche Gesundheitspflege*, no. 2 (1878): 260–64.
83 Yuri Lotman, *The Structure of the Artistic Text*, trans. Ronald Vroon (Ann Arbor: Michigan Slavic Contributions, 1977), 237 (emphasis added); "dress circle of a theatre" is presumably a mistranslation for *bel étage*.
84 Dölger, "Einfluss der Höhenlage," 444.
85 Flügge, *Großstadtwohnungen*, 41.
86 Musil, *Törless*, 83. Further citations of this edition will be in parentheses following the quote.
87 Hauptmann, *Rats*, 348. Further citations of this edition will be in parentheses following the quote.
88 Ibsen, *Wild Duck*, 455. Further citations of this edition will be in parentheses following the quote.
89 Kafka, *The Trial*, 73–74. Further citations of this edition will be in parentheses following the quote.
90 Benno von Wiese, "Wirklichkeit und Drama in Gerhart Hauptmanns Tragikomödie 'Die Ratten,'" *Jahrbuch der deutschen Schillergesellschaft* 6 (1962): 315. It is noteworthy that von Wiese's analysis makes a connection to Kafka's *Trial*: "The distance from Kafka's ramified, labyrinthine court offices and their oppressive stuffiness is not as far as is usually thought." On the spatial structure of *The Rats*, see also Brigitte Stuhlmacher, "Berliner Hauser in modernen Dramen: Exempel Hermann Sudermann und Gerhart Hauptmann," in *Literarisches Leben in Berlin, 1871–1933*, ed. Peter Wruck (Berlin: Akademie-Verlag, 1987), 204–53.
91 Neumann, "Zauber," 123.
92 Ibid.
93 Kafka, *Der Proceß*, 168.
94 See Hiebel, *Henrik Ibsens psycho-analytische Dramen*, esp. 115–16; on the spatial structure of *The Wild Duck*, see also Knut Brynhildsvoll, "Die Antinomie von Drinnen und Draußen als strukturbildendes Prinzip in den Dramen Henrik Ibsens," in *Studien zum Werk und Werkeinfluss Henrik Ibsens* (Leverkusen: Literaturverlag Norden M. Reinhardt, 1988), 33–64.
95 Hiebel, *Henrik Ibsens psycho-analytische Dramen*, 124.
96 See Moshe Idel, *Golem: Jewish Magical and Mystical Traditions of the Artificial Anthropoid* (Albany: State University of New York Press, 1990).
97 Freud, "The 'Uncanny,'" 220.
98 Ibid., 241.
99 Ibid., 245.

100 Neumann, "Zauber," 122.

101 Klaus Wagenbach, *Kafkas Prag: Ein Reiselesebuch* (Berlin: Wagenbach, 1993), 42.

102 Bachelard, *Poetics*, 17 – 18.

103 Gilles DeLeuze and Félix Guattari, *Kafka: Für eine kleine Literatur* (Frankfurt am Main: Suhrkamp, 1976), 104.

104 Bachelard, *Poetics*, 25.

105 "In Paris there are no houses, and the inhabitants of the big city live in superimposed boxes." Ibid., 26.

106 Joachim Hintze, *Das Raumproblem im modernen deutschen Drama und Theater* (Marburg: Elwert, 1969), 110.

107 By 1905, twenty German cities had adopted the graduated building code; by 1911 the number was thirty-eight. See Gemünd, "Neuere Bestrebungen," 415.

108 *Bauordnung Wien*, § 39, p. 38; almost identical wording is in *Neue Bau-Ordnung Prag*, § 70, p. 369.

109 Quoted in Geist and Kürvers, *Berliner Mietshaus*, 376 – 77.

110 See Friedrich Eugen Hopf, *Bericht über den III. Internationalen Kongress für Wohnungshygiene in Dresden vom 2. bis 7. Oktober 1911* (Dresden: Güntzschen, 1912), especially the opening speech by Carl Flügge, chairman of the Hygienic Institute at the University of Berlin, 64 – 78.

111 At least in the copy archived in the library of the Deutsches Museum in Munich.

112 Jaffé, "Forderung."

113 "Villenwohnung in der vierten Etage," *Bauwelt*, no. 66 (1910): 19 – 20.

114 "Luxuswohnungen im Berliner Westen," *Bauwelt*, no. 120 (1911): 23.

115 M.O., "Der Typ des Dachgarten-Hauses," *Bauwelt*, no. 122 (1911): 29 – 30.

116 Dölger, "Einfluss der Höhenlage," 452.

117 Quoted in Geist and Kürvers, *Berliner Mietshaus*, 373.

118 Gemünd, "Neuere Bestrebungen."

119 Dölger, "Einfluss der Höhenlage," 454.

120 Josef Redlich, *Hygiene, Bauordnung und Parzellierung* (Berlin: Ernst, 1914), 14.

121 *Pretty Woman*, directed by Garry Marshall (Touchstone Pictures/Silver Screen Partners IV, 1990).

122 Quoted in Geist and Kürvers, *Berliner Mietshaus*, 257.

123 Siegfried Ascher, *Die Wohnungsmiethen in Berlin von 1890 bis 1910: Eine statistische Untersuchung als Beitrag zur Theorie der Miethe* (Berlin: Heymann, 1918), 19.

124 Ibid., 125.

125 Ibid., 22.

126 Ibid., 22, 107.

127 Ibid., 22.

128 See especially Cromley, *Alone Together*; Hawes, *New York, New York*; and Ruttenbaum, *Mansions*.

129 Hawes, *New York, New York*, 35.

130 Ibid., 96.

131 Ibid.

132 Ibid., 198.

133 Ibid., 230.

134 He is said to have designed more than five hundred apartment houses. See ibid., 235.

135 Ruttenbaum, *Mansions*, 58; for the design of the facades, see the reproductions on 59–64.

136 See, for example, the entry "penthouse" in the 1929 edition of the *Encyclopaedia Britannica*, 494–95, where even "in modern usage" the term is applied to various kinds of rooftop appendages, including "water tanks, elevator machinery and occasionally living quarters." The first German lexographical recording of the concept is in the 1927 edition of the standard *Brockhaus Enzyklopädie*, 361, where it is defined as a "bungalow-like apartment on the flat rooftop of a multistory residential building."

137 Ruttenbaum, *Mansions*, 68.

138 Ibid., 69–71.

139 Hawes, *New York, New York*, 231.

140 Ibid.

141 See ibid., 221; and Hans-Ulrich Gumbrecht, *1926: Ein Jahr am Rand der Zeit* (Frankfurt am Main: Suhrkamp, 2001), 80–84.

142 The first issue of *Penthouse* was published in 1965.

143 Quoted in Johnson, *Roof Gardens*, 4.

144 See ibid., 8, 37, 78.

145 Ibid., 8.

146 Quoted in ibid., 27.

147 Ibid., 9; see also 37, 59, 110 on the elevators in other roof gardens.

148 Ibid., 4–5.

149 Ibid., 71.

150 Kellermann, *Tunnel*, 61.

151 Johnson, *Roof Gardens*, 59.

152 Kellermann, *Tunnel*, 47–48.

153 Ibid., 63.

154 See Hawes, *New York, New York*, 101, 133, 159.

155 See Walter Spickendorff, "Dachgärten und ihre Bodenkonstruktionen," *Bauwelt*, no. 2 (1913): 28–30.

156 "Eine Anregung," *Bauwelt*, no. 11 (1910): 12.

157 "Die brennende Frage der Dachgärten für Berlin," *Bauwelt*, no. 17 (1910): 20.

158 Wendt, "Dachgärten," 646.

159 W[endt], "Erleichterung," 114.

160 Wendt, "Dachgärten," 648.

161 Flügge, *Großstadtwohnungen*, 41.

162 Wendt, "Dachgärten," 648.

163 W[endt], "Erleichterung," 114.

164 See Johnson, *Roof Gardens*, 51–76, esp. 71–73.

165 See ibid., 89.

166 Jaffé, "Forderung," 5.

167 See, for example, the issues of *Bauwelt* from March and July 1922.

168 It states, "To alleviate the housing shortage, spaces in the cellar and the attic story whose use for long-term human residence is forbidden by the building code may be outfitted as apartments.   . The length of use of these apartments is limited to five years." See Willert, *Zusammenstellung*, 786.

169 See the detailed list of bylaws between 1918 and 1941 in Olaf Piechottka, *Dachraumnutzung—Städtebauliches Planungsinstrument zur Erhaltung und Verbesserung der Stadtstruktur* (Berlin: Kiepert, 1978), 36.

170 "Erlass vom 3. Januar 1921, betr. Errichtung von vielgeschossigen Bürohäusern," in *Volkswohlfahrt, Amtsblatt und Halbmonatsschrift des Preußischen Ministeriums für Volkswohlfahrt*, vol. 2 (Berlin, 1921), 39.

171 Max Jahn, *Handwörterbuch des Baurechts* (Leipzig: Jänecke, 1928), 129.

172 "Europahaus und Wohlfahrtsminister," *Zentralblatt der Bauverwaltung*, no. 7 (1928): 111.

173 See, for example, Neumann, *Hochhäuser*, 169; and Rainer Stommer and Dieter Mayer-Gürr, *Hochhaus: Der Beginn in Deutschland* (Marburg: Jonas, 1990), 244.

174 On this topic, see Neumann, *Hochhäuser*, passim; for example on p. 60, the decree published on July 25, 1934, in the *Zentralblatt der Bauverwaltung* demanding "the greatest restraint" in granting permission for new high-rises because of concern about aerial attacks. But Neumann also mentions that the discussion of the problem of protecting high-rises from aerial bombardment reached back to 1927, before the National Socialists came to power. See also Buff, *Bauordnung im Wandel*, 86: "From 1939 to 1948, normal construction activity ceased in Germany."

175 Berlin introduced a system of five "building classes" in 1925. The highest class continued to be subject to the limit of six stories, "unless special provisions have been made for a public, commercial, or factory building." *Bauordnung Berlin*, 10. Very similar language is in the *Münchner Baupolizeirecht und die*

Münchner Staffelbauordnung (Munich, Berlin, Leipzig: Schweitzer, 1927), 84n1.

176 *Bauordnung Berlin*, 11; almost identical wording in *Bauordnung für die Stadt München* (Munich, 1927), 84.

177 Roman Heiligenthal, *Rasse und Wohnung in der großen Agglomeration* (Heidelberg: Winter, 1937), 88. On this book, see also Geist and Kürvers, *Berliner Mietshaus*, 266.

178 A construction magazine described the first German residential high-rise in Düsseldorf in 1927: "The building contains 18 most elegant 6- and 7-room apartments with very large rooms, two passenger elevators, as well as all possible amenities." "Wohnhaus in Düsseldorf," *Baugilde*, no. 4 (1927): 179. On the two Düsseldorf high-rises built in 1929, see Oelmann, "Haus am Rheinufer," *Deutsche Bauzeitung*, supplement "Moderner Wohnbau" (1929): 13–18.

179 Musseleck, "Aufzug," 990.

180 "Mitteilungen," *Der Neubau: Halbmonatsschrift für Baukunst*, no. 2 (1926): 24.

181 *Ministerialamtsblatt*, 1051–54.

182 See, for example, *Bauordnung Berlin*, 232ff.: "Richtlinien für Hochhäuser" (Guidelines for high-rises). In the first nationwide building code for Germany, the *Musterbauordnung* (Model building code) of 1960, the provisions of these "guidelines" were integrated in various places, that for an elevator in "buildings with more than 5 stories above the ground floor," for example, in § 44, section 10. See *Einführung in die Musterbauordnung*, Part B, "Die Vorschriften im Einzelnen" (Recklinghausen: Kommunal-Verlag, 1960), 74.

183 *Ministerialamtsblatt*, 1054.

184 Ibid.

185 See, for example, Fritz, *Menschen in Büroarbeitsräumen*; Pélegrin-Genel, *Büro*; Albrecht, *On the Job*.

186 See Kurt Alsleben, *Büro und Großraum* (Quickborn: Schnelle, 1961); Eberhard Schnelle and Alfons Wankum, *Architekt und Organisator: Probleme und Methoden der Bürohausplanung* (Quickborn: Schnelle, 1965); as well as the other writings of the Quickborn Group of "office organizers" who are considered the inventors of the office landscape concept.

187 See Fritz, *Menschen in Büroarbeitsräumen*, 69–79; and Wiener, *Warenhaus*, 323.

188 Freytag, *Soll und Haben*, 28. Again, the English translation of 1858, available online from Project Gutenberg, is inaccurate and leaves out entire phrases and clauses of the original.

189 Ibid., 107.

190 See Equitable Life, *Hyde*, 119. On this historic date, see also Thomas Hine, "Office Intrigues: The Interior Life of Corporate

Culture," in Albrecht and Broikos, *On the Job*, 135; Logan, "Onward," 139; Eric Sundstrom, *Work Places: The Psychology of
the Physical Environment in Offices and Factories* (New York:
Cambridge University Press, 1986), 28; and Young, *Art and Enterprise*, 16.

191 Logan, "Onward," 140. Evidence that the Equitable Life also followed this practice in the 1860s is in Equitable Life, *Hyde*, 54.

192 See Young, *Art and Enterprise*, 39.

193 Quoted in ibid., 16.

194 See Hyde's memory of this struggle in Equitable Life, *Hyde*,
119 – 20: "It is a very singular fact that at the time the first Equitable Building was approaching completion there was not a
single elevator in New York in a structure devoted exclusively
to office purposes. All the members of the building committee,
except myself, were opposed to the introduction of elevators,
but finally consented to have one erected. It required quite a
struggle on my part to obtain their consent to put two in the
building."

195 See Mujica, *History*, 22.

196 Logan, "Onward," 140.

197 Ibid., 149; see also the examples for the conquest of the higher
stories in Robinson, "Tall Office Buildings," esp. 198 – 202.

198 Steffens, "Modern Business Building," 44.

199 Pélegrin-Genel, *Büro*, 166.

200 Young, *Art and Enterprise*, 40.

201 See ibid., 35.

202 Schuyler, "Evolution," 425.

203 A letter of February 11, 1898, quoted in Young, *Art and Enterprise*, 52.

204 Quoted in ibid., 55.

205 See Logan, "Onward," 152.

206 Quoted in ibid.

207 Ibid., 153.

208 Ibid., 156.

209 See the statistics in Steffens, "Modern Business Building," 59.

210 Shultz and Simmons, *Offices*, 207.

211 See Fritz, *Menschen in Büroarbeitsräumen*, 69, on the increasingly hierarchical structuring of counting houses in the early
nineteenth century: "The more screened-off and concealed a
workplace is, the higher the prestige."

212 Joachim Ritter, "Landschaft: Zur Funktion des Ästhetischen
in der modernen Gesellschaft," in *Subjektivität* (Frankfurt am
Main: Suhrkamp, 1974), 141 – 61; on Petrarch, see also Dieter
Groh and Ruth Groh, "Petrarca und der Mont Ventoux," in *Die
Außenwelt der Innenwelt: Zur Kulturgeschichte der Natur*, vol. 2
(Frankfurt am Main: Suhrkamp, 1996), 17 – 82.

213 Dölger, "Einfluss der Höhenlage," 454 (emphasis in original).

214 Quoted in Equitable Life, *Hyde*, 119.

215 Daniel Defert, "Foucault, der Raum und die Architekten," in *Politics-Poetics: Das Buch zur Documenta* (Ostfildern: Cantz, 1997), 281.

216 Marchand, *Advertising*, 238–47.

217 Ibid., 238–39.

218 Ibid., 241.

219 Ibid., 242.

220 See, for example, "Das Geschäftshaus Fr. Hahn in Berlin," *Bauwelt*, no. 115 (1911): 51.

221 See A. Wedemeyer, "Groß-Kraftwerk Klingenberg in Berlin-Rummelsberg," *Deutsche Bauzeitung*, nos. 1–2 (1928): 18–26.

222 See Hans Bahn, "Das Hochhaus des Hannoverschen Anzeigers in Hannover," *Deutsche Bauzeitung*, no. 63 (1928): 537–44.

223 See "Verwaltungsgebäude des Lenz and Co.-Konzerns, Berlin," *Deutsche Bauzeitung*, nos. 1–2 (1929): 8–12.

224 See "Das Tagblatt-Turmhaus in Stuttgart," *Deutsche Bauzeitung*, nos. 1–2 (1929): 13–18.

225 See "Magdeburgs erstes Hochhaus," *Deutsche Bauzeitung*, nos. 31–32 (1931): 185–90.

226 See Hertlein, "Wernerwerk"; and Siemens, *Carl Friedrich zu Siemens*.

227 See Zimmermann, *Von der Wohnungsfrage*; on the design competition, see "Verwaltungsgebäude I.G. Farbenindustrie A.-G., Frankfurt am Main," *Baugilde*, no. 22 (1928): 1663–66.

228 See Münter, "Verwaltungsgebäude"; and Lukasz Krzywka, "Das Hochhaus der Städtischen Sparkasse am Breslauer Ring," in *Hochhäuser für Breslau*, ed. Jerzy Ilkosz and Beate Störtkuhl (Delmenhorst: Aschenbeck und Holstein Verlag, 1997).

229 Münter, "Verwaltungsgebäude," 764.

230 See Regina Stephan, *Studien zu Waren- und Geschäftshäusern Erich Mendelssohns in Deutschland* (Munich: Tuduv, 1992), 69.

231 Siemens, *Carl Friedrich zu Siemens*, 256.

232 Hertlein, "Wernerwerk," 1510.

233 Hermann Seeger, *Bürohäuser der privaten Wirtschaft* (Leipzig: Gebhardt, 1933), 11.

234 See Badische Anilin, *Hochhaus der BASF*.

235 See Jürgen Joedicke, "Bürogebäude und Automobilmuseum der Daimler-Benz AG, Stuttgart-Unterrürkheim," *Deutsche Bauzeitung*, no. 5 (1962): 339–78.

236 See Farbenfabriken Bayer AG, *Bayer-Hochhaus*.

237 See Peters, *Verwaltungsgebäude*.

238 Badische Anilin, *Das Hochhaus der BASF*, 11.

239 Ibid., 13.

240 See Farbenfabriken Bayer AG, *Bayer-Hochhaus*, 23.

NOTES

241 Ibid., 24.

242 Siegfried Schulze and Carl Krause, *Bürobauten* (Stuttgart and Bern: Krämer, 1967), 58.

243 Ibid., 59.

244 See Friedrich Wilhelm Kraemer, "Das Großraumbüro, eine neue Bauaufgabe unserer Zeit," *Deutsche Bauzeitung*, no. 4 (1966), esp. the cross-section of the BP building, 291. See also "Engerer Bauwettbewerb für den Neubau eines Verwaltugs-gebäudes der BP Benzi- und Petroleum-Aktiengesellschaft, Hamburg, 1964," *Deutsche Bauzeitung*, no. 10 (1964): 771: "The executive floor is generously proportioned in accordance with the importance of this group of rooms."

245 Wolfgang Schnelle, *Hierarchische Ordnung im Büro: Rang- und Gruppenprobleme in Verwaltungen* (Quickborn: Schnelle, 1961), 28.

246 Peters, *Verwaltungsgebäude*, 31.

247 Ibid., 37.

NOTES TO CHAPTER 3

1 Generlich et al., *Fahrstuhlführer*, 1.

2 Ibid.

3 "Polizei-Verordnung" (1893), 259. A commentary in the official gazette of the Berlin building inspector states that the regulations were "the first of their kind issued in Prussia." Garbe, "Ueber die Einrichtung und den Betrieb von Aufzügen (Fahrstühlen)," *Zentralblatt der Bauverwaltung*, 1893, 164. Simmen and Drepper are mistaken in stating that the earliest Prussian elevator regulations are from 1884 (*Fahrstuhl*, 141).

4 *Polizei-Verordnung* (1908), 32.

5 Hintz, *Handbuch*, 60–61.

6 Ibid., 62.

7 Fürst, "Aufzüge," 81.

8 Ibid.

9 Quoted in Simmen and Drepper, *Fahrstuhl*, 55.

10 *Instructionen für Fahrstuhlführer: Auszug aus der Polizei-Verordnung vom 6. September 1898 nebst zusätzlichen Anweisungen* (Berlin: Siemens, 1900), 4.

11 Mann, *Confessions*, 149.

12 Ibid., 167.

13 Ibid., 168.

14 See "Examination of Elevator-Runners"; and "Improving the Control over Elevators in New York," *American Architect and Building News*, no. 1499 (1904): 89.

15 "Elevator Inconveniences," *American Architect and Building News*, no. 814 (1891): 61–62.

16 See the description of the mechanism in George Edward

Harding, "Electric Elevators," *American Architect and Building News*, no. 983 (1894): 33.

17 Maurice Saglio, "City Apartment Houses in Paris," *Architectural Record*, April 1896, 352.

18 Thus, in retrospect, Hintz, *Handbuch*, 65.

19 See Ernst, "Entwurf."

20 P. Schwehm, *Elektrisch betriebene Aufzüge, ihr Wesen, Anlage und Betrieb* (Hannover: Jänecke, 1901), 41.

21 "Sitzungen der Bezirksvereine: Lausitzer Bezirksverein. Sitzung vom 25. April 1903," *Zeitschrift des Vereins deutscher Ingenieure*, 1903, 1535.

22 Drews, "Moderne Aufzüge," 625.

23 Carl Flohr, *Fest-Schrift zur Feier des 25jährigen Geschäftsjubiläums am 2. Juli 1904* (Berlin: Maschinenfabrik Carl Flohr, 1904), 14.

24 The clearest description of the control system is in Drews, "Moderne Aufzüge," 626–28.

25 See "Fahrstuhl für Dienstboten."

26 *Polizei-Verordnung* (1908), 14–15; for the restriction of this regulation to apartment houses, see the "Ausführungsanweisung" (Instructions for implementation) of § 32 in ibid., 33.

27 Ibid., 32.

28 *Abänderung der Polizeiverordnung vom 30. Mai 1913 über die Einrichtung und den Betrieb von Aufzügen (Fahrstühlen), (Aufzugsverordnung): Polizeiverordnung vom 4. Januar 1917* (Berlin: Seydel, 1917), 7.

29 H. Jahr, ed., *Polizeiverordnung (Musterverordnung zur Aufzugsverordnung von 1926) über die Einrichtung und den Betrieb von Aufzügen sowie Technische Grundsätze für den Bau von Aufzügen* (Hagen in Westfalen: Hammerschmidt, 1926), 2–3.

30 "Hebel- oder Druckknopf-Steuerung bei Personenaufzügen," *Zentralblatt der Bauverwaltung* 82 (1907): 536.

31 See *Fahrstuhlführer-Prüfung: Fragen, welche gelegentlich der Fahrstuhlführer-Prüfung vom Sachverständigen gestellt werden, und Beantwortung dieser Fragen* (Berlin: Seydel, 1917).

32 Generlich et al., *Fahrstuhlführer*, 21.

33 Kafka, *Amerika*, 145.

34 Anton de Nora, *Der Liftboy: Novellen, Grotesken und Skizzen* (Leipzig: Staakmann, 1920), 7 (emphasis added).

35 "Examination of Elevator-Runners."

36 Fürst, "Aufzüge," 82.

37 Ibid.

38 Maar and Heidelbach, *Aufzug*, n.p.

39 Blumenberg, "Lebenswelt," 35.

40 Mayer, "Ueber Auslösung," 413.

41 Benjamin, "On Some Motifs in Baudelaire," 328.

42 The push button leads Roland Barthes to say in his book on photography that "the photographer's organ is not his eye (which terrifies me) but his finger." *Camera Lucida*, 15.

43 See Simmen and Drepper, *Fahrstuhl*, 168.

44 Frank, *Feuerwehrbuch*, 36.

45 Ibid., 37.

46 Ibid.

47 Ibid., 38.

48 F. A. Förster, "Die Druckknopfsteuerung als Wirtschaftlichkeitsfaktor," *Der graphische Betrieb*, 1929, 257.

49 Blumenberg, "Lebenswelt," 36.

50 Frank, Feuerwehrbuch, 41.

51 Hugo Koch, "Fenster, Thüren und andere bewegliche Wandverschlüsse," in *Handbuch der Architektur*, ed. Josef Durm et al., vol. 3, no. 1 (Darmstadt, 1896), 333.

52 Mayer, "Ueber Auslösung," 416.

53 Ibid.

54 "Das aktuelle Lexikon: Atomkoffer," *Süddeutsche Zeitung*, December 28, 1991, 2.

55 Blumenberg, "Lebenswelt," 36.

56 See James Gleick, *Faster—The Acceleration of Just About Everything* (New York: Vintage, 2000), 30.

57 James Gleick, "Himmelfahrtskommando," *SZ-Magazin* 9 (2000): 45.

58 See Florian Felix Weyh, *Die ferne Haut: Wider die Berührungsangst* (Berlin: Aufbau-Verlag, 1999), 68.

NOTES TO CHAPTER 4

1 See Geist and Kürvers, *Berliner Mietshaus*, 244; although this word occurred in the Berlin building code for the first time in 1853, the encyclopedic dictionary of the Grimm brothers has a citation from Goethe, who died in 1832.

2 Willert, *Zusammenstellung*, 129.

3 Josef von Kerschensteiner, "Die Hygiene der Treppen und des Treppenhauses," *Deutsche medizinische Wochenschrift* 45 (1893): 1140.

4 Emmerich and Recknagel, "Wohnung," 428.

5 Ibid., 428–29.

6 Ibid., 429.

7 Ibid.

8 Ibid., 431.

9 Hobrecht, *Gesundheitspflege*, 16.

10 Ibid., 14.

11 Ibid., 14–15.

12 Ibid., 16.

13 Wasserfuhr, "Gesundheitsschädlichkeiten," 196.

14 Ibid., 197.
15 Herman Melville, *Bartleby, the Scrivener*, in *Great Short Works of Herman Melville* (New York: HarperCollins, 2004), 68.
16 Wilhelm Gemünd, "Die Abortfrage," *Zeitschrift für Wohnungswesen* 4 (1906): 47–49.
17 See Josef Redlich, "Baupolizeiverordnung für die Stadt Düsseldorf," *Zeitschrift für Wohnungswesen* 7 (1908): 92–94, who reports on one of the first German draft laws of this kind.
18 Weisbach, "Wohnhäuser," 39.
19 See the statistics in Herbert Croly, "The Contemporary New York Residence," *Architectural Record*, 1902, 705; and the commentary in Charlotte Perkins Gilman, "The Passing of the Home in the Great American Cities," *Cosmopolitan*, December 1904, 140, that private houses are "no longer built in numbers worth mentioning compared with apartment-houses."
20 See Cromley, *Alone Together*; Hawes, *New York, New York*; Ruttenbaum, *Mansions*; and Stern et al., *New York 1880*. The following pages profited especially from the first two.
21 "A Revolution in Living," *New York Times*, June 3, 1878, 4.
22 Stern et al., *New York 1880*, 543.
23 "Apartment-Houses—II," *American Architect and Building News*, no. 777 (1890): 98.
24 Blanke, "Cliff-Dwellers," 355.
25 Carroll, "Apartment-Houses," 532.
26 "Houses on the European Plan," 1.
27 Vaux, "Architecture."
28 Ibid.
29 "Houses on the European Plan," 3.
30 Ibid.
31 Carroll, "Apartment-Houses," 530, 531.
32 "Apartment-Houses and Tenement-Houses."
33 See Lawrence Veiller, *Tenement House Legislation in New York, 1852–1900* (Albany: Brandow, 1900), 147–48: "The first tenement-house act defined a tenement-house as any building which was occupied as the home or residence of more than three families living independently of each other and doing their cooking upon the premises; or a building occupied by two families or more upon one floor, so living and cooking and having a common right in the public parts of the building, that is, the halls, stairways, yards, etc."
34 "Apartment-Houses and Tenement-Houses."
35 See "New Building Law Code," *New York Times*, September 6, 1899, 12.
36 Carroll, "Apartment-Houses," 530.
37 Hubert et al., "New York Flats and French Flats," 56.
38 Ibid., 57–58.

39 Ibid., 58.

40 Ibid. (emphasis in original).

41 Ibid., 55.

42 "Houses on the European Plan," 3.

43 Hubert et al., "New York Flats and French Flats," 58.

44 "The Cooperative-Apartment Craze of a Score of Years Ago," *American Architect and Building News*, no. 1383 (1902): 97.

45 "The Radical Evil of Life in Apartment-Houses," *American Architect and Building News*, no. 1619 (1907): 1.

46 Ibid.

47 Ibid.

48 Ibid.

49 See Gray, *Ascending Rooms*, 62.

50 See documentation and Benno Wagner's brilliant commentary on the incident in Franz Kafka, *Amtliche Schriften*, ed. Klaus Hermsdorf and Benno Wagner (Frankfurt am Main: Fischer, 2004), 721–41, 963–71.

51 Howells, *Elevator*, 304.

52 Ibid.

53 As quoted in Gray, *Ascending Rooms*, 53.

54 Gutermuth, "Mitteilungen," 774.

55 Flohr Maschinenfabrik, *Personen- und Lastenaufzüge*, 14.

56 See Gray, *Ascending Rooms*, 80.

57 See Carroll, "Apartment-Houses," 533.

58 "French Flats: The Parisian System of Living," *New York Times*, December 26, 1876, 2.

59 "Fast Time in Elevators: Ascending Nine Flights in Thirty Seconds," *New York Times*, September 3, 1882, 12.

60 Ibid.

61 See the quote from the New York Building Act in "The New Building Code," *New York Times*, September 7, 1899, 3: "In every building now erected,   . at least one passenger elevator shall be kept in readiness for immediate use by the Fire Department, during all hours of the night and day, including holidays and Sundays."

62 Criticism of this regulation was not raised until the late 1920s. The author of a 1928 article entitled "The Elevator in the Modern Apartment Building" demands "doing away with the key that opens the doors to the shaft. It should be replaced by a simple door so that anyone can use the elevator, including people who do not live in the building." Musseleck, "Aufzug," 991.

63 See *New York Regular Session Laws 1885*, 108th Legislature (New York, 1885), 763. This regulation did not apply to hotels and office buildings.

64 Hawes, *New York, New York*, 65.

65 "A Modern Apartment House," *Plumber and Sanitary Engin*eer, February 1880, 106.

66 "New York Building Department to Exercise Supervision over Elevators," *Sanitary Engineer* 8 (October 1885): 369.

67 "Sitzungsberichte der Bezirksvereine: Berliner Bezirksverein," *Zeitschrift des Vereins deutscher Ingenieure*, 1894, 622.

68 The first American building to be equipped with indirect-hydraulic elevators was the 1878 Boreel Building in New York; see Thomas E. Brown, "Passenger Elevators—I," *American Architect and Building News*, no. 1507 (1904): 51. In Germany, this type of elevator was introduced by the Otis Company in the mid-1880s; see Reuleaux, *Gutachten*.

69 Werner von Siemens, "Der elektrische Aufzug," *Elektrotechnische Zeitschrift*, November 1880, 373.

70 In the words of an 1890 sales brochure quoted in Gray, *Ascending Rooms*, 172.

71 Flohr Maschinenfabrik, *Personen- und Lastenaufzüge*, 11.

72 Ibid., 43.

73 Schivelbusch, *Railway Journey*, 115n7.

74 "Elevator Sickness," *Scientific American*, July 12, 1890, 17.

75 Ibid.

76 Ibid.

77 Schivelbusch, *Railway Journey*, 165.

78 Ibid, 166.

79 Thomas Katz, "Lehren aus dem amerikanischen Fahrstuhlbau," quoted in Simmen and Drepper, *Fahrstuhl*, 117.

80 Foucault, *Archaeology*, 52–53 (emphasis in original).

81 Schivelbusch, *Railway Journey*, 151.

82 Consider, for instance, the intensity of debate about the danger of radiation from cell phones. Families have moved away from locations near power transmission lines or broadcasting towers for the same reason. It is highly probable that researchers in the future will read about these things with the same ironic smile with which we react to the behavior of early elevator passengers. And yet one cannot dismiss these contemporary complaints as pure delusions.

83 Radkau, *Zeitalter der Nervosität*, 14.

84 "The Elevator Sickness," *Washington Post*, October 14, 1894, 17.

85 Westphal, "Agoraphobie," 138.

86 Ibid. Westphal mentions a Viennese doctor named Benedict who reported a case of "Platzschwindel" (spatial vertigo) as early as 1870 (151).

87 Ibid., 154.

88 Ibid., 143.

89 Ball, "Claustrophobie," 378.

90 See ibid., 380: "I've seen this patient only twice."

91 Ibid., 386.

92 Müller, *Handbuch*, v.

93 See especially Anson Rabinbach, *The Human Motor: Energy, Fatigue, and the Origins of Modernity* (New York: Basic, 1990); and Radkau, *Zeitalter der Nervosität.*

94 See Beard, *Neurasthenia,* 5, where the German translator states in his foreword that Beard's earliest essays on the topic were published in 1869.

95 Müller, *Handbuch,* 33.

96 Beard, *American Nervousness,* vi (emphasis in original).

97 Ibid.

98 Ibid., 146.

99 Müller, *Handbuch,* 38.

100 Ibid., 37.

101 H. Emminghaus, *Psychopathologie: Zur Einführung in das Studium der Geistesstörungen* (Leipzig, 1878), 80.

102 Westphal, "Agoraphobie," 148.

103 Vidler, *Warped Space,* 25.

104 Ibid., 29.

105 Quoted in ibid.

106 Camillo Sitte, *Der Städtebau nach seinen künstlerischen Grundsätzen,* 3rd ed. (Vienna: Graeser, 1900), 53; see also Vidler, *Warped Space,* 265–66.

107 Vincent [pseud.], "Confessions of an Agoraphobic Victim," *American Journal of Psychology* 30 (1919): 295–99.

108 Benjamin, "Charles Baudelaire," 191.

109 Hans Reinecker, *Phobien: Agoraphobien, soziale und spezifische Phobien* (Göttingen: Hogrefe/Verlag für Psychologie, 1993), 31.

110 Asch, "Claustrophobia," 716.

111 See Clarence P. Oberndorf, "Analysis of a Claustrophobian," *Medical Record: A Weekly Journal of Medicine and Surgery* 88 (1915): 350.

112 See Betram D. Lewin, "Claustrophobia," *Psychoanalytic Quarterly* 4 (1935): 228; and Edwin R. Eisler, "Regression in a Case of Multiple Phobia," *Psychoanalytic Quarterly* 6 (1937): 87.

113 William B. Terhune, "The Phobic Syndrome: A Study of Eighty-Six Patients with Phobic Reactions," *Archives of Neurology and Psychiatry* 62 (1949): 165.

114 Mayer, "Aufzüge," 177.

115 See Paul Virilio, "Das Pannenmuseum," in *Ereignislandschaft* (Munich: Hanser, 1998), 93.

116 "In an Elevator."

117 Howells, *Elevator,* 312 (emphasis in original).

118 See Schivelbusch, *Railway Journey,* 134–49.

119 See English Bagby, "The Etiology of Phobia," *Journal of Abnormal Psychology and Social Psychology* 17 (1922): 16–18.

120 See Emanuel Miller, "The Analysis of Agora-Claustrophobia: A Passive Anamnesis," *British Journal of Medical Psychology* 10 (1930): 253–67.

121 Asch, "Claustrophobia," 712, calls it a "classic article."

122 See Rainer Hank, "Topik und Topographie: Seelenlandschaft und Stadtlandschaft im Wien der Jahrhundertwende," in *Die Großstadt als "Text,"* ed. Manfred Smuda (Munich: Fink, 1992), 217–38.

123 Beard, *Neurasthenia*, 41.

124 See Ball, "Claustrophobie," 385.

125 Raymond Gehl, "Indecision and Claustrophobia," *International Journal of Psycho-Analysis* 54 (1973): 51.

126 See Hawes, *New York, New York*, 92–98.

127 Cromley, *Alone Together*, 154; see also Birmingham, *Life at the Dakota*, 37.

128 Hawes, *New York, New York*, 237.

129 Ibid., 205; see also Ruttenbaum, *Mansions*, 130ff., on similar arrangements at the Beresford and the San Remo on the Upper West Side.

130 Virginia Pope, "New York Now Has Mansions in Flats," *New York Times Magazine*, June 27, 1926, 9.

131 Ibid.

132 Hawes, *New York, New York*, 238.

133 See ibid.

134 Bernhard Siegert, *Relais: Geschicke der Literatur als Epoche der Post* (Berlin: Brinkmann and Bose, 1993), 127.

135 Cromley, *Alone Together*, 254–55; see also Birmingham, *Life at the Dakota*, 37, who calls the four service elevators "a novelty in themselves in the 1880s."

136 Ernst Lesser, "Tausend Mark pro Zimmer," *Bauwelt* 12 (1910): 9.

137 "Ein moderner Wohnpalast," *Bauwelt* 34 (1910): 20. A similar description had appeared two issues earlier: "Das Tausend-Mark-Zimmer," *Bauwelt* 32 (1910): 15.

138 "Fahrstuhl für Dienstboten."

139 Ibid.

140 Ibid.

141 Weisbach, "Wohnhäuser," 39.

142 Ibid., 41.

143 See the illustrations in Müller, *Dienstbare Geister*, 184; see also Peter Wiek, "Das großstädtische Etagenhaus: Vergleiche zwischen Hamburg, Berlin und Wien," *Österreichische Zeitschrift für Kunst und Denkmalpflege*, 1982, 156: "The stairs for servants and delivery men . are a matter of course in all 'grand' apartment houses in Berlin."

144 See the extensive bibliography in Müller, *Dienstbare Geister*.

145 "Apartment-Houses," *New York Times*, September 7, 1870, 4.

146 Ernst, "Entwurf," 1287.

147 The assumed average weight of elevator passengers has remained the same for almost a century, but it was not always so, as an 1884 article by Adolf Ernst shows. For a hydraulic elevator in a Berlin hotel, "a carrying capacity of five persons = 300 kg is assumed." Adolf Ernst, "Hebezeuge: Hydraulische Aufzüge," *Zeitschrift des Vereins deutscher Ingenieure*, 1884, 566. A good twenty years before the first unified legal regulations, Prussian elevator passengers were fifteen kilograms lighter on average.

148 Hedda Adlon, *Hotel Adlon: Das Haus, in dem die Welt zu Gast war* (Munich: Kindler, 1955).

149 So declared Katharina Schratt's niece decades later in an interview quoted by Simmen and Drepper, *Fahrstuhl*, 134. In their book, Schratt's move to this apartment is said to have been in 1890, but biographies of the actress date it to 1908. See Joan Haslip, *Die Freundin des Kaisers: Franz Joseph und die Schauspielerin Katharina Schratt* (Stuttgart: Engelhorn, 1985), 361; and Georg Markus, *Katharina Schratt: Die heimliche Frau des Kaisers* (Vienna: Amalthea, 1982), 220.

150 See Goodwin, *Otis*, 111.

151 Zimmermann, "Normen für Personen- und Krankenaufzüge: Aufgestellt vom Normenausschuß der Deutschen Industrie," *Baugilde* 5 (1927): 252. See also Deutscher Normenausschuss, *DIN Normblattverzeichnis: Stand der Normung Herbst 1927* (Berlin, 1927).

152 Jürgen Freiherr von Kruedener, *Die Rolle des Hofes im Absolutismus* (Stuttgart: Fischer, 1973), 60–61.

153 Walter Benjamin, "The Work of Art in the Age of Mechanical Reproduction," in *Illuminations*, trans. Harry Zohn (New York: Schocken, 1969), 222.

154 Bayer, "Treppenstudie," 258. Apropos the following analysis, see also Mielke, *Treppen*, 131, 212–14.

155 Bayer, "Treppenstudie," 258.

156 Mielke, *Treppen*, 214.

157 On *Zeremonialwissen*, or the science of ceremonials, see Milos Vec, *Zeremonialwissenschaft im Fürstenstaat: Studien zur juristischen und politischen Theorie absolutistischer Herrschaftsrepräsentation* (Frankfurt am Main: Klostermann, 1998); and Paulmann, *Pomp*.

158 Harald Keller, "Das Treppenhaus im deutschen Schloß- und Klosterbau des Barock," quoted in Jansen, "Grand Escalier," 20.

159 Julius Bernhard von Rohr, *Einleitung zur Ceremoniel-Wissenschaft der grossen Herren*, ed. Monika Schlechte (Leipzig: Edition Leipzig, 1989), 365.

160 Jansen, "Grand Escalier," 14; for the following discussion, see

also Peter Burke, *The Fabrication of Louis XIV* (New Haven: Yale University Press, 1992), 75–78, 86f., 158, 172.

161 Ibid., 55; on the design of the Grand Escalier, see also Karl Möseneder, *Zeremoniell und monumentale Poesie: Die "Entrée solennelle" Ludwigs XIV. 1660 in Paris* (Berlin: Gebr. Mann, 1983), 203–4.

162 Ibid., 83.

163 See Paulmann, *Pomp*, 195: "A general rule for the meeting of monarchs and state visits was never published in the nineteenth century." At the court in Vienna, they still made do (as the Lord High Steward wrote to his French colleague in 1854) with variations of the "elaborate protocols . that have been followed on all ceremonial occasions continuously since the year 1652" (298).

164 "Preliminary Draft of How His Majesty the King of England Would Like to Be Received during His Imminent Arrival" (circa September, 1821), unpublished document quoted by Paulmann, *Pomp*, 228.

165 Ibid.

166 Mielke, *Treppen*, 212.

167 Gotthardt Frühsorge, "Vom Hof des Kaisers zum 'Kaiserhof': Über das Ende des Ceremoniells als gesellschaftliches Ordnungsmuster," *Euphorion* 3 (1984): 262.

168 Morehouse, *Waldorf-Astoria*, 179.

169 Elgin Burroughs, "Elevator Etiquette at Washington," *Harper's Weekly* 4 (1910): 31.

170 Ibid.

171 "If there is a mythology of modernity, the place from which it is narrated and to which it is tied is the city." Lothar Müller, "Die Großstadt als Ort der Moderne: Über Georg Simmel," in Scherpe, *Unwirklichkeit*, 14.

172 For more recent studies, see Scherpe, *Unwirklichkeit*; Susanne Hauser, *Der Blick auf die Stadt: Semiotische Untersuchungen zur literarischen Wahrnehmung bis 1910* (Berlin: Reimer, 1990); Christof Forderer, *Die Großstadt im Roman: Berliner Großstadtdarstellungen zwischen Naturalismus und Moderne* (Wiesbaden: Deutscher Universitäts Verlag, 1992); Becker, *Urbanität*; and Roskothen, *Verkehr*.

173 Baudelaire, *Painter*, 13.

174 Hermann Doetsch, *Flüchtigkeit: Archäologie einer modernen Ästhetik bei Baudelaire und Proust* (Tübingen: Narr, 2004), 1.

175 There is an English translation that contains some inaccuracies: Peter Altenberg, "Elevator," in *Telegrams of the Soul*, trans. Peter Wortsman (New York: Archipelago, 2005), 79; see also Gruber, "Yankee."

176 Goffmann, *Relations*, 30, 32.

177 Ibid., 32.

178 Christian Bock, "Im Fahrstuhl," in *Die Luftschaukel*, ed. Wilmond Haacke (Berlin, 1939), 50–51.

179 Ibid.

180 See Stefan Hirschauer, "Die Praxis der Fremdheit und die Minimierung von Anwesenheit: Eine Fahrstuhlfahrt," *Soziale Welt* 50 (1999): 221–46.

181 Umberto Eco, *Einführung in die Semiotik* (Munich: Fink, 1972), 344.

182 See Karl Gutzkow, *Die Ritter vom Geiste*, vol. 1 (Berlin, 1876), iv-v (foreword to the first edition): "The old novel presented the sequence of artfully intertwined incidents.   . The new novel is the novel of simultaneity." See also the foreword to the third edition: "People could understand [the concept of the 'novel of simultaneity'] if they would think of a drawing of a mine or a warship in cross-section: the simultaneity of lives existing side by side in hundreds of rooms and cabins, invisible to each other but visible to the outside observer as a unity" (ix).

183 Gerhard Hoffmann, *Raum, Situation, erzählte Wirklichkeit: Poetologische und historische Studien zum englischen und amerikanischen Roman* (Stuttgart: Metzler, 1978), 18–19.

184 Volker Klotz, *Die erzählte Stadt: Ein Sujet als Herausforderung des Romans von Lesage bis Döblin* (Munich: Hanser, 1969), 430.

185 Nabokov, *Mary*, 30.

186 Ibid., 2–3.

187 Ibid., 3.

188 Fechter, *Ruck*, 234.

189 See ibid., 99 and 297.

190 Ibid., 489.

191 Hailey, *Hotel*, 40.

192 Ibid., 76.

193 Ibid., 326.

194 Ibid., 373.

195 Nicholson Baker, *The Mezzanine* (New York: Weidenfeld and Nicholson, 1986), 76.

196 Billy Wilder and I. A. L. Diamond, screenplay for *The Apartment*, directed by Billy Wilder (Panavision, 1959), http://www.daily-script.com/scripts/apartment.html.

197 Malle's film changes elements of the novel's ending.

198 On the concept of a non-place, see Marc Augé, *Orte und Nicht-Orte: Vorüberlegungen zu einer Ethnologie der Einsamkeit* (Frankfurt am Main: Fischer, 1994).

199 Calef, *Fahrstuhl*, 186.

200 Ibid., 34.

201 *Some Like It Hot*, directed by Billy Wilder (United Artists, 1959).

202 *The Secret of My Success*, directed by Herbert Ross (Universal, 1986).

203 Oskar Bie, *Der Technische Sinn*, cited in Gruber, "Yankee," 91.

204 A Hollywood movie like *Sleepless in Seattle* (1993) exploits this dramaturgic similarity in its final shot, as the elevator doors of the Empire State Building close.

205 "In an Elevator," *Harper's Weekly*, May 1875, 362.

206 Howells, *The Elevator*, 304.

207 Ibid., 305.

208 Ibid., 308.

209 Ibid., 312.

210 *Abwärts*, directed by Carl Schenkel (Laura/Mutoskop/Dieter Geissler Filmproduktion, 1984).

211 Simmen and Drepper, *Fahrstuhl*, 149.

212 Boccaccio, *Decameron*, 184ff. (Third Day, Third Tale) and 416 ff (Seventh Day, Fifth Tale).

213 See the illustrations in Alfred Wiesenhütter, "Beichtstuhl," in *Reallexikon zur deutschen Kunstgeschichte*, ed. Otto Schmitt, vol. 2 (Stuttgart: Metzler, 1948), 183–99. On the history of the confessional, see Schlombs, *Entwicklung des Beichtstuhls*; Max Tauch, *Der Beichtstuhl in den katholischen Kirchen des deutschen Barock* (Bonn: Rheinische Friedrich-Wilhelms-Universität, 1969); Franz Kohlschein, "Beichtstuhl," in *Lexikon für Theologie und Kirche*, vol. 2, rev. ed. (Freiburg im Breisgau: Herder, 1994), 162; Schick, "Außerhalb des Beichtstuhles"; E. Jombart, "Confessional," in *Dictionnaire de Droit Canonique*, vol. 4 (Paris: Letouzey, 1949), 63–66; Salome Zajadacz-Hastenrath, *Das Beichtgestühl der Antwerpener St. Paulskirche und der Barockbeichtstuhl in den südlichen Niederlanden* (Brussels: Arcade, 1970); and John Bossy, "The Social History of Confession in the Age of Reformation," *Transactions of the Royal Historical Society*, Fifth Series, vol. 25 (1975): 21–38.

214 Schlombs, *Entwicklung des Beichtstuhls*, 37.

215 Charles Borromeo, *Instructionem fabricae ecclesiasticae et superlectilis ecclesiasticae libri duo*, chap. 23, quoted in Schlombs, *Entwicklung des Beichtstuhls*, 134.

216 Schick, "Außerhalb des Beichtstuhles," 212.

217 In this sense, Norbert Elias's reflections on the "civilizing process" can be related to the history of the confessional. One of the central elements of his extensive study is his attention to space and the shifting border between the visible and the hidden. "It will be seen again and again how characteristic of the whole process that we call civilization is this movement of segregation, this hiding 'behind the scenes' of what has become distasteful" (Elias, *Civilizing Process*, 121). It is no surprise that the confessional box goes back to the same century

as the clearest shift in Elias's "threshold of embarrassment" and it is evidence of the truth of his observation. In an epoch of marked growth in the sense of shame, the confessional ensures the concealment of affect.

218 Heinrich Klee, *Die Beichte: Eine historisch-kritische Untersuchung* (Frankfurt am Main, 1828), 309–10.

219 On the discussion of the incompatibility of the telephone and confession, see Alfred E. Hierold, "Beichte per Telefon? Bemerkungen zum 'Ort für das Bußsakrament,'" in *Fides et Ius: Festschrift für Georg May zum 65. Geburtstag*, ed. Winfried Aymans et al. (Regensburg: Pustet, 1991), 163–76. On the ongoing debate about confession on the Internet, see articles such as "Vatikan wünscht keine Online-Beichte," *Süddeutsche Zeitung*, June 6, 2001, 16, where the American archbishop is quoted as saying that confession must continue to "always take place in the sacramental framework of a personal encounter."

220 Gerhard Kraus and Gerhard Müller, eds., *Theologische Realenzyklopädie*, vol. 5 (Berlin: de Gruyter, 1980), 430.

221 Original screenplay by Nora Ephron and Delia Ephron at http://sfy.ru/?script=youve_got_mail.

222 See Reinhard Messner, ed., "Sakramentliche Feiern: Feiern der Umkehr und Versöhnung," in *Handbuch der Liturgiewissenschaft*, ed. Hans Berhard Meyer et al., pt. 7.2 I/2 (Regensburg: Pustet, 1992).

223 Georg Simmel, *Philosophie des Geldes*, vol. 6 of *Complete Works* (Frankfurt am Main: Suhrkamp, 1989), 665. See also Lothar Müller, "Die Großstadt als Ort der Moderne: Über Georg Simmel," in Scherpe, *Unwirklichkeit*, 14–36.

224 Helmut Lethen, *Verhaltenslehre der Kälte: Lebensversuche zwischen den Kriegen* (Frankfurt am Main: Suhrkamp, 1994), 45 (emphasis added).

225 Ibid.

BIBLIOGRAPHY

Albrecht, Donald, and Chrysanthe B. Broikos, eds. *On the Job: Design and the American Office.* New York: Princeton Architectural Press, 2000.

"Apartment-Houses and Tenement-Houses." *American Architect and Building News*, no. 111 (1878): 45.

Aristotle, *Poetics*, London: Penguin, 2012.

Asch, Stuart S. "Claustrophobia and Depression." *Journal of the American Psychoanalytical Association* 14 (1966): 711–29.

Bachelard, Gaston. *The Poetics of Space.* Trans. Maria Jolas. Boston: Beacon, 1994.

Badische Anilin und Soda-Fabrik AG. *Das Hochhaus der BASF: Planung—Ausführung—Erfahrungen.* Stuttgart: Hoffmann, 1958.

Ball, Benjamin. "De la Claustrophobie." *Annales Médico-Psychologiques*, 6th series, vol. 2 (1879): 378–86.

Balzer, Willi H. "Das Hochhaus in den USA: Baugeschichtliche Voraussetzungen des 19. Jahrhunderts, Entfaltung 1871 bis 1895, weitere Entwicklung bis 1939." Diss., Technische Hochschule Aachen, Fakultät für Bauwesen, 1973.

Barthes, Roland. *Camera Lucida: Reflections on Photography.* Trans. Richard Howard. New York: Hill and Wang, 1981.

Baudelaire, Charles. *The Painter of Modern Life and Other Essays.* Trans. Jonathan Mayne. London: Phaidon, 1964.

Bauordnung für die K. K. Reichs- und Residenzstadt Wien. Vienna, 1893.

Bauordnung für die Stadt Berlin vom 3. November 1925. Berlin: Ernst, 1925.

Bauordnung für die Stadt München. Munich, 1927.

Bayer, Josef. "Eine Treppenstudie." In *Baustudien und Baubilder: Schriften zur Kunst.* Jena: Diederichs, 1919.

Beard, George M. *American Nervousness: Its Cause and Conse-quence.* New York, 1881.

——. *Die Nevernschwäche (Neurasthenia): Ihre Symptome, Natur, Folgezustände und Behandlung.* Leipzig, 1881.

Becker, Sabina. *Urbanität und Moderne: Studien zur Großstadt-wahrnehmung in der deutschen Literatur, 1900–1930.* St. Ingbert: Röhrig, 1993.

Benjamin, Walter. *The Arcades Project.* Trans. Howard Eiland and Kevin McLaughlin. Cambridge: Harvard University Press, 1999.

——. "On Some Motifs in Baudelaire." In *Selected Writings*, vol. 4, *1938-1940*, 313-355. Cambridge: Harvard University Press, 2003.

——. "The Paris of the Second Empire in Baudelaire." In *The Writer of Modern Life*, trans. Harry Zohn, 46–133. Cambridge: Harvard University Press, 2006.

Berger, Otto, ed. *Bauordnung der Stadt Breslau von 1605 bis 1925.* Breslau: Graß, Barth, 1926.

Birmingham, Stephen. *Life at the Dakota, New York's Most Unusual Address.* New York: Random House, 1979.

Blanke, Everett N. "The Cliff-Dwellers of New York." *Cosmopolitan*, July 1893, 354–62.

Blumenberg, Hans. "Lebenswelt und Technisierung unter Aspe-kten der Phänomenologie." In *Wirklichkeiten, in denen wir leben: Aufsätze und eine Rede*, 7–54. Stuttgart: Reclam, 1981.

Boccaccio, Giovanni. *The Decameron.* Trans. Richard Aldington. New York: Dell, 1962.

Bohny, F. "Amerikanische Hochbauten, sogenannte Wolkenkratzer." *Zeitschrift des Vereins deutscher Ingenieure*, 1906, 362–66.

Bornhardt, Wilhelm. *Wilhelm August Julius Albert und die Erfind-ung der Eisendrahtseile: Gedächtnisschrift zu Ehren des um den Oberharzer Bergbau hochverdienten Mannes zur Jahrhundertfeier seiner Erfindung.* Berlin: VDI-Verlag, 1934.

Bryan, John Albury. *Evolving the Elevator.* St. Louis: American Lithographing, 1947.

Buff, Albert. *Bauordnung im Wandel: Historisch-politische, soziolo-gische und technische Aspekte.* Munich: Callwey, 1971.

Calef, Noël. *Fahrstuhl zum Schafott.* Munich: Desch, 1958.

Canguilhem, Georges. "Der Gegenstand der Wissenschaftsge-schichte." In *Wissenschaftsgeschichte und Epistemologie: Gesam-melte Aufsätze*, ed. Wolf Lepenies, 22–37. Frankfurt am Main: Suhrkamp, 1979.

Carroll, Charles. "Apartment-Houses." *Appleton's Journal* 5 (1878): 529–35.

Cromley, Elizabeth. *Alone Together: A History of New York's Early Apartments.* Ithaca: Cornell University Press, 1990.

Dölger, Robert. "Was ist bisher über den Einfluss der Höhenlage (Stockwerklage) der Wohnungen in den Grossstädten statistisch festgestellt? Wie lässt sich dieser Einfluss erklären?" *Deutsche Vierteljahrsschrift für öffentliche Gesundheitspflege*, no. 3 (1901): 444–55.

Drews, K. "Moderne Aufzüge." *Dinglers Polytechnisches Journal*, October 3, 10, and 17, 1908, 625–28, 641–45, 657–60.

Eberstadt, Rudolf. *Handbuch des Wohnungswesens und der Wohnungsfrage.* 4th ed. Jena: Fischer, 1920.

Elias, Norbert. *The Civilizing Process: The History of Manners.* Trans. Edmund Jephcott. Oxford: Basil Blackwell, 1978.

Emmerich, R., and G. Recknagel. "Die Wohnung." In *Handbuch der Hygiene*, ed. Max Pettenkofer and H. von Ziemssen, pt. 1, sect. 2, fascicle 4. Leipzig, 1894.

Engels, Friedrich. "Zur Wohnungsfrage." In *Werke*, by Karl Marx and Friedrich Engels, 18:211–87. Berlin, 1962.

Englert, Kerstin, and Alfred Englert. *Lifts in Berlin.* Berlin: Jovis, 1998.

Equitable Life Assurance Society of the United States. *Henry Baldwin Hyde: A Biographical Sketch.* New York: De Vinne, 1901.

Ernst, Adolf. "Entwurf einer Polizeiverordnung, betreffend die Einrichtung und den Betrieb von Aufzügen (Fahrstühlen)." *Zeitschrift des Vereins deutscher Ingenieure*, 1900, 1285–90.

Ewald, François. *Der Vorsorgestaat.* Frankfurt am Main: Suhrkamp, 1993.

"Examination of Elevator-Runners as a Preventive of Elevator Accidents." *American Architect and Building News*, no. 1496 (1904): 65.

"Der Fahrstuhl für Dienstboten." *Bauwelt*, no. 2 (1910): 13.

Farbenfabriken Bayer AG, Leverkusen. *Bayer-Hochhaus.* Detmold: Deutscher Bauzentrum-Verlag, 1963.

Fechter, Paul. *Der Ruck im Fahrstuhl.* Stuttgart: Deutsche Verlags-Anstalt, 1926.

Fleck, Ludwik. *Entstehung und Entwicklung einer wissenschaftlichen Tatsache: Einführung in die Lehre vom Denkstil und Denkkollektiv.* Frankfurt am Main: Suhrkamp, 1980.

Flohr Maschinenfabrik. *Personen- und Lastenaufzüge: Mit einem Vorwort über ihre Entwicklung.* Berlin, 1900.

Flohr, Willy. "Neuere Aufzugsanlagen für Wohngebäude vom Standpunkte der Unfallsicherheit." In *Bericht über den III. Internationalen Kongress für Wohnungshygiene in Dresden vom 2. bis 7. Oktober 1911*, ed. Friedrich Eugen Hopf, 269–80. Dresden, 1912.

Flügge, Carl. *Großstadtwohnungen und Kleinhaussiedlungen in ihrer Einwirkung auf die Volksgesundheit.* Jena: Fischer, 1916.

Foucault, Michel. *Archaeology of Knowledge.* Trans. A. M. Sheridan Smith. London: Routledge, 2002.

———. *Discipline and Punish: The Birth of the Prison.* Trans. Alan Sheridan. New York: Pantheon, 1977.

————. *The History of Sexuality.* Vol. 1, *An Introduction.* Trans. Robert Hurley. New York: Vintage, 1980.

Frank, Paul Arthur. *Das deutsche Feuerwehrbuch.* Dresden: Groh, 1929.

Freud, Sigmund. "The 'Uncanny.'" Trans. Alix Strachey. In *The Standard Edition of the Complete Psychological Works of Sigmund Freud,* 17:217–56. London: Hogarth, 1955.

Freud, Sigmund, and Josef Breuer. *Studien zur Hysterie.* In *Gesammelte Werke,* by Sigmund Freud, 1:75–312. London: Imago, 1952.

Freytag, Gustav. *Soll und Haben.* Munich and Zurich: Droemer, 1957. http://projekt.gutenberg.de/?id=5&xid=733&kapitel=1#gb_found (German text), http://www.gutenberg.org/files/19754/19754-h/19754-h.htm (flawed 1858 English translation).

Fritz, Hans-Joachim. *Menschen in Büroarbeitsräumen: Über langfristige Strukturwandlungen büroräumlicher Arbeitsbedingungen mit einem Vergleich von Klein- und Großraumbüros.* Munich: Moos, 1982.

Fürst, Artur. "Aufzüge." In *Das Weltreich der Technik: Entwicklung und Gegenwart,* 4:75–87. Berlin: Ullstein, 1927.

Gavois, Jean. *Going Up: An Informal History of the Elevator from the Pyramids to the Present.* [New York]: Otis Elevator Company, 1983.

Geist, Johann Friedrich, and Klaus Kürvers. *Das Berliner Mietshaus, 1862–1945.* Munich: Prestel, 1984.

Gemünd, Wilhelm. "Neuere Bestrebungen auf dem Gebiete der Wohnungs- und Städtehygiene." *Deutsche Vierteljahrsschrift für öffentliche Gesundheitspflege,* no. 3 (1912).

Generlich et al., *Der Fahrstuhlführer: Beschreibung der wichtigsten Teile einer Aufzugsanlage nebst Betriebs- und Bedienungsanleitung.* Berlin: Seydel, 1909.

Giedion, Sigfried. *Mechanization Takes Command: A Contribution to Anonymous History.* New York: Oxford University Press, 1948.

————. *Space, Time and Architecture: The Growth of a New Tradition.* 4th ed. Cambridge: Harvard University Press, 1965.

Goffman, Erving. *Relations in Public: Microstudies of the Public Order.* New York: Basic, 1971.

Goodwin, Jason. *Otis: Giving Rise to the Modern City.* Chicago: Ivan R. Dee, 2001.

Gray, Lee E. *From Ascending Rooms to Express Elevators: A History of the Passenger Elevator in the 19th Century.* Mobile: Elevator World, 2002.

Greville, Charles. *Memoirs.* Vol. 1, ed. Lytton Strachey and Roger Fulford. London: Macmillan, 1938.

Gruber, Eckhard. "'Der Yankee findet den Fahrstuhl gut, er steigt nicht gern die Treppe...': Zur 'Anbetung von Fahrstühlen' in

der modernen Literatur," in *Vertikal: Aufzug Fahrtreppe Paternoster: Eine Kulturgeschichte vom Vertikal-Transport*, ed. Vittorio
Magnago Lampugnani et al. Berlin: Ernst, 1994.

Gugerli, David, and Daniel Speich. *Topografien der Nation: Politik,
kartographische Ordnung und Landschaft im 19. Jahrhundert.*
Zurich: Chronos, 2002.

Gutermuth, M. F. "Mitteilungen über eine Studienreise nach Nordamerika." *Zeitschrift des Vereins deutscher Ingenieure*, 1888,
774–77, 793–97.

———. "Neuere Konstruktionen der amerikanischen Person-
enaufzüge." *Zeitschrift des Vereins deutscher Ingenieure*, 1893,
1089–1100, 1539–48, 1573–80.

Hahn, Hugo. *Jena: Seine 7 Wunder und sonstige Denkwürdigkeiten.*
Jena, 1895.

Hailey, Arthur. *Hotel.* New York: Doubleday, 1965.

Hand, Wayland D. "Bergmännische Lebens- und Arbeitsweise
in den USA: Der Übergang von lokalen und regionalen Da-
seinsformen zur nationalen Großindustrie." *Der Anschnitt:
Zeitschrift für Kunst und Kultur im Bergbau*, nos. 2–3 (1977):
121–31.

Hauptmann, Gerhart. *The Rats.* Trans. Ludwig Lewisohn. In
The Dramatic Works of Gerhart Hauptmann. Vol. 2, *Social
Drama.* New York: Viking, 1929. Also Project Gutenberg
EBook #9972 (2006), http://www.gutenberg.org/cache/
epub/9972/pg9972.html.

Hawes, Elizabeth. *New York, New York: How the Apartment House
Transformed the Life of the City, 1869–1930.* New York: Knopf,
1993.

Heilfurth, Gerhard. *Der Bergbau und seine Kultur: Eine Welt
zwischen Dunkel und Licht.* Zurich: Atlantis, 1981.

Hertlein, Hans, "Der neue Wernerwerk-Hochbau in Berlin-Siemensstadt: Verwaltungsgebäude der Siemens und Halske A.-G."
Baugilde, no. 19 (1931): 1510–16.

Hiebel, Hans H. *Henrik Ibsens psycho-analytische Dramen: Die Wie-
derkehr der Vergangenheit.* Munich: Fink, 1990.

Hintz, Ludwig. *Handbuch der Aufzugstechnik.* Berlin: Seydel, 1908.

Hobrecht, James. *Über öffentliche Gesundheitspflege und die Bil-
dung eines Central-Amts für öffentliche Gesundheitspflege im Sta-
ate.* Stettin, 1868.

Hoffmann, E. T. A. "My Cousin's Corner Window." In *The Golden
Pot and Other Tales*, trans. Ritchie Robertson, 377–401. New
York: Oxford University Press, 1992.

"Houses on the European Plan." *Real Estate Record and Builders'
Guide* 8 (1869): 1-3.

Howells, William Dean. *The Elevator.* In *The Complete Plays*,
300–313. New York: New York University Press, 1960.

Hubert, Pirsson and Hoddick. "New York Flats and French Flats." *Architectural Record*, 1893, 55–64.

Hude, v. d., and Hennicke. "Das Central-Hotel in Berlin." *Zeitschrift für Bauwesen*, 1881, 175–88.

Hugh McAtamney and Company. *The Master Builders: A Record of the Construction of the World's Highest Commercial Structure*. New York: Hugh McAtamney and Company, 1913.

Ibsen, Henrik. *The Wild Duck*. Trans. Rolf Fjelde. In *The Complete Major Prose Plays*, 387–490. New York: Farrar Straus and Giroux, 1978.

"In an Elevator." *Harper's Weekly*, May 1875, 362.

Jaffé, Franz. "Das sechste bis achte Stockwerk: Eine Forderung für die City." *Bauwelt*, no. 1 (1910): 5–6.

Jansen, Birgit. "Der 'Grand Escalier de Versailles.'" Diss., University of Bochum, 1981. Microfilm.

Johnson, Stephen Burge. *The Roof Gardens of Broadway Theatres, 1883–1942*. Ann Arbor: UMI Research Press, 1985.

Kafka, Franz. *Amerika*. Trans. Edwin Muir. New York: New Directions, 1946.

———. *Der Proceß: Apparatband*. Ed. Malcolm Pasley. In *Schriften, Tagebücher, Briefe: Kritische Ausgabe*. Frankfurt am Main: Fischer, 1990.

———. *The Trial*. Trans. Breon Mitchell. New York: Schocken, 1998.

Kellermann, Bernard. *Der Tunnel*. Berlin: Fischer, 1931.

Kennedy, Sloane W. "The Vertical Railway." *Harper's Monthly*, November 1882, 888–94.

Koolhaas, Rem. *Delirious New York: A Retroactive Manifesto for Manhattan*. New York: Monacelli, 1994.

Lampugnani, Vittorio Magnago et al., eds. *Vertikal: Aufzug Fahrtreppe Paternoster: Eine Kulturgeschichte vom Vertikal-Transport*. Berlin: Ernst, 1994.

Logan, Andy. "Onward and Upward with the Arts." *New Yorker*, October 21, 1961, 139–65.

Maar, Paul, and Nikolaus Heidelbach. *Der Aufzug*. Weinheim: Beltz and Gelberg, 1993.

Malmedie, J. "Über Fangevorrichtungen für Fördergefäße." *Zeitschrift des Vereins deutscher Ingenieure*, 1868, 353–66.

Mann, Klaus. *Der Vulkan: Roman unter Emigranten*. Frankfurt am Main: Fischer, 1956.

Mann, Thomas. *Confessions of Felix Krull, Confidence Man (The Early Years)*. Trans. Denver Lindley. New York: Knopf, 1955.

Marchand, Roland. *Advertising the American Dream: Making Way for Modernity, 1920–1940*. Berkeley: University of California Press, 1985.

Mayer, Julius Robert. "Ueber Auslösung." In *Die Mechanik der Wärme*, ed. Hans Peter Münzenmayer, 413–16. Heilbronn: Stadtarchiv, 1978.

Mayer, Philipp. "Aufzüge." In *Handbuch der Architektur: Dritter Theil; Die Hochbau-Constructionen*, ed. Josef Drum et al. Vol. 3, fascicle 2, *Anlagen zur Vermittlung des Verkehrs in den Gebäudenm* 163–99. Darmstadt, 1892.

Melville, Herman. *Bartleby, the Scrivener: A Story of Wall Street.* Project Gutenberg EBook #11231, 2005. http://www.gutenberg.org/files/11231/11231.txt.

Mielke, Friedrich. *Die Geschichte deutscher Treppen.* Munich: Ernst, 1966.

Ministerialamtsblatt der bayerischen inneren Verwaltung. Munich: Bavarian State Ministry of the Interior, 1954.

Morehouse, Ward, III. *The Waldorf-Astoria: America's Gilded Dream.* New York: Evans, 1991.

Mujica, Francisco. *History of the Skyscraper.* New York: Da Capo, 1977.

Mülder-Bach, Inka. "Poetik des Unfalls." *Poetica*, 34, nos. 1–2 (2002): 193–221.

Müller, Franz Carl, ed. *Das Handbuch der Neurasthenie.* Leipzig, 1893.

Müller, Heidi. *Dienstbare Geister: Leben und Arbeitswelt städtischer Dienstboten.* Berlin: Dietrich Reimer, 1985.

Münter, Georg. "Verwaltungsgebäude der Städtischen Sparkasse Breslau." *Zentralblatt der Bauverwaltung*, no. 52 (1931): 761–64.

Musil, Robert. *Young Törless.* Trans. Eithne Wilkins and Ernst Kaiser. New York: New American Library, 1964.

Musseleck, E. "Der Aufzug im neuzeitlichen Wohnhaus." *Baugilde*, no. 13 (1928): 990–91.

Nabokov, Vladimir. *Mary.* Trans. Michael Glenny in collaboration with the author. London: Penguin, 2004.

Neue Bau-Ordnung für die königliche Hauptstadt Prag und deren Vororte. Prague, 1886.

Neumann, Dietrich. "Deutsche Hochhäuser der zwanziger Jahre." Diss., Technische Universität Munich, 1989.

Neumann, Gerhard. "Der Zauber des Anfangs und das 'Zogern vor der Geburt'—Kafkas Poetologie des 'riskantesten Augenblicks.'" In *Nach erneuter Lektüre: Franz Kafkas 'Der Proceß,'* ed. Hans Dieter Zimmermann, 121–43. Würzburg: Königshausen and Neumann, 1992.

Otis, Charles R. *E. G. Otis, Inventor: Originator of Otis Safety Elevator Business, 1811–1861.* New York, 1911.

Otis Elevator Company. *The First Hundred Years.* New York, 1953.

———. *The Otis Bulletin: Special 125th Anniversary Edition.* September 20, 1978.

Palme, Arthur. "Das Woolworth-Gebäude in New York." *Zeitschrift des Vereins deutscher Ingenieure*, 1914, 249–56.

Paulmann, Johannes. *Pomp und Politik: Monarchenbegegnungen in Europa zwischen Ancien Régime und Erstem Weltkrieg.* Paderborn: Schöningh, 2000.

Pélegrin-Genel, Elisabeth. *Büro: Schönheit—Prestige—Phantasie.* Cologne: DuMont, 1996.

Peters, Paulhans. *Klöckner-Humboldt-Deutz AG, Verwaltungsgebäude.* Munich: Callwey, 1965.

Petersen, L. A. *Elisha Graves Otis, 1811–1861, and His Influence upon Vertical Transportation.* New York: Newcomen Society, 1945.

"Polizei-Verordnung über die Einrichtung und den Betrieb von Aufzügen (Fahrstühlen) in Berlin." *Deutsche Bauzeitung*, May 27, 1893, 258–60.

Polizei-Verordnung vom 11. September 1908 über die Einrichtung und den Betrieb von Aufzügen (Fahrstühlen). Berlin: Seydel, 1908.

Radkau, Joachim. *Das Zeitalter der Nervosität: Deutschland zwischen Bismarck und Hitler.* Munich: Hanser, 1998.

Rappold, Otto. *Der Bau der Wolkenkratzer: Kurze Darstellung auf Grund einer Studienreise für Ingenieure und Architekten.* Munich: Oldenbourg, 1913.

Reuleaux, Franz. *Gutachten über Bauart und Sicherheit der Aufzüge der amerikanischen Aufzugbau-Gesellschaft.* Berlin, 1886.

Riehl, Wilhelm Heinrich. *Die Naturgeschichte des Volkes als Grundlage einer deutschen Social-Politik.* Vol. 3, *Die Familie.* 2nd printing. Stuttgart, 1854–55.

Robinson, John Beverly. "The Tall Office Buildings of New York." *Engineering Magazine* 1 (1891): 185–202.

Roskothen, Johannes. *Verkehr: Zu einer poetischen Theorie der Moderne.* Munich: Fink, 2003.

Ross, Frank J., Jr. *Writings on Early American Architecture.* Columbus: Ohio State University Press, 1943.

Roth, Joseph. *Hotel Savoy.* Trans. John Hoare. New York: Overlook, 2003.

Ruttenbaum, Steven. *Mansions in the Clouds.* New York: Balsam, 1986.

Scherpe, Klaus R., ed. *Die Unwirklichkeit der Städte: Großstadtdarstellungen zwischen Moderne und Postmoderne.* Reinbek bei Hamburg: Rowohlt Taschenbuch, 1988.

Schick, Ludwig. "'Außerhalb des Beichtstuhles dürfen Beichten nur aus gerechtem Grund entgegengenommen werden' (c. 964 §3 CIC): Kanonisch-pastorale Überlegungen zum Beichtort." In *Iuri canonico promovendo: Festschrift für Herbert Schmitz zum 65. Geburtstag*, ed. Winfried Aymans and Karl-Theodor Geringer, 207–26. Regensburg: Pustet, 1994.

Schivelbusch, Wolfgang. *The Railway Journey: The Industrialization of Time and Space in the 19th Century*. Berkeley: University of California Press, 1986.

Schlombs, Wilhelm. *Die Entwicklung des Beichtstuhls in der katholischen Kirche*. Düsseldorf: Schwann, 1965.

Schmitz. "Hydraulische Aufzüge für Personen und leichte Lasten." *Deutsche Bauzeitung*, 1874, 283–85, 326–27.

Schönberg, Heinrich. "Die technische Entwicklung der Fördergerüste und –Türme des Bergbaus." In *Die Architektur der Förder- und Wassertürme*, ed. Bernhard Becher and Hilla Becher. Munich: Prestel, 1971.

Schuyler, Montgomery. "The Evolution of the Skyscraper." In *American Architecture and Other Writings*, 2:419–36. Cambridge: Belknap, 1961.

———. "The 'Sky-Scraper' Up to Date." *Architectural Record* 3 (January–March 1899): 231–57.

Selbach. "Kritik der Fangvorrichtungen an Förderkörben." *Zeitschrift für das Berg-, Hütten- und Salinenwesen*, vol. 28, pt. B (1880): 1–78.

Sennett, Richard. *Flesh and Stone: The Body and the City in Western Civilization*. New York: Norton, 1996.

Shultz, Earle, and Walter Simmons. *Offices in the Sky*. Indianapolis: Bobbs-Merrill, 1959.

Siemens, Georg. *Carl Friedrich zu Siemens: Ein großer Unternehmer*. Freiberg: Alber, 1960.

Simmel, Georg. *Soziologie: Untersuchungen über die Formen der Vergesellschaftung*. Vol. 11 of *Complete Works*. Frankfurt am Main: Suhrkamp, 1992.

Simmen, Jeannot, and Uwe Drepper. *Der Fahrstuhl: Die Geschichte der vertikalen Eroberung*. Munich: Prestel, 1984.

Speich, Daniel. *Helvetische Meliorationen: Die Neuordnung der gesellschaftlichen naturverhältnisse an der Linth (1783–1823)*. Zürich: Chronos, 2003.

Spiess, Edmund. *Die sieben Wunder von Jena: Ein Beitrag zur Geschichte der Städtewahrzeichen*. Jena, 1878.

Steffens, J. Lincoln. "The Modern Business Building." *Scribner's Magazine* 22 (1897): 37–61.

Stern, Robert, Thomas Redlins, and David Fishman. *New York 1880: Architecture and Urbanism in the Gilded Age*. New York: Monacelli, 1999.

Suhling, Lothar. *Aufschließen, Gewinnen und Fördern: Geschichte des Bergbaus*. Reinbek bei Hamburg: Rowohlt, 1983.

Sullivan, Louis H. "The Tall Office Building Artistically Considered." In *Kindergarten Chats and Other Writings*, 202–13. New York: Wittenborn, Schultz, 1947.

Tieck, Ludwig. *Des Lebens Überfluss.* In *Schriften in zwölf Bänden.* Vol. 12, *Schriften, 1836–1852.* Ed. Uwe Schweikert. Frankfurt am Main: Deutscher Klassiker, 1986.

Urban, Georg. *Unfallverhütung im Fahrstuhlbetrieb: Eine Darstellung der Unfallgefahren im Fahrstuhlbetrieb; Vorschläge zu ihrer Beseitigung unter Anführung der Sicherheits-Einrichtungen.* Berlin, 1917.

Vaux, Calvert. "Architecture." *Crayon,* July 1857, 218.

Verein für die bergbaulichen Interessen im Oberbergamtsbereich Dortmund. *Die Entwicklung des Niederrheinisch-Westfälischen Steinkohlen-Bergbaues in der zweiten Hälfte des 19. Jahrhunderts.* Vol. 5, *Förderung.* Berlin, 1902.

Vidler, Anthony. *Warped Space: Art, Architecture and Anxiety in Modern Culture.* Cambridge: MIT Press, 2000.

Wasserfuhr, Hermann. "Die Gesundheitsschädlichkeiten der Bevölkerungsdichtigkeit in den modernen Miethshäusern." *Deutsche Vierteljahrsschrift für öffentliche Gesundheitspflege,* no. 2 (1886): 185–203.

Webster, Carson J. "The Skyscraper: Logical and Historical Considerations." *Journal of the Society of Architectural Historians,* no. 4 (December 1959): 126–39.

Weisbach, Karl. "Wohnhäuser." In *Handbuch der Architektur,* ed. Max Hasak, pt. 4, half volume 2, fascicle 1. Stuttgart: Bergsträsser, 1902.

W[endt]. "Erleichterung bei der Anlage von Dachgärten in Berlin." *Zentralblatt der Bauverwaltung,* no. 18 (1917): 114–15.

Wendt, E. "Dachgärten in Berlin." *Zentralblatt der Bauverwaltung,* no. 98 (1915): 646–48.

Westphal, Carl Otto. "Die Agoraphobie, eine neuropathische Erscheinung." *Archiv für Psychiatrie und Nervenkrankheiten* 3 (1872): 138–61.

Wiener, Alfred. *Das Warenhaus: Kauf-, Geschäfts-, Büro-Haus.* Berlin: Wasmuth, 1912.

Willert, Paul-Friedrich, ed. *Zusammenstellung der für die Anwendung des § 110 Abs. 1 BauO Bln wesentlichen früheren Bauordnungsvorschriften aus der Zeit vom 1. Juli 1853 bis zum 30. November 1925.* Berlin, n.p., 1975.

Wischermann, Clemens. "Mythen, Macht und Mängel: Der deutsche Wohnungsmarkt im Uranisierungsprozess." In *Geschichte des Wohnens,* ed. Jürgen Reulecke, 3:333–502. Stuttgart: Wüstenrot-Stiftung, 1997.

Wolfsgruber, Cölestin. *Die Kaisergruft bei den Kapuzinern in Wien.* Vienna, 1887.

Young, Eve Marie. *Art and Enterprise: The Nineteenth Century Administration Buildings of a U.S. Life Insurance Company.* Bonn, 1991.

Zimmermann, Clemens. *Von der Wohnungsfrage zur Wohnungspolitik: Die Reformbewegung in Deutschland, 1845–1914*. Göttingen: Vandenhoeck and Ruprecht, 1991.

Zola, Émile. *L'Assommoir*. Translator not identified. Project Gutenberg EBook #8558, 2005. http://www.gutenberg.org/dirs/etext05/8asmr10h.htm.

———. *Pot Luck*. Trans. Brian Nelson. New York: Oxford University Press, 1999.

ABOUT THE AUTHOR

Andreas Bernard is Editor of *Süddeutsche Zeitung*, Germany's largest daily newspaper, and is Visiting Professor of Cultural Studies at Leuphana University of Lüneburg. He received his PhD in Cultural Sciences from the Bauhaus University Weimar.

ABOUT THE TRANSLATOR

David Dollenmayer is a literary translator and emeritus professor of German at the Worcester Polytechnic Institute in Worcester, Massachusetts. He has translated works by Bertolt Brecht, Elias Canetti, Peter Stephan Jungk, Michael Kleeberg, Michael Köhlmeier, Perikles Monioudis, Anna Mitgutsch, Mietek Pemper, Moses Rosenkranz, and Hansjörg Schertenleib and is currently at work on a translation of Martin Walser's novel *A Gushing Fountain*. He is the recipient of the 2008 Helen and Kurt Wolff Translator's Prize and the 2010 Translation Prize of the Austrian Cultural Forum in New York.